MARS
AT LAST!

ALSO BY MARK WASHBURN:

The Armageddon Game

MARS
AT LAST!

By Mark Washburn

G. P. PUTNAM'S SONS · NEW YORK

SBN: 399-11935-3

Library of Congress Cataloging in Publication Data

Washburn, Mark.
  Mars, at Last!

  Includes index.
  1. Mars (Planet)—Addresses, essays, lectures.
I. Title.
QB641.W29   523.4'3   77-8509

PRINTED IN THE UNITED STATES OF AMERICA

For my parents,
and for Dicky Shuck,
who would have liked it.

Author's Note

As a reader of books, I am sometimes annoyed by the long, seemingly irrelevant lists of acknowledgements which many authors insist on including at the beginning of their books. As the writer of this book, I at last understand the reason for including those long lists. It would have been utterly impossible to write this book without the cooperation and encouragement of a lot of people, some of whom are listed here, not out of duty, but out of gratitude. The list could easily be much longer than it is, but to those mentioned here, I owe a special debt. They all made substantial contributions to the writing of this book; naturally, any errors of fact or interpretation are my own doing.

First, a thousand thank-yous to all the men and women at the Jet Propulsion Laboratory Public Information Office. Their labors made my job (and the jobs of hundreds of other journalists) much easier. The scientists and engineers of the Viking Project were cooperative beyond anything I had hoped for. I particularly want to thank Alan Binder, Fred Brown, Mike Carr, Win Farrell, Ted Flinn, Paul Fox, Jim Martin, Hal Masursky, Bill O'Neill, Carl Sagan, Joe Veverka, and Tom Young. Special thanks to Don Bane, who knows everything, and Shirley Arden, bionic secretary. Among the members of the media, I'm especially grateful to Jon Lomberg, of CBC, Tim Ferris, of *Rolling Stone,* and David Salisbury, of *The Christian Science Monitor,* for sharing their thoughts and perceptions with me.

On general principles, thanks to: John Hartnett, Karen Keating, Bob Webb, Dianne Marr, Mike Germer, Steve and Brenda Halpert, Jack and Kathy Sheets, Karen Nelson, Lisa Hutchinson, Tom Campbell, Clay Steinman, and Mitch and George in Somerville.

Finally, eternal thanks to my old friend Dave Pieri, without whom this book probably would not have been started, and my new friend, Jonathan Eberhart, who helped make it happen.

Contents

PART I   GODS, MEN, AND CANALS

1/   The Martian Mystique   13

2/   The Shoulders of Giants   22

3/   Canals and Controversy   49

PART II   FLIGHTS OF FANCY

4/   "The Martians Are Coming! The Martians Are
       Coming!"—
       The Mars of H.G. Wells and Edgar Rice Burroughs   69

5/   "The Earthmen Are Coming! The Earthmen Are
       Coming!"—
       The Mars of Clarke, Heinlein, and Bradbury   79

6/   Other Voices, Other Barsooms—
       Radical Visions of the Red Planet   91

PART III   FLIGHTS OF FACT

7/   The View from Earth   105

8/   Mars from *Mariner*   121

9/   New Mars, New Moons—
      The Mars of *Mariner 9*   141

PART IV   VISIT TO A SMALL PLANET

10/   *Viking*: Portrait of a Spacecraft   157

11/   The Plain of Gold   194

12/   The Search Begins:
      The Mars of *Viking*   218

13/   Looking for Life—
      "Nobody Wants to be Wrong . . ."   245

14/   Utopia and Beyond   260

      Selected Bibliography   278

      Appendices   279

      Index   283

MARS
AT LAST!

PART ONE

Gods, Men, and Canals

1

The Martian Mystique

It was Mars, the God of War, and for me, the fighting man, it had always held the power of irresistable enchantment. As I gazed at it on that far-gone night it seemed to call across the unthinkable void, to lure me to it, to draw me as the lodestone attracts a particle of iron.
—Edgar Rice Burroughs
The Princess of Mars, 1911

I

"Well, we're coming down, we're coming down!"

Dr. Albert Hibbs, the Voice of *Viking* Mission Control, was trying valiantly to maintain a detached, professional calm, but he was losing the battle. In the final minutes before the *Viking 1* spacecraft made its rendezvous with the surface of the planet Mars, Hibbs' detailed, technical commentary was reduced to the self-evident, nonscientific observation that, "We're coming down!"

Down to Mars.

For the million or so years that mankind and its ancestors had been aware of the existence of the glaring red light in the sky that *Viking* was now approaching, Mars had always been *up.* Suddenly, it was *down.*

Over four hundred journalists and VIP guests were assembled in the Von Karman Auditorium of the Jet Propulsion

Laboratory to be present for the *Viking* landing on Mars. The actual event was taking place some two hundred million miles away, but in the early morning hours of July 20, 1976, that crowded hall in Pasadena was as close as one could get to Mars and still be on earth. A closed-circuit television network relayed Hibbs' commentary to the anxious observers in Von Karman. Amid the tension and excitement and the torrent of incoming data, Hibbs' nervous comment was all but ignored; and yet it was probably the best expression of the meaning of the moment. Mars was *down*. Never before in history could such a thing have been said.

The planet Mars had always been up, out, away, distant, remote, the insubstantial object of a thousand speculations, dreams, and fears. Mars was the symbol of war and ruin, the eternal omen of suffering and pain, a baleful, blood-red beacon in the cold night sky. It was the home of hideous monsters and beautiful princesses, of cool, evil intelligences and mindless beasts. The flying saucers came from Mars. The human race came from Mars. Insidious invaders from Mars were already among us. Mars was the place where terrible things were always just about to happen. Mars was the Great Unknown.

The arrival of the *Viking* spacecraft was to change forever our perception of Mars. Investigation caught up with and passed Imagination. The exotic, poetic Mars of Burroughs and Bradbury dissolved, replaced by a desolate landscape of rocks and sand. The world that we had once known only through the works of Wells and Heinlein was now revealed to us by Lander Imaging, analyzed by the XRFS and GCMS, and interpreted by the staffs of SFOF and FOVLIP. On the ochre desert where John Carter once saved Dejah Thoris from the tharks, an ugly robot from earth now intruded, like some sloppy American tourist in a temple, snapping photos of the sunset, digging holes, scattering trash.

For many of the people in Von Karman Auditorium that

night, Mars was much more than simply the latest target of applied technology. It was a special place, a world more of mind than of matter, a mystical homeland of the imagination. "I have always looked on myself as some sort of Martian," science-fiction writer Ray Bradbury had written; Bradbury was there at JPL, waiting for his first look at his distant native land in the sky. Although the author of *The Martian Chronicles* may have had a proprietary interest in the Red Planet, Bradbury's claim of Martian citizenship was not unique. We had all been there before, many times.

The *Viking* spacecraft descending toward the surface of Mars carried with it a computerized, automated biochemical laboratory of awesome sophistication. It was designed and built, with great cost and incredible difficulty, for the purpose of answering one of mankind's most enduring questions: is there life on Mars? More than a year after *Viking*'s successful landing, the question remains unanswered. Although the spacecraft has sent back to earth literally billions of bits of new data about Mars, it has been unable to give us a simple yes or no on the question of life.

The new Mars of *Viking* is our latest version of the Red Planet, but it almost certainly will not be the final one. If we learned nothing else from *Viking*, we learned how little we know about our planetary neighbor. Nearly every pre-*Viking* theory about Mars has proved to be wrong; many of the early post-*Viking* theories will probably have a similar fate. We are gradually getting closer to the true story of Mars, but there is still a very long way to go. The trip is worth making, though, because as we learn about Mars, we learn about ourselves.

Compared with what we have yet to learn, our fund of knowledge about Mars is still very limited, but after centuries of observation and study, we at least have possession of some basic facts:

Mars is the fourth planet from the sun. Of the nine planets in the solar system, only Mercury and Pluto are smaller. Mars has a mean diameter of about 4,240 miles, compared with 7,926 miles for the earth. Because of its small size and mass, the force of gravity at the surface of Mars is only about 38 percent as strong as it is on earth; a man who weighs 150 pounds on earth would only weigh about 60 pounds on Mars.

Mars revolves around the sun at a mean distance of 141.5 million miles. Its orbit is much more elliptical than the nearly circular orbit of earth. At its closest approach, Mars comes within 128.4 million miles of the sun, and at its most distant point, it is more than 154.9 million miles away. In contrast, earth never varies from its 93 million mile mean distance from the sun by more than 1.5 million miles in either direction.

The Martian year lasts 687 terrestrial days. Because Mars, like the earth, is tilted on its axis, Mars possesses four distinct seasons. However, the elliptical Martian orbit causes the planet to move around the sun at a variable speed, resulting in seasons of unequal length. Spring in the Martian Northern Hemisphere lasts for 199 terrestrial days, while autumn lasts for only 147 days.

Mars is also similar to the earth in that it has polar ice caps. The polar caps, which are visible as bright white spots through a good telescope, change in size and shape according to the Martian seasons. The north polar cap expands during the northern winter and shrinks during the summer, while the southern cap waxes and wanes in a complementary fashion.

A Martian day lasts 24 hours, 37 minutes, and 22.7 seconds, or about 41 minutes longer than a terrestrial day. During the *Viking* mission, the Martian day was known as a "sol," to distinguish it from earth time.

Mars has two known satellites, both of them small, irregular chunks of rock. Phobos, the inner moon, revolves around Mars in just 7.7 hours, while Deimos takes 30.3 hours to make the circuit. Both moons possess some rather peculiar properties and have been the subject of intense speculation in their own right.

16

As seen from earth, Mars is a ruddy red in color and has a surface which is mottled with markings of some darker hue, variously described as green, blue, or neutral gray. The surface markings visible from earth are generally constant in shape and size, although one of the greatest of Martian mysteries over the years has been the apparent seasonal alteration of some of the dark areas.

Twice during each Martian year, the center points of Mars and the earth line up with the center point of the sun. When the two planets are on opposite sides of the sun, the alignment is known as superior conjunction; the maximum distance between Mars and earth at superior conjunction is 247.9 million miles. When the lineup occurs with both planets on the same side of the sun, they are said to be in opposition. The mean distance at opposition is 48.7 million miles, and the closest approach is 34.6 million miles. During opposition, Mars is one of the brightest objects in the night sky, outshone by only Venus and Jupiter.

All of these facts were known about Mars long before *Viking* touched down on the sands of the Martian region known as Chryse Planitia. Some of them were known by the ancients several thousand years ago. Others were learned only in this century. Until *Viking,* we could be confident about these bare-bones statistics, but to go much beyond them took us into the realm of theory and speculation. With the addition of the new *Viking* data, we can go much farther than ever before, but the new Mars will still be a world constructed more from guesswork than from fact.

Facts, Norman Mailer once said, are nothing without nuance. Even if we had *all* the facts about Mars, we would still not have the complete story. The data from *Viking* and future space probes will give us only a part of the true picture of Mars. To try to understand Mars through facts alone would be like describing Willie Mays through statistics alone. One can say with complete accuracy that Mays was a baseball player who collected 3,283 hits in 22 years, hit 660 home runs, and had a lifetime batting average of .302, but the statistics tell nothing about the over-the-head catches, the daring base-running, the perpetual grin on the face of the Say-Hey Kid. Mays is more than the sum of his statistics, just as Mars is more than sum of its science.

Stripped of myth and mystery, Mars is simply a large hunk of rock and metal floating in space. Gold, too, is just rock and metal, yet much of human history has revolved around that otherwise unremarkable substance. It has value and importance because of what people think about it and the things they have done to discover it. Similarly, the planet Mars is important because of our attitudes about it and the history of our efforts to "discover" it. Mars has exerted an influence on the earth far stronger than just gravity.

In some ways, the lure of Mars has been diminished by the recent discoveries of *Viking*. One can hardly deny that Mars would have been more attractive if it had been populated by the tharks and thoats of Burroughs or the Ancient Ones of Heinlein. Even a blade or two of grass would have helped. Yet, even as it dispelled old mysteries, *Viking* discovered new ones. Mars may not harbor any exotic monsters or ancient astronauts, but it is still a source of wonder. Consider:

Viking orbital photos of the Martian north polar region revealed huge sheets of what looks like very thin, translucent ice stretching across chasms and gulleys in a straight line extending for miles. Scientists have no idea what caused such formations.

Other orbital photos showed a region that looks as if it had been contour plowed, like a farmer's field in Iowa. Another region looks like a drive-in theater seen from the air. These topographic features are unique to Mars. No one knows how they were formed.

Geological evidence indicates that Mars once possessed huge rivers, lakes, and seas. They are all gone now, and no one can say for sure what happened to them. No one can be sure that the same thing won't happen to earth.

There is something in the Martian soil that behaves like nothing ever seen on earth. It may be a biological entity or a purely chemical phenomenon; whatever it is, there is nothing like it on this planet.

The questions posed by Mars—both the old Mars and the new—are not merely intellectual exercises for scientists or make-work projects for the overeducated. The answers to some age-old terrestrial mysteries may well come from knowledge gained in the study of Mars. There are many questions right here on earth that we would like to have answered, and a few that we *must* have answered—and soon.

Viking scientist Richard S. Young, writing in 1975, gave his view of the situation: "I think our problems here on earth are so serious that we haven't got more than thirty or forty years more to begin to answer some of the questions that plague us. Unfortunately, man doesn't have a history of solving the next generation's problems; he leaves them to the next generation. Here we have a chance, I think, to be visionary . . . I'm very optimistic about the potential payoff from *Viking*. I really think it is going to help us understand the earth better."

Ray Bradbury expressed the same concerns as Young in 1973: "We are all . . . children of the universe," wrote Bradbury. "Not just earth, or Mars, or this system, but the whole grand fireworks. And if we are interested in Mars at all, it is only because we wonder over our past and worry terribly about our possible future."

Young's hopes for *Viking* have already been partially fulfilled, but the ultimate payoff may be years in coming. We have only begun to learn the lessons that Mars can teach us. It may well be that from Mars we will finally discover the secrets of earthquakes and climatic change and the basic processes of life itself.

The most exciting thing about Mars, and the most challenging, is that the answers to the ancient questions are within the grasp of those of us alive today. As I sat in Von Karman Auditorium, listening to Dr. Hibbs describe *Viking*'s descent toward Mars, I thought of my grandmother. When she was a small child in Dayton, Ohio, just before the turn of the century, she lived down the street from a bicycle shop run by two eccentric brothers named Orville and Wilbur Wright. She thought they were crazy; they weren't. My grandmother lived long enough to see the first men leave the earth.

Then, I thought of my parents. My mother was born on a farm near the small town of St. Marys, Ohio, which is about a dozen miles down the road from the even smaller town of Wapakoneta. In an era when women didn't normally do such things, my mother became a private pilot. Her career as an aviatrix was brief and undistinguished, but she learned to fly on the same grass airstrips where a kid from Wapakoneta first earned his wings a few years later. The kid was Neil Armstrong, the first man to set foot on the moon. My father was also a pilot. His introduction to aviation came at the Cleveland Air Races in the twenties and thirties, where he spent most of his youth watching brave men in glorified kites straining to reach the dizzy speed of 400 miles per hour.

I was born in 1948; I grew up watching *Captain Video* and *Tom Corbett, Space Cadet* and, somewhat later, *Star Trek* and *2001: A Space Odyssey.* In between those two eras of space fantasy, a real-life space spectacular was going on. *Sputnik* burst upon us in 1957 and then, in rapid succession, *Explorer, Vanguard, Ranger, Vostok, Lunik, Mercury, Gemini, Surveyor, Mariner, Apollo, Pioneer, Soyuz, Skylab*—and *Viking.* If I am allotted my full threescore and ten, I expect to return to JPL in about forty years for the first manned landing on Mars.

Those of us who were there at JPL on July 20, 1976, and the millions who watched on television, and the four billion other residents of this small planet, all shared a unique privilege. As Carl Sagan has said, you can only land on Mars for the first time once. We all have had the incredible luck of being alive to see it happen.

If our luck holds, and if we are willing to accept the challenge, *Viking* will be only the beginning of an age of discovery unparalleled in history. Dr. Michael McElroy, one of the most articulate of the *Viking* scientists, put it this way: "If we are the generation that has the privilege of exploring the solar system, of really making the earth part of its immediate environment and not some unique isolated body whose inhabitants do not know the difference between Mars and a star in the sky, I think that will be a great step forward. Man's perception of himself will change . . . . If we are the generation that does that, then I think our place in history is assured."

2

The Shoulders of Giants

"E pur, si muove."
Nevertheless, it moves.
—attributed to Galileo

On some unmarked night, perhaps a million years ago, in the shelter of a dry, dusty African valley, the first astronomer—naked, frightened, not yet truly a man but no longer a beast—looked toward the glittering sky and noticed for the first time the planet Mars. Of all the objects in the heavens, save the sun and the moon, it was the one most certain to attract his attention and engage his awakening mind.

Mars was not the brightest light to be seen, although it shone more steadily and radiantly than most of the others. And it didn't follow or precede the sun, the way some of the lights did.

Something else about this bright blaze in the sky held his eyes. Its color was unique in the night sky—a ruddy, hard, glowering red that flickered malevolently and unmistakably. The astronomer's remotest descendants would come to associate that color with fires, wars, plagues, and calamities that were far beyond his poor ability to imagine. But it was a color he knew.

It was the color of blood.

Ever since that far-gone night, mankind has been held in the thrall of the Red Planet. The moon and sun were familiar and benevolent, proper objects for worship. But Mars was something to be feared. This bloody omen in the sky could not be ignored. Early man's survival depended on his keeping alert to every possible danger in a hostile universe, in the heavens no less than on the earth. He began to keep track of the movements of those cold, frightening lights above him.

We have no records of just how and when mankind's interest in the heavens took the great leap from fearful apprehension and simple curiosity to "scientific" observation. The earliest remaining evidence—what appears to be a lunar calendar carved on an antler—suggests that sometime following the last great ice age, perhaps fifteen to twenty thousand years ago, man was at least aware of the periodic and repetitive nature of celestial phenomena. Not until the development of the first agricultural societies, about ten thousand years ago, did men begin serious and systematic observation of the skies.

The skies foretold the future. When a given set of stars appeared in the evening, it was time for planting. Other stars gave warning that the spring floods were about to come, or that harvest was approaching. Such events were the most important in the lives of the early farming communities, and the ability of the stars to foretell them was certainly portentious: perhaps the stars could foretell other events as well.

Thus was born the first science—astrology. Astrology deserves the rank of science because in the beginning it was indistinguishable from what we now call astronomy. Over the years, however, it has evolved into something altogether different. The separation of the two was a very gradual process and was not complete until relatively recent times. By the end of the nineteenth century, in the West at least, astrology was generally viewed as no more than an intellectual curiosity.

In recent years, though, astrology has made a powerful and somewhat disturbing comeback, particularly among the young. Perhaps this resurgence is due to the same forces which created astrology in the first place—fear and uncertainty in a universe which seems, at best, indifferent to the fate of man. Whatever the cause, the new fascination with astrology has been a source of concern for serious scientists, who almost unanimously view the whole "science" of astrology as totally nonscientific.

In 1975, 186 scientists signed a statement entitled "Objections to Astrology," which expressed indignant alarm over the growth of astrology. The predictable result was a storm of controversy, led by the astrologists but also fueled by debate within the scientific community. Some scientists complained that, while astrology was undeniably bunk, you couldn't prove it simply by signing your name on a letter. Scientific authoritarianism, in its own way, was as bad as astrological mysticism. Partly as a result of the controversy, several groups of respectable scientists have now begun to investigate seriously the claims of the astrologists, as well as other bizarre phenomena such as ESP, astral projection, reincarnation, and UFOs. The results of the investigations are not likely to placate either the dyed-in-the-wool mystics or the hard-nosed pragmatists. The important thing, however, is that the studies represent an attempt to achieve an objective and empirical understanding of some of the world's baffling and mysterious phenomena—which is exactly how science got started in the first place.

As the early societies grew more complex, so did their problems. There were wars, plagues, famines, royal assassinations and successions, religion, and laws to worry about. The men who watched the skies to foretell spring planting evolved into a class of high priests whose job it was to coordinate heavenly signs with earthly events. It was a formidable task.

We know that such high priests were in business as early as five thousand years ago in China and Sumeria, and possibly elsewhere. Their main problem was keeping track of the planets, rather than the stars, sun, and moon, which seemed to take care of themselves. But the planets required careful study, for their behavior was independent and sometimes alarmingly capricious. The five planets (the word comes from the Greek word for "wanderers") visible to the ancients—Mercury, Venus, Mars, Jupiter, and Saturn—each seemed to have very distinct characteristics. Mercury and Venus followed or preceded the sun. Jupiter and Saturn were bright and moved at a stately, regal pace. But Mars was erratic and perplexing. Its motion through the sky was relatively fast, but it moved in fits and starts, sometimes even moving backward. And then, there was its menacing red color, unique among the wanderers. Clearly, the motions of Mars were not to be taken lightly.

Not surprisingly, then, Mars became associated with wars, disasters, and bad luck in general. A surviving fragment of Babylonian text informs us that, "When Nergal (Mars) is dim, it is lucky, when bright, unlucky." Nergal also happened to be the name of the god of battle and death; the red light in the sky was simply the abode of Nergal.

The identification of Mars with war was consistent across many cultures. The Persians knew it as Pahlavani Siphir, the Celestial Warrior. For the Egyptians, it was Harmakhis. The Greeks called it Ares, the Norse, Tiu (from which we get Tuesday), and the Romans, Mars (from which the French, Spanish, and Italians get their words for Tuesday). Although Mars was not the god-in-chief (Jupiter's distinction), its fearsome associations demanded special attention. Members of one Babylonian sect known as the Sabians devoted themselves to placating Nergal by meeting on Tuesdays dressed in red and smearing themselves with blood. Even today, we pay homage to Mars' violent reputation—the astronomical symbol for Mars is the aggressive-looking descendant of a shield and spear: ♂

Over the centuries, the priests built up a considerable body of data about the motions of the planets. Eventually it became possible to predict with some precision the positions of the planets at a given moment. Little or no attempt was made to explain these motions, but careful descriptions of planetary movements allowed the priests to perform their jobs.

Celestial events sometimes caught the priests by surprise, however, as in the case of two Chinese astronomers of the twenty-second century B.C. The astronomers, named Hi and Ho (believe it or not), failed to predict a solar eclipse. The Emperor Chung K'ang punished this regrettable error by putting them to death.

The fate of Hi and Ho was not unique; as a natural consequence, the prudent astronomer-priests put a high premium on both accuracy and what modern politicians might call "deniability." Predictions were couched in ambiguous, metaphorical terms, so that if things went wrong, the priest could tell an angry king, "My prediction was right, but your interpretation of it was wrong." The classic example is the Greek oracle at Delphi's prediction that Athens would be saved by its "wooden walls." The walls might be either literal wooden ramparts, or the metaphorical "wooden walls" of the naval fleet; the oracle didn't specify which one it meant. If Athens hadn't been saved, the oracle would have been out of a job anyway. The modern equivalent of the oracle can be seen in the horoscope column of your daily newspaper, which leans heavily on broad generalities rather than on specific advice.

A priest might save his neck by ambiguity, but accuracy was a much safer way. By the fourth century B.C. the Chaldean astronomers of Babylon had devised a reasonably accurate lunar calendar, based on a nineteen-year period which included seven years of thirteen months. This nineteen-year period later became the basis for the Hebrew calendar.

Another major achievement of the Chaldeans was the development of the zodiac. They had observed that the sun,

26

moon, and planets moved around the sky following a relatively narrow pathway. They divided the stars along this path into distinct constellations, such as Pisces, Taurus, Scorpio, and the rest of the heavenly menagerie. In addition to their astrological implications, the signs of the zodiac were important because they provided convenient reference points for plotting the positions of the planets.

Over the span of centuries, the Chaldeans also devised accurate tables which one could use to calculate the dates of planetary oppositions. Since the planets shone brightest at the time of opposition, their powers over the affairs of men were presumed to be strongest then; predicting oppositions was one of the astronomers' most important functions. The Chaldeans discovered that Mars was at opposition once every 779.9 days.

With this information available, the Chaldeans were able to make accurate predictions about some of the motions of Mars and the other planets. But although they could be sure that Mars would be at opposition once every 779.9 days, its position during the intervening period was less easy to predict.

The problem which stumped the Chaldeans—and everyone else until the time of Copernicus and Kepler—was the occasional retrograde motion of Mars and the other outer planets. The normal motion of the planets is eastward across the background of stars. At times, however, Mars, Jupiter, and Saturn may appear to stop and then reverse their motion. They may move westward for weeks or months before resuming their direct, eastward motion. This seemingly erratic behavior made it impossible for the Chaldeans to confidently predict the future positions of the outer planets.

The Chaldeans' failure was in theory, rather than observation. Like virtually every other ancient civilization, the Babylonians had a geocentric concept of the universe—the earth in the center, with everything else in creation revolving around it. There were myriad variations on this theme—goddesses holding up the sky, the sun sailing around in a boat, and dozens of others—but as long as the earth remained in the center, there was no hope of evolving an orderly universe or a reliable astronomy.

The Chaldeans weren't even particularly interested in finding out the how and why of things; their religion adequately answered those questions. They were descriptive astronomers; theoretical astronomy had to wait for the Greeks.

The civilization of ancient Greece produced the first truly scientific theories of cosmology. With a single exception, their theories were wrong, but the Greeks contributed the important concept of universal law. The universe, they said, was not simply the plaything of arbitrary and capricious gods; it was an orderly place bound by rules and principles which might be discovered and understood by men.

There were many early Greek versions of the universal order. Anaximander (611-546 B.C.) had the earth as a cylinder and the heavenly bodies as wheels with holes in them, through which their internal fires were visible. Anaximenes (585-526 B.C.) thought that "the stars are like nails" tacked up on the sky. Pythagoras (sixth century B.C.), friend of geometry students, was probably the first to declare that the earth was a sphere. The notion of a spheroid earth became popular and was never seriously challenged thereafter. Even in Columbus' time, contrary to popular belief, very few educated people believed in a flat earth.

In all of the early Greek models, the earth was still at the center of the universe. (More precisely, *Greece* was at the center of the universe, and Delphi was "the navel of the world.") A later Greek astronomer, Aristarchus of Samos, suggested that perhaps the sun was in the center, with the earth and other planets revolving around it, but he was ignored. The weight of learned opinion remained firmly on the side of geocentrism.

The definitive Greek work on astronomy was a book written by Aristotle (384-322 B.C.). Aristotle accepted a spherical earth—he even attempted to demonstrate scientifically why this must be so—but he absolutely prohibited any earthly motion. The universe, he believed, was perfect, and the center of a perfect universe does not move.

This obsession with perfection led Aristotle to ascribe perfect, regular circular motions to the heavenly bodies. He postulated the existence of a total of fifty-five perfect crystal spheres in the heavens, along which the planets moved. The large number of spheres was necessary in order to account for the troublesome motions of the outer planets.

These extra circles were called epicycles. They were small circles along the rim of the main circles, called deferents. Moving with uniform velocity around the epicycles while following the larger deferent, a body, as seen from earth, would seem to slow down at times, or even move backward. The epicycles apparently accounted for the retrograde motions of the outer planets, but complicated the workings of Venus and Mercury. Heraclitus, a contemporary of Aristotle, attempted to solve this problem by having the epicycles of Mercury and Venus take them around the sun, while their deferents carried them around the earth.

The last of the great Greek astronomers was Ptolemy, who worked at Alexandria during the second century A.D. Ptolemy refined and codified the Aristotelian system of spheres and epicycles. His version of the universe had the earth at the center, circled by the moon, Mercury, Venus, the sun, Mars, Jupiter, and Saturn, in that order. Even Ptolemy had difficulty in making his system work, however. "I do not profess to be able to account for all the motions at the same time," he admitted.

Ptolemy's observations and theories, lost for a while, came back to Europe via the Arabs in the form of a book known as the *Almagest,* which was the bible of astronomy until the sixteenth century. Despite all its complexities and defects (including an increasingly out-of-phase calendar), the

Ptolemaic system remained at the center of European thought for fifteen hundred years, as immovable as the earth itself.

The Romans did nothing to advance the Greek concepts of the universe; they were too busy conquering this world to pay much attention to the others. Only Mars held any real significance for them, for as the home of the War God, its appearance in the sky usually signaled the start of another campaign. Not that they needed much prodding from the gods. By the time the Roman Empire reached its zenith, Mars was regarded as a much more influential deity than his nominal boss, Jupiter.

As the old religion gave way to Christianity, the influence of Mars, and the planets in general, declined. The Bible had little to say about other worlds. Mars may or may not have been mentioned once, in the book of Amos (5:26): "But ye have borne the tabernacle of your Moloch and Chiun your images, the star of your god. ... " Chiun, according to some scholars, refers to the Syrian word for Saturn; other experts believe it refers to Mars. Either way, it is no more than a passing reference.

The Arabs were excellent observational astronomers, but made no contributions to theory, other than preserving the ancient Greek texts. Not all of them, however. The great library at Alexandria was supposedly burned by a Moslem caliph who decreed that any book which disagreed with the Koran was heretical, and any book which agreed with it was superfluous.

The Chinese were meticulous observers of the skies, and recorded the supernova of 1054, whose debris now appears as the Crab Nebula. No one in Europe looked up that year, or if anyone did, he didn't bother to write down what he saw, for the Chinese record of the event is the only one we have. Chinese cosmology was as xenophobic as Chinese society; the center of the universe was China, and anyone who did not live there was a barbarian.

In the New World, the Mayans produced a better calendar than the Europeans used, but it died with their civilization. The American Indians clung to poetic, nature-oriented versions of cosmology, but they did have enough interest in the skies to build a kind of American Stonehenge, known as the Big Medicine Wheel.

Although every civilization and culture, from the South Sea Islanders to the Laplanders, had its own unique version of the universe and the heavens, our attention has to remain on Europe. When the true nature of the solar system was finally discovered, Europeans did the discovering.

The most important discovery was made by the Polish scholar Nicolaus Copernicus. Born at Toruń in 1473, Nikolaj Kopernik (later latinized, in the fashion of the times, to Copernicus) was the son of well-to-do middle-class parents. With the help of his uncle, the Bishop of Warmia, young Nicolaus enrolled at the University of Cracow in 1491. His uncle intended to install him as the canon of Frombork, so Copernicus studied canon law.

Scholarship at that time consisted mainly in rediscovering the works of the ancients. The credo in European universities was, if Aristotle hadn't said it, then it wasn't true. At many universities professors were required to swear an oath that they agreed completely with the views of Aristotle on every subject. The intellectual climate was hardly conducive to original research and creative thought.

Copernicus might never have blossomed as a scholar if he had remained at Cracow. Fortunately, he went to Italy in pursuit of a Doctorate in Law at the University of Bologna. While there, he struck up a friendship with Domenico Maria Novara, a professor of astronomy, and Novara successfully infected Copernicus with a fascination for the heavens.

Copernicus stayed in Italy until 1503, studying law and medicine, but it was mainly astronomy that held his interest. We don't know exactly when Copernicus began to doubt the geocentric theory, but it must have been during those years in

Italy. If so, he made no mention of it, even though his reputation as an astronomer won him invitations to lecture in Rome.

He returned to Poland as canon of Frombork in 1503. His duties as canon kept him busy; Copernicus was actively involved in the stormy politics of the region, and was responsible for reforming the Polish monetary system. He was also famous for his skills as a doctor. Somehow, he found time to devote to astronomy, and his studies led him to devise his heliocentric theory. He was convinced that the sun was in the center of the solar system, regardless of the entrenched wisdom of Aristotle. However, it was a bad time to promulgate a radical new theory of the universe. The Protestant Reformation was under way, and both Martin Luther and the Catholic Church took violent exception to anything that smelled of heresy.

That may explain Copernicus' caution and his reluctance to publish his theory. He had come up with the idea as early as 1507, but his great book, *De Revolutionibus,* was not published until shortly before his death in 1543. (Legend has it that he received a copy on his deathbed; if he did, he was in no position to appreciate it, since he spent his last few days in a coma.)

Copernicus did, however, write a brief twenty-page pamphlet in 1507, known as the *Commentary.* Only a few handwritten copies were circulated, but it was enough to give his theory a certain limited fame in scholastic circles. In essence, the *Commentary* was a short summary of the basic elements of the heliocentric theory.

The core of the theory was that the sun was at the center of the universe (or near it), and that the celestial bodies, including earth, revolved around it. That was the *theory,* which was fundamentally correct. The Copernican *system* is another matter. In his description of the motions of the planets, Copernicus was as wrong as his predecessors. For one thing,

32

he clung to the concept of circular oribts, spheres, deferents, and epicycles. Another problem was that Copernicus was an abysmally poor observer. The high latitude of Poland made observations of the planets difficult, since they follow an equatorial path—he may never even have seen Mercury. Still, Copernicus placed stars as much as four degrees out of position, an unforgivable error at any latitude. The inaccurate observations and the inadequacies of the system served to undermine the credibility of the theory. Nevertheless, planetary tables based on the Copernican theory were somewhat more accurate than the old Ptolemaic tables.

Copernicus described his theory and system in great detail in *De Revolutionibus,* which was probably written sometime around 1530. Although unpublished, the theory had already drawn the attention of the Church—some of it, surprisingly, favorable. But the great book might not have been published at all if it had not been for the enthusiasm of a young mathematician who called himself Rheticus. After spending two years with Copernicus, Rheticus published a short book called *Narratio Prima* (First Account), which introduced the theory to the public. With the cat out of the bag anyway, Copernicus finally agreed to publish *De Revolutionibus.*

The attacks started even before publication. Since Copernicus was a Catholic, the most vociferous assaults naturally came from Martin Luther, who said of Copernicus, "This fool seeks to overturn the whole art of astronomy."

Copernicus' intentions were actually somewhat more modest, but the impact of the theory was undeniable. One did not casually accept the removal of man from the center of creation. Concerned over the possible repercussions, the Lutheran clergyman, Andreas Osiander, who supervised the publication of *De Revolutionibus,* tacked on an unauthorized preface, which he hoped would soften the expected blow. The unsigned preface asserted that the book that followed was simply a theory—an intellectual exercise—and was not to be taken literally. Many readers thus thought that Copernicus himself had authored this "just kidding, folks" introduction. It is impossible to judge the full effect of the preface, but it undoubtedly delayed the acceptance of the Copernican theory.

One of those who did not accept the theory was Tycho Brahe, perhaps the greatest observational astronomer of all time. He was born of Danish nobility in 1546, three years after the death of Copernicus. We don't know a great deal about Tycho's early years, except for the interesting fact that he was once kidnapped by his uncle. Possibly that accounts for his personality, which was uncommonly abrasive. A better explanation might be the duel he fought as a young man. The quarrel was inspired by a disagreement over a mathematical problem, and ended with Tycho's having a large part of his nose chopped off. Tycho then built himself a new nose from gold, silver, and wax. Evidently believing that a new nose is a good nose, Tycho became friendly with the man who wounded him, but seems to have held a grudge against the rest of the world.

Tycho was a man of towering ego, but he had talents to match it. He made a name for himself with his detailed observations of the supernova of 1572 (known as Tycho's Star), and managed to parley his reputation into an appointment by Frederick II as Denmark's official astronomer. Tycho received money to build an observatory on the island of Hven (or Hveen, now Ven), and was made landlord of the island. The observatory, called Uraniborg ("Castle of the Heavens") was a strange Flemish-style combination of scientific efficiency and aristocratic luxury. It was equipped with the latest astronomical instruments, running water, a jail for delinquent tenants, and a pet dwarf named Jep.

Although Tycho sometimes neglected his official duties, such as tending an important lighthouse, he was painstakingly meticulous about his astronomical observations. He catalogued the positions of more than 700 stars and made no errors greater than about one-quarter of the width of the full moon. His observations of the planets, particularly of Mars, were so precise that when Johannes Kepler later found a discrepancy between his own calculations and the observations of Tycho, he scrapped the calculations, rather than doubt Tycho.

As the Chaldeans had proved, however, good observations don't necessarily lead to sound theory. Tycho found that the distance to Mars was less than the distance to the sun, which was impossible according to the Ptolemaic theory. But he couldn't accept the Copernican theory either. He believed that under the heliocentric theory, the stars would have to be unthinkably far away, since they showed no parallax, which he felt they should if the earth were in motion. (In fact, some stars do show a parallax, but it is too small to be measured without more sophisticated instruments than those available to Tycho. And the stars *are* unthinkably far away.) Unwilling to accept either an earth in motion or superdistant stars, Tycho concluded that Copernicus was as wrong as Ptolemy. He was sure that he could come up with a theory of his own which would explain everything.

The result has been called "Tycho's Folly," but it was actually a fairly reasonable attempt to solve the seeming paradoxes of geocentrism and heliocentrism. Tycho compromised by leaving the earth at rest in the center of the universe, but he put the planets in motion around the sun, which in turn orbited the earth. It was ingenious, but it was wrong.

Meanwhile, back on earth, things began to go wrong for Tycho in a more personal way. Frederick II died in 1588, leaving Tycho without a patron. Never popular with his fellow nobles, Tycho got embroiled in a number of feuds, large and small, and finally wrote a letter of complaint to the new king, who was not pleased by it. Tycho left in a huff and found a new sponsor in Bohemia, Rudolf II, the Holy Roman Emperor. He became the Imperial Mathematician, but he died in

1601 after only two years at his new post. The tragic irony of Tycho's life is that all his observations were made without the aid of a telescope; but just nine years after his death, the telescope was being used by Galileo.

During Tycho's last years at Prague he had for an assistant a young German mathematician named Johannes Kepler. The two got along surprisingly well, considering the vast differences in their backgrounds and temperaments. In contrast to Tycho's aristocratic forbears, Kepler was born into an on-the-skids middle-class family. His grandfather had been a mayor, but his father was a wastrel and drifter and his mother was a malicious gossip who was once tried for witchcraft.

At the age of eighteen, in 1589, Kepler received a scholarship for "poor but pious people" and went off to the University of Tübingen with the intention of becoming a Lutheran pastor. There, much like the young Copernicus in Italy, he became acquainted with a professor of astronomy, Michael Mästlin. Although the official line was still that the earth did not move, Mästlin apparently gave Kepler a shove in the direction of heliocentrism.

In 1594 a Protesta seminary at Graz offered Kepler a job as a teacher of mathematics and astronomy. Kepler accepted, bidding goodbye to the life of a clergyman. The pay was low, so Kepler supplemented his income by casting horoscopes.

At Graz, Kepler began to concern himself with what he referred to as "the harmony of the universe." The old idea of "music of the spheres" (supposedly caused by the friction between Aristotle's crystal spheres) had gone out the window with Copernicus. Spheres simply wouldn't fit into the observed orbits of the planets. Kepler thought about the problem and came up with a set of replacements for the spheres. He envisioned the five regular solids of geometry occupying the now vacant space between the planets; where Aristotle had placed spheres, Kepler put cubes and icosahedrons. He was totally wrong, of course, but Kepler thought he had made a great discovery, and he published a book about it in 1596.

The book did contain one interesting idea. As a theorist, rather than an observer, Kepler was concerned not only with where the planets moved, but how and why they moved. He conjectured that there must be some sort of pushing force exerted by the Sun. It had to be something invisible, and its power seemed to decline with distance, thus accounting for the slower motions of the outer planets. Kepler was within a stone's throw of discovering the law of gravity.

Tycho read Kepler's book, and although he didn't agree with it, he recognized Kepler's talent and invited him to come to Prague. When Tycho died, Kepler replaced him as Imperial Mathematician. Tycho left Kepler with not just a job, but a specific goal: he was to take Tycho's observations and prepare tables of planetary motion that would prove once and for all the truth of Tycho's theory.

Kepler tried valiantly, but for all his skill as a mathematician, he couldn't get Tycho's theory to agree with his observations.

The main problem was Mars. Tycho had paid special attention to the Red Planet and had left Kepler with a marvelously precise set of observations. Unless he could find some new explanations for the motions Tycho had described, Kepler would be forced to doubt the accuracy of Tycho's observations. That was out of the question, so Kepler scrapped the theory in order to save the observations.

The sticking point was the retrograde motion of Mars. Ptolemy's epicycles were an attempt to explain it, but they were inadequate because they were based on a geocentric model. Working from a Copernican viewpoint, Kepler realized that Mars' apparent backward motion in the sky was really an optical illusion. As earth and Mars approach opposition, the faster moving earth overtakes and passes Mars, making it seem to slow down, stop, and then move in reverse, as seen from earth. Kepler knew what caused the retrograde motion, but he was unable to get Tycho's observations to agree with what Copernicus had said was the circular orbit of Mars. Finally, Kepler abandoned the circular orbit and tried an ellipse. It worked.

It was fortunate that Kepler had chosen to concentrate his studies on Mars, which has a highly elliptical orbit around the sun. If he had devoted himself to Venus, which has an almost perfectly circular orbit, he might never have evolved his laws of planetary motion.

Building on his discovery that the Martian orbit was elliptical, Kepler proceded to work out three laws which govern the motions of the planets. Kepler's mathematical genius, combined with Tycho's observational genius, added up to a revolution in astronomy. Kepler's laws did away with Aristotle's uniform motions along perfect spheres, and Ptolemy's Rube Goldberg collection of epicycles and deferents. Moreover, Kepler provided the much needed mathematical proof of heliocentrism.

Although Kepler supplied a mathematical confirmation of the Copernican theory, it was still difficult for most people to accept. Anyone who looked at the night sky could see for himself that everything in the heavens revolved around the earth. There was no obvious visual evidence that anything in the sky revolved around a different center.

But if you had a telescope to look through, there was evidence aplenty. As far as we know, the first man to use a telescope for astronomical purposes was the great Italian scientist, Galileo Galilei. And it was Galileo who finally dispelled any lingering doubts about heliocentrism.

Galileo was born at Pisa in 1564 and showed an early aptitude for mathematics and physics. What separated Galileo from other scientists of his time was his penchant for performing experiments. Virtually everyone else was willing to simply accept Aristotle's word on every subject, even in cases where the simplest of experiments would have disproved the Master. In that sense, Galileo was the first modern scientist; he wanted to see for himself how things worked. And what he saw, in almost every case, was a refutation of Aristotle. He wrote, somewhat scornfully, that Aristotle "was ignorant not only of the deeper and more abstruse discoveries of geometry, but even of its most elementary principles."

Galileo had an appointment as a professor at the University of Pisa when he began his attacks on Aristotle. His colleagues were more than a little annoyed by his impiety, so Galileo moved to Padua in 1592. It was there that he performed most of his important experiments concerning bodies in motion; the famous Leaning Tower of Pisa demonstration may or may not have occurred—we don't really know, and it probably doesn't matter. Like Kepler, Galileo came very close to discovering the law of gravity, but didn't quite make it. He realized that a falling body accelerates, but he supposed that after it reached its "proper" velocity, the acceleration would cease—for Galileo, an uncharacteristically Aristotelian notion.

We know that by the time Galileo moved to Padua, he was an ardent Copernican. Nevertheless, he did not publicly mention his beliefs until 1604. The Church was becoming less and less patient with such radical theories, as it had demonstrated in the case of Giordano Bruno. Bruno was a philosopher, not a scientist, but he went several steps farther than Copernicus. He said that not only was the earth not the center of the universe, but neither was the sun. It was simply another star, one of millions, around which whirled many other planets and civilizations. Bruno wandered around Europe spreading his heresy until he made the fatal mistake of returning to Italy. He was promptly arrested, tried, and burned at the stake in Rome in 1600. With the memory of Bruno fresh in his mind, Galileo was initially cautious in his defense of Copernicus.

The invention of the telescope changed everything. Galileo

began using one in 1610, but the telescope had been around, in one form or another, for several years before that. Italians had been making lenses for eyeglasses since the thirteenth century, and by about 1600 a number of enterprising Dutch lens grinders were putting two lenses together to produce the first telescopes. Exactly who should get credit for this innovation is unclear, but the names most commonly mentioned are Zacharias Jansen and Hans Lippershey. Lippershey, knowing a good thing when he saw through it, sold his telescopes to the Dutch army for a handsome figure and applied for a patent. His application was denied, on the grounds that too many other people already knew how to make telescopes. Indeed, by 1609 one could buy small telescopes in a shop in Paris for 90 guilders, a tidy but not enormous sum.

Galileo built his own "in the course of one night." It was a simple affair, two lenses connected by a tube, and its magnifying power was probably no greater than about thirty, with a small field of view. But that was more than enough to open up many of the mysteries of the heavens. Galileo turned his telescope skyward and saw things that no one had ever dreamed of before.

The moon was rocky, craggy, and covered with mountains, plains, and huge craters. Venus showed a disc at times (final proof that the planets were unlike the stars, which never showed more than a single point of light), and at other times it displayed phases similar to the moon's. That meant that Venus had to be closer to the sun than the earth, another confirmation of Copernicus.

Saturn was a bafflement to Galileo. Through his small telescope, Saturn appeared to have a somewhat lopsided shape. Galileo guessed that this was due to two nearby moons, but when he viewed Saturn two years later in 1612, the moons were gone. Galileo was completely perplexed. Without realizing it, Galileo had actually seen Saturn's rings. Christian Huygens properly identified the rings in 1656. The rings are so thin that when seen edge-on, as in 1612, they are nearly invisible; thus, the disappearance of Saturn's two "moons."

Galileo thought the rings might have been moons because he had already discovered four moons in orbit around Jupiter. The importance of this observation was enormous, for it showed beyond question that at least one other body in the solar system had objects revolving around it. There was no longer any reason to believe that earth was the center of everything.

Mars was a disappointment. Even through his best telescope, Galileo could see no more than a fuzzy blob of red. There was not much he could learn about Mars from watching it, except that since it was much closer than Jupiter, it also had to be much smaller.

Galileo was naturally excited by his discoveries, and, abandoning caution, he announced them to the world in a book published in 1610. Because it offered very persuasive proof that the earth moved, it was more troublesome to the Church than anything Copernicus had written. By 1612, Galileo was in hot water. In 1616, after four years of controversy, Pope Paul V tried to settle the matter by convening a board of experts to consider the possibility that the sun was in the center of the universe. The experts quickly replied that it was an absurd idea, and Galileo was ordered to stop talking about his false doctrine. His writings were placed on the Index of Prohibited Books. There they stayed for more than two centuries.

Galileo was frustrated, but not completely silenced. He published a book about comets under a false name, in which he managed to get in a few licks for heliocentrism. Still more effective was a *Dialogue Concerning the Two Chief World Systems,* published in 1632. Using the old Greek format of a debate, Galileo ostensibly defended the official view of Aristotle, when in fact he destroyed it with ridicule. Unfortunately, Galileo chose to give his defender of Aristotle the rather too transparent name of Simplicio. The Church was not amused.

The Pope, who had been an old friend of Galileo's in his pre-papal days, ordered the scientist to come to Rome and stand trial for heresy. Aged and ill, Galileo endured a grueling nine-month trial, and in the end he signed a document in which he admitted that he had been in error. According to legend, after signing the confession, Galileo supposedly muttered, "E pur, si muove." ("Nevertheless, it [earth] moves.") Like so many good stories, this one probably isn't true. But whether he said it or not, the earth *does* move, and Galileo, who spent his last years under house arrest, at least had the satisfaction of knowing he was right. He must have known that, sooner or later, he would be vindicated.

Galileo's vindication was not long in coming. Eleven months after Galileo's death in 1642, Isaac Newton was born. Newton's accomplishments are far too numerous to list here, but he was always careful to note that if he was able to see farther than others had, it was because he stood on the shoulders of giants—men like Copernicus, Kepler, Tycho, and Galileo.

Kepler had explained how the planets move, but he couldn't explain why they moved as they did. Newton's laws of motion provided that explanation and brought the universe to order. Newton's mathematics were irrefutable; it was no longer possible to doubt that the sun was at the center of the solar system and that the earth was one of the wanderers.

Astronomers throughout Europe continued the observations Galileo had begun. The early telescopes were crude and usually homemade, but they made possible the gradual accumulation of knowledge about the solar system. In 1646 the first rough drawing of Mars was made by a Neapolitan named Francesco Fontana. The dominant feature on the surface of Mars, according to Fontana, was a large black dot (a "pill," he called it) in the center of the disc. Since Fontana subsequently discovered the same black dot on the surface of Venus, we can be sure that what he was actually observing was an imperfection in his own telescope.

The first reliable sketch of Mars was produced in 1659 by the Dutch lensmaker Christian Huygens. It shows a large dark feature, roughly triangular in shape, near the Martian equator. The dark area was what we now call Syrtis Major, the most readily identifiable of Martian surface features. Huygens also noted in 1672 that there was a prominent white spot covering the south pole of Mars. (It should be mentioned here that because of the inversion of telescopic images, almost all astronomical drawings and photographs are oriented with north at the bottom of the picture and south at the top. Only the recent spacecraft photos and maps show the planets with north at the top.)

Huygens also found that the rotation period of Mars was about the same as that of earth, 24 hours. In 1666, this figure was revised to 24 hours and 40 minutes by the Italian astronomer Giovanni Domenico Cassini, who changed his name to Jean-Dominique Cassini when he became the director of the Paris Observatory. His nephew, Giacomo Filippo Maraldi, cut a minute off that time in 1704, coming close to the actual rotational period of 24 hours and 37 minutes. These early estimates were made by careful observation of the appearance and disappearance of identifiable surface features as Mars spun about on its axis.

There was a limit to how much could be learned about Mars with the first small telescopes; consequently the study of Mars did not advance much beyond Maraldi's observations until the late eighteenth century. By then, a number of astronomers were using large, recognizably modern instruments. One of them was a gifted amateur named Friedrich Wilhelm Herschel.

Friedrich Wilhelm Herschel was born in Hanover, Germany in 1738, the son of an oboist in the band of the Hanoverian

43

Foot Guards. Herschel followed his father into the military music trade and eventually, through the vagaries of the Seven Years War, found himself in England, an unemployed veteran. He managed to keep himself alive by working as a musician and music teacher. In 1767 he was offered a job as organist at the Octagon Chapel in Bath. At Bath, with his salary and teaching and concert fees, he led a prosperous, comfortable life.

The mathematical relationships inherent in music fascinated Herschel, and his study of them led him into other branches of mathematics and science. By 1774, he was giving eight music lessons a day and devoting his nights to astronomical observations using telescopes of his own construction. Soon he cut back on the music lessons in order to spend more time on astronomy.

Herschel began corresponding with the Fellows of the Royal Society about matters relating to astronomy. The professional scientists were at first reluctant to take Herschel's observations very seriously, since their own observations did not coincide with Herschel's. The reason for the discrepancy, they discovered, was that Herschel's homemade telescopes were vastly superior to anything in use by the Fellows of the Royal Society.

In 1781, Herschel discovered what he initially thought was a new comet. Continued observation proved that it wasn't a comet after all—it was a new planet. The five planets that had been known since antiquity suddenly had a new brother. Herschel wanted to name it after King George III, but wiser heads prevailed, and the new planet was christened Uranus. In recognition of his achievement, Herschel was elected to the Royal Society. He was later knighted.

Herschel became a full-time astronomer and telescope maker. The largest of his telescopes had a metal mirror that was two feet in diameter and weighed a ton. Herschel was primarily interested in making a complete survey of the heavens, including all visible nebulae and double stars, but he also made some of the first detailed observations of Mars.

With his large telescopes, Herschel was able to see the bright white patches at the Martian poles. He suggested in 1784 that these white spots were probably polar ice caps, analagous to those on earth. Herschel noted that the polar caps, as well as some of the other surface features he had observed, seemed to change in shape and size as the Martian seasons changed. He also saw what he took to be clouds above the surface of Mars, evidence that Mars possessed an atmosphere. All in all, he concluded, "its inhabitants probably enjoy conditions analogous to ours in several respects."

That Mars should have inhabitants was not a particularly radical proposition. During this period it was widely assumed that all of the planets were inhabited. Giordano Bruno had been executed two hundred years earlier for voicing such ideas, but times had changed. Eighteenth-century Protestants could not believe that God would be so wasteful as to create planets without putting people on them. Herschel even thought that some of the cooler regions of the sun might be inhabited.

Astronomy, then as now, was an expensive science to pursue. Telescopes cost more than test tubes, so the advancement of astronomical studies depended to a great extent upon the continuing interest of people who had money. Many of the early observatories in the United States were funded entirely by private benefactors. To a slightly lesser extent, this was also true in Europe.

One of the most enthusiastic of these patrons of astronomy was a Berlin banker named Wilhelm Beer. He constructed his own private observatory in the Tiergarten and, with the help of J. H. von Mädler, produced the first truly detailed maps of both the moon and Mars. The Mars map, drawn around 1840, showed a planet mottled by dark and light splotches. If one assumed the dark areas to be seas, then the light regions looked much like earthly continents. As a result of this resemblance, many features on Mars were given names that implied the existence of great Martian seas.

Whether water actually existed on Mars was something that had yet to be established. The first rigorous attempt to find an answer was carried out in 1867 by physicists Pierre Jules César Janssen and Sir William Huggins. They failed to find any evidence of either water vapor or oxygen in the atmosphere, but their results were deemed inconclusive. Nevertheless, the experiment was indicative of the fact that Mars was coming to be considered as a planet and not simply an interesting object in the sky.

By the middle of the nineteenth century, astronomers had built up a modestly detailed and not entirely inaccurate picture of Mars. They knew it was a world smaller than earth, with consequently weaker gravity, that it had an atmosphere, and that it had a heterogeneous surface which was subject to seasonal changes. They did not, however, know if Mars had any moons.

For centuries, ever since Galileo's discovery of the four moons of Jupiter, there had been predictions that Mars would be found to possess two moons. The originator of this idea was probably Kepler, whose fascination with the "harmony of the universe" had led him to believe that since Venus had no moons, earth one, and Jupiter four, Mars therefore ought to have two. Kepler's supposition became something of an article of faith, since the great mathematician had been right about so many other things.

In 1726, Jonathan Swift wrote his great fantasy, *Gulliver's Travels*. Swift's hero came in contact with a variety of odd people, including the Laputans, who lived on an island in the sky. The Laputans were gifted astronomers, and Gulliver wrote of them: "They have likewise discovered two lesser stars, or satellites, which revolve about Mars, whereof the innermost is distant from the centre of the primary planet exactly three of his diameters, and the outermost five; the former revolves in the space of ten hours, and the latter in twenty-one and an half. . . ." The Laputans' observations turned out to be surprisingly accurate.

As of 1877, the Laputans were the only ones who had seen the Martian moons. No one was even sure if they existed at all. During the opposition of 1877, American astronomer Asaph Hall, of the U.S. Naval Observatory in Washington, decided that the time had come to settle the question once and for all. He launched an intensive search for the hypothetical moons of Mars.

Hall watched Mars carefully for weeks as it neared the earth, but with no success. He started his search at a good distance from the planet, then gradually moved in closer to it. He was ready to give up in frustration, but his wife, the former Angelina Stickney, told him, "Asaph, you get back to that telescope and find those moons," or words to that effect. Asaph did go back to his telescope and on the night of August 11, he spotted Mars' outer moon. Bad weather closed in and prevented further observations until the sixteenth, when Hall again found the satellite. The next night, while waiting for the moon to appear, he discovered a second moon, much closer to Mars. Hall named the inner satellite Phobos (Fear) and the outer one Deimos (Panic). These names are generally mentioned as being the names of the horses which pulled the chariot of Ares, as Mars was called by the Greeks. However, in the fifteenth book of the *Iliad,* Fear and Flight are not the horses, but the attendants of the War God. Either way, the names did nothing to diminish the warlike reputation of the Red Planet.

The moons themselves are small chunks of rock, no more than a few miles in diameter. Deimos revolves around Mars once every 30 hours and 18 minutes; Phobos makes its shorter trip in only 7 hours and 39 minutes, making it the only satellite in the solar system which revolves around its planet

47

faster than the planet itself rotates on its axis. As a result of this odd phenomenon, to an observer standing on Mars, Phobos would appear to rise in the west. That was not the only odd thing about Phobos, however, and a century later one of the world's leading astronomers was led to speculate that Phobos might be an artificial satellite constructed by an intelligent civilization on Mars.

Hall's discovery of the Martian moons was an odd confirmation of the predictions of Kepler and Swift. Odd, because Kepler had predicted the right answer for the wrong reasons. Kepler thought that Mars should have two moons because Jupiter had four; but we now know that Jupiter actually has at least fourteen moons. So much for the harmony of the universe. As for the accuracy of Swift, we can probably ascribe it to a shrewd guess, rather than inside information. The Laputans' moons had to be small, otherwise they would have been seen by nonmythical astronomers. Their orbits and periods of revolution were dictated by the laws of Newton and Kepler, of which Swift was well aware. His predictions were remarkable, but hardly miraculous.

And concerning Angelina Stickney Hall, history has duly honored her contribution to the exploration of the solar system. The most prominent surface feature on Phobos now bears the proud name of Stickney—which may not sound as imposing as Fear or Panic, but is probably more appropriate.

3

Canals and Controversy

In our exposition of what we have gleaned about Mars, we have been careful to indulge in no speculation. . . . Our conclusion is this: that we have in these strange features, which the telescope reveals to us, witness that life, and life of no mean order, at present inhabits that planet.

—Percival Lowell, 1908

The canals of Mars have been something of an embarrassment to planetary astronomers. . . .

—Carl Sagan and Paul Fox, 1975

The canals of Mars—the phrase has a certain ring to it. Like the Lost Continent of Atlantis or the Golden City of Cibola, they were ancient, grand, and mysterious. Were they real? Or were they just a shimmering mirage in the distant red deserts.

When the Spanish explorers first came to the New World, they were enthralled by stories of a magnificent city called Cibola, whose streets and buildings were said to be made of gold. Many refused to give credence to these fabulous tales, but others, men like Coronado, spent years crisscrossing the American Southwest in search of the secret of Cibola. There were even those who claimed to have seen the Golden City—and there were also those who abandoned the quest, disillusioned and convinced that there was no such place.

Centuries later, when modern astronomers began to get their first good look at another new world, the planet Mars, a debate arose that echoed the passion and persistence of the conquistadores. There appeared to be strange markings on the surface of Mars—long dark lines that stretched for hundreds of miles and intersected with geometrical precision. And like Cibola, there were those who saw the markings and were convinced of their reality, and there were those who never saw them and did not believe they existed. The Martian controversy became one of the most intriguing scientific debates of all time.

In the summer of 1877, Mars approached earth in one of the closest oppositions of the century. It was a rare opportunity for astronomers to get a relatively close-up look at our planetary neighbor; in America, Asaph Hall took advantage of the occasion and discovered the two Martian moons. But Hall's discovery was almost overlooked in the furor aroused by the work of an Italian astronomer, Giovanni Virginio Schiaparelli.

While doing a trigonometric study of the planet, Schiaparelli noticed dark, linear streaks against the characteristic red-ochre color of the surface. Earlier astronomers had seen similar markings and labeled them "straits," probably because the larger dark areas on Mars were assumed to be seas. But Schiaparelli chose to call his streaks "canali."

"Canali" is an Italian word which means "channels" or "grooves," and that is the sense in which Schiaparelli intended the appellation. But, perhaps inevitably, "canali" was translated as "canals"—and the consequences were enormous.

The term "canal" implies artificiality. Canals don't just happen; they are built. And that implies intelligent life. Schiaparelli never said that he thought the canals were necessarily artifacts of a Martian civilization (although he was also careful "not to combat the suggestion, which contains

50

nothing impossible"); he simply reported what he had observed. Nevertheless, his observations set off a storm of controversy.

Schiaparelli could not be dismissed as a crackpot or a poor observer. He had been the Director of the Milan Observatory since 1862, and was the discoverer of the asteroid Hesperia. For his work on meteors, he had been awarded the Lalande Prize of the Paris Academy of Science in 1868. As a prominent and respected astronomer, Schiaparelli had to be taken seriously.

The controversy was mainly one-sided—against Schiaparelli—for several years, for the very good reason that no one but Schiaparelli had ever seen a canal. Others looked but were unable to find them. Even Hall, who had discovered the two tiny rocks that served as Mars' moons, failed to see any evidence of Schiaparelli's "canali."

Schiaparelli not only saw them, he saw them in fine detail. He said they looked as if they had been "laid down by rule and compass." Two years after his initial announcement, he reported seeing some canals double, or "germinate." Where there had been a single canal, said Schiaparelli, another parallel canal a short distance away would sometimes appear, almost overnight. These strange observations did nothing to enhance his credibility.

Undeterred, Schiaparelli proceeded to draw detailed maps of the canals, as well as of other prominent surface features. As was his right as the discoverer, Schiaparelli assigned names to the features he saw, most of them classical references such as Elysium, Hellas, Solis Lacus, and Utopia. Many of Schiaparelli's place names are still in use.

Most astronomers remained skeptical about the canals, but in 1886 two French astronomers at Nice finally confirmed Schiaparelli's observations of the canals. They were there, all right. Whatever the canals were, they were not simply products of the imagination of Giovanni Schiaparelli.

The difficulty in seeing the canals was due to a phenomenon which astronomers call "seeing." That refers not to the eyesight of the astronomers, but rather to conditions in the night sky. Depending on factors such as air currents, dust, ice crystals, smog, temperature inversions, and the latitude of the observer, Mars, even when seen through a large telescope, often reveals no more than splotches of light and dark coloring. In the inelegant phrase of one astronomer, it looks like "a moldy tangerine."

Under very good conditions, however, the splotches resolve into distinct features. But excellent seeing may last for only a few moments—not long enough to take a photograph. The unpredictability of seeing has been a continuing frustration for planetary astronomers; more than a few of them have spent a lifetime without seeing a Martian canal. "If wishful thinking could conjure up canals," Dr. Robert S. Richardson of the Mount Wilson Observatory lamented in 1954, "I'd have seen them long ago." Two years later, Richardson did see a canal, so perhaps wishful thinking has some value.

Schiaparelli, working in the clear air of northern Italy, was consistently able to see the canals. Others who reported observing the canals also tended to be based in locales where the seeing was usually good. The better the seeing, apparently, the easier it was to find the canals.

Although astronomical seeing was good in Milan, Schiaparelli's sight was deteriorating. His failing eyes forced him to give up his observations of Mars in the 1890s. He devoted the rest of his life to a study of the ancient Babylonians and Jews, although he continued to argue in favor of the existence of the Martian canals.

Schiaparelli's work was continued. His discovery of the canals had made Mars an object of paramount interest for astronomers all over the world. The leader among those who followed in the Italian's footsteps was a Boston Brahmin named Percival Lowell.

According to Massachusetts tradition, the Cabots speak only to the Lowells, and the Lowells speak only to God. As a tenth-generation Lowell, Percival's blood ran so blue that he needn't even have spoken to God. He was a nephew of James Russell Lowell, the abolitionist, and a brother of Amy Lowell, the cigar-smoking poet. He was named for old Percival Lowell himself, founder of the dynasty.

Old Percival was a prosperous English merchant, born in 1571. At the age of sixty-seven, fed up with high taxes and unstable English politics, he moved his entire clan to Massachusetts and quickly established himself as one of the leaders of the colony. He died at ninety-three in 1664, secure in the knowledge that his progeny would carry on the family name and business. That they did, and by the time the younger Percival was born, in 1855, the Lowells were the closest thing America had to a royal family. They were Old Money, which, as everyone knows, is vastly preferable to New Money. Vanderbilts and Rockefellers might come and go, but the Lowells endured.

Percival had the kind of education and upbringing that one might expect. As a child, he spent two years in Paris, where he displayed an early facility for languages. He excelled in the classics and once wrote several hundred lines of heroic Latin hexameters about the wreck of his toy sailboat. He was also interested in astronomy, and had a small 2¾-inch telescope.

He graduated from Harvard in 1876 and, as was the fashion of the time for those who could afford it, embarked with a classmate on the Grand Tour of Europe. Despite his heritage of Brahmin reserve, Percival knew how to enjoy himself. He enthusiastically sampled the delights of the Continent and at one point, he and his companion even tried to get into the Serbo-Turkish War. On which side, his brother and biographer, Abbott Lawrence Lowell, does not say.

Of those to whom much is given, much is expected. After his Grand Tour, Percival settled down and went to work in the family business, managing several large trusts and running a cotton mill for his grandfather. This fit the classical pattern of America's leading families. The young men are expected to devote several years to furthering the family finances, after which it is normal for them to pursue some form of public service, such as government or education.

Percival Lowell chose to serve the commonweal by becoming an oriental scholar. He sailed for Japan in 1883 to study the language and culture. While there, he was asked to serve as Foreign Secretary for a special diplomatic mission from Korea to the United States. Lowell wanted to stay in Japan and study, but he reluctantly accepted the position and returned home as an envoy of a country he had never even seen. He accompanied the Koreans back to Seoul and spent most of the next decade there and in Tokyo, where he became involved in the writing of the new Japanese constitution.

He also wrote four books on Korean and Japanese culture. Lowell found a similarity between the ancestor worship of the Japanese and that of his own Boston Brahmins, who, he noted, "make themselves objectionable by preferring their immediate relatives to all less connected companions, and cling to their cousins so closely that affection often culminates in matrimony, nature's remonstrances notwithstanding."

Despite his reservations about the Boston life-style, he returned there in 1893, bored with the Far East. For a while he played a lot of polo. A new obsession was growing in Lowell's mind, and before the year ended he acted upon it.

During his sojourn in Asia, Lowell had retained his early interest in astronomy. He had even lugged a 6-inch telescope with him on his world travels. News of Schiaparelli's discoveries excited him, and when the Italian astronomer was forced to retire, Lowell made up his mind to carry on Schiaparelli's work himself.

Although he had done well in mathematics at Harvard, Lowell's main qualification for becoming an astronomer was his exceptional eyesight. A Boston ophthalmologist said that Percival's eyes were the keenest he had ever examined. Lowell's only other qualification was his being heir to an immense fortune.

He decided to use some of his money to build an observatory for the further study of Mars. He wanted a location that would provide consistently good seeing, and that meant that the observatory would not be built anywhere near Boston, a circumstance which probably delighted Lowell. He later remarked (somewhat inaccurately) that Mars has no weather, "unlike New England, which has more than it can accommodate." Between clouds and cousins, Lowell was not very happy in Boston.

Lowell selected a hill outside Flagstaff, Arizona, as the site for his observatory. The high elevation (about 7,200 feet) and clear weather of the American Southwest made it an ideal location. (It is also interesting that in his search for life on Mars, Lowell chose the same area where three and a half centuries earlier, Coronado had conducted his quest for Cibola.)

Flagstaff itself was a sleepy town of 800 inhabitants, but it was on the railroad so transportation was no problem. The townspeople were excited by the project and cooperated by deeding the hill to Lowell and building a road to it from the town.

As a novice astronomer, Lowell knew that he would need expert help if his observations were to be a success. To that end, he enlisted the aid of fellow Bostonian William H. Pickering, who had carried out successful studies of Mars at Arequipa in Peru in 1892. Pickering stayed in Boston during the winter of '93 to supervise the design and construction of the observatory, which was shipped out to Flagstaff early in 1894. Lowell acquired an 18-inch refractor from the famed telescope maker John Brashear, and began observations on April 23, 1894, just six weeks after the groundbreaking.

Lowell's rush to complete the observatory was dictated by the approaching opposition of Mars, an event he didn't want to miss.

Lowell began his observations of Mars on May 24, 1894, and continued them, almost nightly, until August 3, 1895, during which time he made 917 detailed sketches of the Red Planet. From the beginning, he had no trouble seeing Schiaparelli's canals: "Markings were seen hour after hour, day after day, month after month," he later wrote. His maps confirmed those of Schiaparelli and added many new canals and other surface features. With uncharacteristic understatement, Lowell commented, "it is patent that here are phenomena which are passing strange."

Following the opposition of '94-95, Lowell published a book entitled, simply, *Mars*. It was a unique and important book because it was not merely a report to his fellow astronomers; rather, it was aimed at the general reading public, and it catapulted the canal debate out of purely scientific circles and into the arena of popular opinion. Largely due to this book and the two that followed *(Mars and Its Canals, Mars As an Abode of Life)*, Lowell's theories and opinions were to overshadow virtually every discussion of Mars for the next sixty years.

Lowell was convinced that the canals had been constructed by a highly advanced Martian civilization. He believed that no other explanation could account for all the observed phenomena. "Not a single thing has been detected which it does not explain," Lowell declared. His critics—and they were legion—refused to accept the idea. Swedish chemist Svante Arrhenius argued: "The theory that intelligent men exist on Mars is very popular. With its help everything can be explained, particularly if we attribute an intelligence vastly superior to our own to these beings ... the trouble with these 'explanations' is that they explain anything, and therefore in fact nothing."

Lowell was not surprised by the attacks on him and his theory. He had anticipated them, and addressed himself to the problem in his first book:

> Startling as the outcome of these observations may appear at first, in truth there is nothing startling about it whatever. Such possibility had been quite in the cards ever since the existence of Mars itself was recognized by the Chaldean shepherds . . .
>
> To be shy of anything resembling himself is part and parcel of man's own individuality. Like the savage who fears nothing so much as a strange man, like Crusoe who grows pale at the sight of footprints not his own, the civilized thinker instinctively turns from the thought of mind other than the one he himself knows. To admit into his conception of the cosmos other finite minds as factors has in it something of the weird. Any hypothesis to explain the facts, no matter how improbable or even palpably absurd it be, is better than this. . . . Surely all this is puerile and should as speedily as possible be outgrown. . . .

Some of the theories put forth to counter Lowell were, indeed, "palpably absurd." Many of them seem to have been evolved with no other purpose than to disprove Lowell's ideas. Consequently, some of the competing theories strained credibility even more than Lowell's.

Lowell argued that the large dark areas on Mars consisted of vegetation. Earlier theories that they were seas had been disproved before the turn of the century. Schiaparelli had pointed out that if the dark areas were seas, we should be able to observe brilliant flashes as the sun reflects off them. More recent calculations show that even a body of water as small as 300 meters across would display observable sun flashes; but none have ever been seen. Then, in the 1890s, Pickering and Lowell's assistant A.E. Douglass detected what appeared to be canals cutting across the dark areas; obviously, there couldn't be canals in the middle of a sea.

In addition, the dark areas looked green, like vegetation. The green appearance, though, was partially due to the redness of the adjoining desert areas. Another problem was that most nineteenth-century astronomers used refracting telescopes, which tend to distort colors because of a phenomenon known as chromatic aberration. Modern astronomers prefer to use reflecting telescopes, which aren't as subject to this problem.

To Lowell and most other astronomers, the dark areas appeared to be green. Most importantly, they exhibited distinct seasonal changes.

During the Martian summers, the polar caps retreat dramatically, leaving in their wake a "wave of darkening." The green areas take on a darker, denser appearance, and some red regions seem to be engulfed by the expanding dark areas. The dark areas behave exactly as vegetation does following a spring thaw on earth. Conversely, during the Martian winters, as the polar caps expand, the green areas appear to shrink and fade. Some astronomers even thought they could detect bright autumnal colors in the dark areas. The clincher, as far as Lowell was concerned, was that these seasonal changes repeated themselves year after year in the same locations; they had to be caused by some constant, regenerative process. In other words, vegetation.

Whatever caused the changes, the whole process seemed to be intimately connected with the availability of water. Once the sea theory was disproved, astronomers were certain that water was scarce on Mars. Thus, the red areas were probably deserts and not red vegetation, as some had suggested. Another factor limiting the water supply was the thin Martian atmosphere. Although they had no accurate measurements, astronomers believed that due to the weak Martian gravity, the planet could not retain a very dense atmosphere. Thus, air pressure was likely to be very low, similar to high altitudes on earth. Water vapor could not be present in abundance. If there was water on Mars, most of it had to be locked up in the polar caps.

That implied that the polar caps of Mars were indeed composed of frozen H_2O. There were some suggestions that they might actually be composed of dry ice, but the wave of darkening in the Martian summer indicated to most observers that the melting polar caps released a liquid, which could only be water.

The fact that the polar caps melted at all suggested two things to Lowell: first, there had to be fairly high temperatures during the Martian day, well above the freezing point of water; and second, the polar caps could not be very thick—perhaps four or five feet at most. Such a thin ice cap meant that the total amount of water available on Mars had to be quite small. And thus, the canals.

Any Martian civilization would place a high priority on the collection and distribution of water. If most of the water were tied up in the two polar ice caps, it would be extremely scarce near the equator. Yet temperatures were far more clement in the central latitudes. The problem would then be how to get water from the poles to the equator, where temperatures were more suitable for life. Lowell's answer: the canals.

Lowell saw the "canali" of Schiaparelli as literal canals, constructed for the purpose of distributing water from the melting polar caps to the rest of the parched planet. As he continued his observations, Lowell found what he believed to be ample evidence to support his thesis. Three features, in particular, seemed to suggest artificiality: the straightness of the canals, their uniform width, and their confluence.

Of the 437 canals mapped by Lowell, almost all of them extended in straight or nearly straight lines, for distances as long as 1,500 kilometers. There was even some evidence that the canals followed great circle routes. "The straightness of the lines," Lowell declared, "is unhesitatingly attributed to the draughtsman. Now this is a very telling point. For it is a case of the double-edged sword. Accusation of design, if it prove not to be due to the draughtsman, devolves *ipso facto* upon the canals. . . . Let us not cheat ourselves with words. Conservatism sounds finely, and covers any amount of ignorance and fear."

Not only were the canals straight, they also tended to be of uniform width—about thirty miles. "The better we see the lines," wrote Lowell, "the more regular they look." He believed that such regularity could hardly be the result of random natural processes.

Especially significant to Lowell was the confluence of the canals. Even granting that a purely natural phenomenon could produce the long regular lines, the laws of probability could never tolerate as many as seven of these lines converging at a single spot. Only intelligent design could account for that. In addition, Lowell noted that the canals always connected the dark areas. They never began or ended somewhere out in the middle of the Martian desert. As conveyances for polar water, that was only logical.

The network of canals was so extensive that their construction would have been an enormous task. Thus, Lowell believed that "a mind of no mean order would seem to have presided over the system we see . . . Certainly what we see hints at the existence of beings who are in advance of, not behind us, in the journey of life." Mars was thought to be an older planet than earth—possibly a dying planet. Faced with increasingly harsh conditions, a Martian civilization might well decide to construct the canals as a means of surviving. Such a task would be within the capabilities of the Martians, for, as Lowell confidently declared, "age means intelligence."

The idea that the canals had been constructed by a highly advanced civilization had a certain appeal to the late nineteenth-century mind. In a way, it was even flattering, for this was the great age of canal-building on earth. Tremendous advances in technology and social organization had permitted the construction of hundreds of earthly canals earlier in the century. As the railroad supplanted the inland waterways, the canal builders turned to greater challenges, culminating in the completion of the Suez Canal in 1869. The Americans, for their part, had ambitious plans to build a great canal of their own, just as soon as a suitable way to steal Panama could be found. Teddy Roosevelt found it, and the Panama Canal opened for business in 1914.

If great canals could be constructed on earth, people asked, then what was so preposterous about canals on Mars? Indeed, Lowell argued, it wouldn't even be that difficult to build the Martian canals. "If we were transported to Mars," he wrote, "we should be pleasantly surprised to find all our manual labor suddenly lightened threefold." Lowell postulated Martian creatures three times the size of a man, who would thus be 27 times as efficient and have 81 times the effective strength of an earthbound human.

Lowell believed that construction of the canals would not be impeded by mountains. The surface of Mars was thought to be virtually level, with differences in elevation of no more than a few thousand feet over the entire planet. If there were mountains on Mars, Lowell believed that they ought to have been visible from the earth in the same way in which we can discern the mountains of the moon. High lunar peaks can be seen reflecting sunlight when they are slightly on the dark side of the terminator (the sunrise/sunset line), and the mountains of Mars, if any, should have revealed themselves in a similar manner. Lowell searched, but could find no evidence of any Martian mountains. He concluded that Mars was flat, ideal for canal-building.

Some critics suggested that Lowell's canals were too wide, or too narrow, depending on how one looked at them. If they were wide enough to be seen from earth, they had to be some thirty miles across, which seemed extravagant even for an advanced civilization. Moreover, calculations based on the size of the ice caps indicated that there would not be enough water on Mars to fill such huge canals. Even if there were enough water to fill them, it would all evaporate long before it could reach the equator. On the other hand, any more reasonably sized canal would be too small to be seen from earth.

Lowell disposed of the second argument by demonstrating that thin linear objects can be perceived from a great distance, even when they are beyond the theoretical limits of vision. Lowell was able to see thin telegraph wires from several miles away in the Arizona desert. The linear nature of the wires (and canals) made them visible despite their size.

As to the first objection, that the canals were too wide, Lowell had a persuasive answer: "The supposed herculean task of constructing such canals disappears at once; for, if the canals be dug for irrigation purposes, it is evident that what we see, and call by ellipsis the canal, is not really the canal at all, but the strip of fertilized land bordering it—the thread of water in the midst of it, the canal itself, being far too small to be perceptible. In the case of an irrigation canal seen at a distance, it is always the strip of verdure, not the canal, that is visible, as we see in looking from afar upon irrigated country on Earth."

The more Lowell studied Mars, the more evidence he found to support his theory of an advanced civilization. He even believed he could deduce from his observations that the Martians had a form of unified world government, with no wars. The planet-wide system of canals argued against the existence of trivial national boundaries. And any civilization capable of building the canals was surely too intelligent to indulge in childish warfare.

As to the precise nature of the Martian beings, Lowell wrote, "That Mars is inhabited by beings of some sort or other we may consider as certain as it is uncertain what those beings may be ... to talk of Martian beings is not to talk of Martian men. . . . The existence of extraterrestrial life does not involve 'real life in trousers,' or any other particular form of it with which we may be locally conversant."

Lowell's theories were a success among the writers of pulp fiction, but few astronomers were ready to take Lowell's race of canal builders any more seriously than they took John Carter and Dejah Thoris. While they might admire Lowell's meticulous observations, they could not bring themselves to accept the Lowellian system of artificial canals and Martian civilization. But if the canals were not the product of intelligent design, what were they?

A plethora of alternative theories were proposed. Pickering, Lowell's colleague, suggested that the canals were actually volcanic rift valleys radiating from small "craterlets." The gases expelled from the volcanos might include steam, which condensed in the rift valleys to irrigate the vegetation in the dark areas. It was a good theory, but it didn't explain why the canals extended for hundreds of miles in straight lines.

The great British scientist Alfred Russel Wallace wrote an entire book to refute Lowell in 1907. He proposed that the canals were actually great cracks in the crust of Mars, resulting from different rates of cooling following the formation of the planet. If there were a conformity of materials in the crust, the cracks would tend to follow straight lines. Wallace didn't even accept the notion of Martian vegetation, believing that conditions on Mars absolutely prohibited the existence of liquid water.

Swedish chemist Svante Arrhenius believed that the canals were no more than "earthquake" cracks. As for the dark areas and their seasonal changes, he explained them away as the result of chemical changes in "hygroscopic salts" which reacted in the presence of moisture.

Other theorists explained away the canals as the products of tidal interaction with asteroids, meteorite grooves, crater rays, sand storms, naturally migrating vegetation, ridges, depressions, outright fakery, and even the parting of seaweed caused by water currents in a planet-wide ocean. These diverse theories all had two things in common. First, they were all based on difficult telescopic observations from forty million miles away.

And, second, they were all wrong.

Only one explanation was close to the truth. Due to the difficulty in seeing the canals at all, it was suggested that they were optical illusions and not real features.

British astronomer E. Walter Maunder performed an experiment with a group of schoolboys which gave some support to the optical illusion theory. He showed a class a small diagram of Mars, minus the canals. Only the other surface details were shown. Hanging the diagram on the wall in the front of the room, Maunder asked the students to reproduce what they saw. Those who sat close to the front made accurate drawings. But the boys in the back of the room tended to connect the smaller markings with lines which bore a distinct resemblance to the canals.

It was an interesting experiment, but those who had seen the canals put more trust in their own eyes than in the perceptions of untrained English schoolboys. Another British astronomer, Patrick Moore, repeated Maunder's experiment in 1950. Out of a total of 58 boys, only three produced "Lowell-type canals. Of these three boys, two were notoriously inartistic and the third short-sighted."

Some astronomers, though, suggested that the canals were indeed optical illusions, quite apart from the evidence of Maunder's classroom experiment. To observe a canal at all, it was necessary to have unusually good seeing conditions. On rare occasions, however, seeing could be exceptional. One such occasion was September 20, 1909, when the Italian astronomer E. M. Antoniadi viewed Mars through a 33-inch refractor from the Pic du Midi observatory in the Alps. "I thought I was dreaming," wrote Antoniadi, "and scanning Mars from his outer satellite." He saw a "prodigious and

64

bewildering amount of sharp or diffused natural, irregular detail." He saw no canals. It seemed that the canals of Schiaparelli and Lowell were no more than badly observed disconnected surface detail. Yet astronomers kept on seeing the canals, as mapped by both Schiaparelli and Lowell. What kind of optical illusion was so persistent that it looked nearly identical to hundreds of observers at different times and places?

The debate raged on, unresolved. Lowell's theories were popular with the public, but met fierce opposition from most of his fellow astronomers. Eventually, the strain of continuous observation and acrimonious controversy became too much for Lowell, and his health broke. He spent several years on the Riviera, staying well away from his beloved Mars Hill in Flagstaff.

In his final years, Lowell did make a contribution to astronomy that seemed to be beyond debate and controversy, although he didn't live to see the final fruit of his work. Precise observations of the motions of Neptune revealed to Lowell a perturbation in its orbit—evidence of an undiscovered ninth planet in the solar system. The principle involved here is familiar to readers of mysteries: when the visible characters behave erratically for no apparent reason, it is usually because they are being acted upon by some unseen outside personage. Lowell spent years calculating the position of Planet X, as he called it, but did not live long enough to see it. He died at Flagstaff on November 12, 1916, following a cerebral hemorrhage. His last words were, "I have always known it would come like this, but not so soon."

Lowell's will set up a trust to continue the work of his observatory. Fourteen years after his death, Clyde Tombaugh, an astronomer at Flagstaff, discovered the mystery planet near the position calculated by Lowell. The planet was named Pluto, and its astronomical symbol is ♇ —PL, for Percival Lowell.

65

But controversy was to plague Lowell even unto the grave. Later observations of Pluto indicated that it was far too small to account for the calculated perturbations in Neptune's orbit: Pluto could not be the Planet X of Lowell's search. Yet Tombaugh had discovered it in more or less the same patch of sky where Lowell said it would be. Fantastic as it may seem, Pluto's discovery seems now to have been no more than a coincidence. All things considered, it's almost easier to believe in Lowell's canals than in the coincidence responsible for the discovery of the ninth planet.

It is for his work on Mars, though, that Lowell will be remembered. As late as 1965, a few months before *Mariner 4* sent back the first good photographs of Mars, Lowell's canals were still on the map. The official NASA *Sourcebook on Space Sciences* of that year concluded that "most astronomers would probably agree that there are apparently linear markings . . . of considerable length on the surface of Mars."

But there aren't.

The canals never existed. Their mystique, nevertheless, fades slowly, like the grin of a Cheshire cat. What finally happened to the canals will be discussed in the chapters on the *Mariner* missions, but a clue to their birth (and death) is contained, ironically, in a tribute Lowell wrote to Schiaparelli eighty years ago. "Schiaparelli's discoveries," Lowell wrote, "were due solely to the genius of the man—his insight, not his eyesight, for at a telescope eyes differ surprisingly little, brains surprisingly much."

If the canals were gone, they are not forgotten. Nor is the Mars that Lowell imagined—the dry, dying world where intelligent beings labored heroically against the harsh conditions. For over half a century, whenever the writers of speculative fiction have turned their attention toward the Red Planet, it has been with a deep bow to Percival Lowell.

PART TWO

Flights of Fancy

4

"The Martians Are Coming! The Martians Are Coming!"— The Mars of H. G. Wells and Edgar Rice Burroughs

PHILLIPS
Then you're quite convinced as a scientist that living intelligence as
we know it does not exist on Mars?

PIERSON
I should say the chances against it are a thousand to one.
—Howard Koch,
Radio play of *The War of the Worlds,* 1938

If Mars were inhabited by intelligent beings, as Lowell and
others claimed, then it seemed inevitable that earthmen and
Martians would meet someday. That intriguing possibility,
however, was not a subject for scientific speculation. It was
better suited to the talents of writers of fiction, people whose
imaginations need not be shackled by the unbending laws of
science.

Long before Lowell and the canals, writers had dabbled in
the romantic possibilities of extraterrestrial adventure. The
early science fiction tales were usually long on fiction and
extremely short on science, but they did play their part in
expanding man's field of vision. Yes, they said to their
readers, man can go wherever his mind is willing to take him.

Events in the real world seemed to bear out this inspiring
philosophy. By the end of the nineteenth century, Europeans

69

and Americans had explored, conquered, and claimed just about everything in the known world that was worth having. Primitive tribes had fallen before the irresistible march of civilization and science. It was a heady feeling for those who had done the conquering.

In 1898 the British writer Herbert George Wells turned things around. How would it feel, he asked, to be one of those primitive tribes? How would it feel to be crushed by an uncaring race with a vastly superior science? Wells answered his own questions in his classic novel *The War of the Worlds.*

It was naturally to Mars that Wells turned in 1897 when he wanted a supervillain. "Across the gulf of space," he wrote, "minds that are to our minds as ours are to those of the beasts that perish, intellects vast and cool and unsympathetic, regarded this earth with envious eyes, and slowly and surely drew their plans against us."

Wells even provided his Martians with a rational excuse for their imperialism, a manifest destiny at least as compelling as our own. The air of Mars, he wrote, "is much more attenuated than ours, its oceans have shrunk until they cover but a third of the surface, and as its slow seasons change, huge snowcaps gather and melt about either pole and periodically inundate its temperate zones. The last stage of exhaustion, which to us is incredibly remote, has become a present-day problem for the inhabitants of Mars. The immediate pressure of necessity has brightened their intellects, enlarged their powers, and hardened their hearts."

The Wellsian Mars is really a pre-Lowellian Mars, since Wells provided it with oceans which, by 1897, were known not to exist. Wells wasn't particularly concerned with scientific accuracy, though; what he was really doing was creating a suitable abode for the ultimate bogeymen, a kind of extraterrestrial Transylvania. The comparison is fitting, since the Martians feed on the warm blood of their victims.

And there are plenty of victims. The Martians arrive in

70

large cylinders, shot from guns on the surface of Mars. They waste no time in devastating most of the English countryside with their heat rays and clouds of black gas. The plucky British put up a game fight against the huge Martian war machines, but in the end they, together with the rest of the world, are conquered, utterly and finally.

The idea of annihilating one or more of the major countries of the world was not new with Wells. During the eighties and nineties an entire body of literature arose which graphically depicted the destruction of England or America by a powerful invader, usually Germany. It is not entirely clear what was responsible for this fad; probably it was just a reflection of the whole "end of an era" state of mind that was common then. These tales of conquest were simply a way of saying, "If the end is near, then let's go out in style," but they bore little resemblance to the conflagration that ultimately did end the era. Wells' achievement was in casting unearthly aliens in the role of the conqueror, thus lifting the book safely out of the shifting sands of contemporary politics.

The War of the Worlds was also a book designed to humble Victorian arrogance. Not only did the Martians subjugate the Earthmen with ridiculous ease, but the invaders themselves were finally vanquished by "the humblest thing God in His wisdom put on this earth," bacteria. With no built-in resistance to earthly microbes, the Martians were killed off en masse by the common cold.

Wells' Martians were disgusting creatures, perhaps the worst of a generally unattractive lot. They were mostly head and tentacles with no body to speak of; Wells suggested that they may have been descended from "beings not unlike ourselves." It was an idea Wells had used before in *The Time Machine:* evolution need not stop here. The Morlocks and Eloi had degenerated, but the Martians had moved on to other, perhaps better, forms.

The War of the Worlds met with immediate success and

spawned dozens of books about Martians, a few of which were written as sequels to Wells' book. In the sequels, the earthmen usually launched a counterattack against the Martians which devastated the Red Planet and restored earthly pride.

Wells was not the first (and certainly not the last) to write about Martians, he was simply the most successful. The same year *The War of the Worlds* was published, a German writer named Kurd Lasswitz brought out a lengthy novel entitled *On Two Planets.* It was noteworthy because it showed that relations with the Martians would probably not be terribly different from relations among nations. After an initial period of friendship, the Martians take over the earth, but with the help of Martian sympathizers, the Americans gain access to the Martian technology and eventually force a kind of balance-of-power settlement.

Both Lasswitz and Wells had more serious purposes in mind than just scaring people. As good science fiction writers have always done, they used an alien culture to point out truths about our own. However, there was a lot to be said for the value of a good scare, too, and soon dozens of writers were grinding out thrillers about Martians. The trend reached a peak sometime before World War I, but with the coming of the war there was no further need for made-up villains. After the war, although the pulp thrillers continued to flourish, most "serious" writers and readers were more than willing to forget that they had ever been titillated by something as frivolous as an invasion from Mars.

On the night of October 30, 1938, millions of Americans were abruptly shaken out of the same kind of complacency that H.G. Wells had written about. The shaking was done by the twenty-four-year-old boy wonder of the airwaves, Orson Welles.

Welles was the director and star of the CBS radio show, *The*

Mercury Theatre. The show had a large following, but not as large as that of the competition, NBC's Edgar Bergen and Charlie McCarthy. Determined not to be outdrawn by a wooden dummy, Welles planned a special Hallowe'en treat— an adaptation of *The War of the Worlds.* The task of writing the radio play was given to Howard Koch, who later wrote the screenplay of *Casablanca.* Koch wanted out of the project, but Welles was adamant. Somewhat reluctantly, Koch turned to the task of destroying the world.

Koch moved the invasion from England to the United States, specifically, to Grovers Mill, New Jersey, a spot he picked by closing his eyes and poking at a map. At the suggestion of producer John Houseman, Koch dramatized the first half of the book in the form of radio bulletins.

The broadcast began with a typical "dance band remote" and the syrupy music of "Ramon Raquello and his orchestra." The band was interrupted by bulletins announcing the observation of brilliant flashes on the surface of Mars, soon followed by reports of a blazing meteorite crashing to earth in New Jersey.

Before long, there was a reporter broadcasting live from the scene, describing in urgent tones the strange cylinder that had come to rest on the farm of a Mr. Wilmuth. With the deft use of sound effects and a breathless commentary, the first sudden attack of the Martians was recreated in an all-too-realistic manner. As the Martian heat ray turned toward him, the voice of the reporter was abruptly cut off.

In the next fifteen minutes the Martians conquered all of New Jersey and were closing in on New York. The first half of the performance ended with an announcer on the roof of the CBS Building giving a play-by-play account as the Martian war machines waded across the Hudson River and spread their deadly black smoke over Manhattan.

The second part of the broadcast was similar to the original Wells version; the thoughts and recollections of a survivor wandering across the ruined landscape. Anyone who heard this second act would have realized immediately that he was listening to a play, but by then an astounding number of people were no longer listening. The realism of the first act had been enough to send many of them into the streets in screaming panic.

It seems more than a little incredible that so many people could have been taken in by Welles' "Hallowe'en prank." For one thing, it took the Martians less than half an hour to leave their own planet and conquer ours—which is pretty quick, even for superior beings. And anyone who bothered to change stations would have heard the reassuring voices of Edgar Bergen. Nevertheless, a surprising number of otherwise sober and intelligent citizens took the whole thing seriously. A study performed by a group from Princeton (just a few miles from Grovers Mill) estimated that of the six million people who heard the program, at least 1,200,000 believed that an actual invasion was under way.

In Grovers Mill itself a group of courageous farmers grabbed their shotguns and went out looking for Martians; they found one and blasted away at it. When dawn came, they saw that their Martian war machine was just a well-perforated water tower. Many people took to the roads, fleeing the invaders with a lemminglike instinct, oblivious to the fact that if the Martians were taking over the world, there was nowhere to go that would be safe. Others gathered their families together and sat quietly waiting for the end.

There were some near tragedies. A Pittsburgh man returned home to find his wife in the bathroom holding a bottle of poison, screaming, "I'd rather die this way than like that!"

As far as is known, the broadcast was not directly responsible for any deaths, and the millions of dollars worth of lawsuits which were filed against CBS were dropped for lack of precedent. After the initial furor subsided, the general view of Welles and his hoax was actually favorable. Those who hadn't been taken in felt superior, and those who did believe it had learned a valuable lesson, along with the rest of the country. The power of radio was greater than anyone had previously suspected, and people were all too willing to believe whatever they were told.

In the context of 1938, it is perhaps not so surprising that the broadcast was taken seriously by so many. The Martians may not have been real, but Hitler certainly was; the play was credible because it sounded so much like actual reports from Europe.

But there was something else. The magic, potent name of Mars had been invoked, and people responded to it. How many would have believed it if Welles had launched his invasion from Venus? Mars, the God of War, the blood-red light in the sky, was still a force lurking just beneath the surface of the rational mind.

Although the Wells-Welles team may have scared a lot of people, it is doubtful that they influenced as many as another, less respected writer—Edgar Rice Burroughs. When Burroughs wrote about Mars, there was no pretense about making comments on contemporary society, nor was there any other form of redeeming social importance. If the Wellsian Mars was a device for illuminating the problems of our own world, then the Mars of Burroughs was a device for getting away from them.

The career of Edgar Rice Burroughs is an affront to every writer who has ever spent long, impoverished years courting the muses in a vain attempt to produce "art." Burroughs turned to writing at the age of thirty-seven simply because he had failed at everything else. It looked easy enough. He decided that "if people were paid for writing rot such as I read, I could write stories just as rotten."

The "rotten" stories that inspired Burroughs to write *A Princess of Mars* in 1911 appeared in the then flourishing "pulp" magazines. *The All-Story Magazine, The Argosy, The*

Blue Book Magazine, The Cavalier, Famous Story Magazine,
and a host of others filled a growing need for escapism in an
increasingly urban, mechanized, and literate society. Writers
such as Arthur Conan Doyle, Jack London, Rex Stout, Max
Brand, H. Rider Haggard, and H. P. Lovecraft frequented the
pages of the pulps, along with legions of hacks who are best
forgotten. The quality of writing ran the gamut from dreadful
to mediocre, with occasional sallies into regions of actual
literary merit—and Burroughs fit right in.

Burroughs had the kind of can't-win life that naturally
inspired daydreams of a more exciting existence. He flunked
out of prep school, failed the West Point admission exams,
and was eventually invalided out of the cavalry. He ran an
unsuccessful stationery store in Idaho, went broke in a mining
venture, worked as a railroad policeman in Utah, was an
accountant with Sears Roebuck, sold mail-order aluminum
cookware, and wrote self-improvement courses on (fittingly
enough) how to succeed at business. By 1911, he was working
as an agent for a Chicago pencil sharpener company. With a
wife and two children to support, he decided to put down on
paper some of the fantasies of adventure that he had dreamt
during the long years of failure.

The rest is, as they say, history. The first of his John Carter
on Mars tales was an immediate success, and his publisher
clamored for a sequel. Eventually there were eleven Mars
books and dozens of other swashbucklers, including the Tarzan books. The popularity of Burroughs' novels may be
measured, in part, by the fact that Tarzan is probably the only
fictional character ever to have a town named after him—
Tarzana, California.

The Mars of Edgar Rice Burroughs is essentially the same
as the Mars of Percival Lowell, with stage dressing added.
Lowell's theories were in vogue at the time Burroughs began
writing, and he was certainly aware of them, although as time
went on Burroughs paid less and less attention to such foolish
hobgoblins as consistency and scientific accuracy.

Burroughs may have paid a kind of tribute to Lowell, however. Before John Carter's departure to Mars, he was prospecting for gold in the Arizona desert with a man named Powell. Arizona is the location of Lowell's observatory, and Powell could be an elision of P. Lowell. But since Powell got killed by Apaches, it was probably not the sort of remembrance that Lowell would have appreciated.

John Carter himself was the dashing soldier-of-fortune son of an aristocratic Virginia family. He fought for the South in the Civil War (naturally: no one with any real *style* fought for the North), then wandered west in search of fortune and adventure. He finds both, and is cornered in a cave by marauding Indians, with no way out. Percival Lowell had urged his readers to free their minds from "the shackles that of necessity tether our bodies," and Burroughs has Carter do just that, literally. Carter looks up and sees Mars, red and portentious in the desert sky. The god of his vocation, it seems to beckon. Carter heeds the call; closing his eyes, he wishes his way to Mars. When he opens his eyes, he is on Mars. Neat trick, that.

Carter soon encounters an astonishing variety of Martians—green, red, black, yellow, white, headless—and with his quick wits and earth-grown muscles, he conquers them all. As the victor, he gets the spoils, which means Dejah Thoris, the beautiful Princess of Helium. Together, they produce a son, though it is hard to say just how they accomplished this feat, since all Martians are oviparous. John Carter, Virginia gentleman, is far too polite to give us the details.

Mars, or Barsoom, was the kind of place guaranteed to capture the imagination of youngsters, as well as adults who weren't too particular about realism. An entire generation grew up on the nourishment of Burroughs' fantasies, and it would not be an exaggeration to suggest, as Ray Bradbury has done, that Edgar Rice Burroughs was the true father of the space age. Burroughs made us *want* to get to Mars.

When the *Viking* spacecraft touched down on the surface of

Barsoom, sixty-five years after Carter's arrival, it was not surprising that many of those responsible for the achievement credited Burroughs with giving them their first shove in the direction of Mars. Present at the Jet Propulsion Laboratory for the landing were some of the men who carried on the Burroughs tradition—Robert A. Heinlein, Ray Bradbury, and *Star Trek*'s Gene Roddenberry. Said Roddenberry, "I'm an old ERB fan, so I hope they find John Carter up there."

A man more directly involved in the *Viking* Project also gave a nod to Burroughs—Carl Sagan, Director of Cornell's Laboratory for Planetary Studies. Sagan even admitted that as an eight-year-old boy he spent a lot of hours in an empty field with his arms outstretched, trying to wish his way to Mars, a la John Carter.

And on July 20, 1976, Sagan got his wish. Never underestimate the power of a hack writer.

5

"The Earthmen Are Coming! The Earthmen Are Coming!"— The Mars of Clarke, Heinlein, and Bradbury

> They had a house of crystal pillars on the planet Mars by the edge of an empty sea . . .
>
> —Ray Bradbury, 1950

The success of H.G. Wells and Edgar Rice Burroughs proved that Martians were a marketable commodity. The general fiction "pulp" magazines gave way to specialized fantasy and science fiction periodicals such as *Astounding, Astonishing,* and *Amazing,* and by the 1930s science fiction had entered what is often referred to as its Golden Age. Writers explored such bizarre themes as time travel, suspended animation, space flight, atomic bombs, overpopulation, telepathy, and a raft of others; but they kept returning to Mars. The Red Planet was soon overrun with exotic LGMs (Little Green Men) and BEMs (Bug-Eyed Monsters), and occasional visiting earthmen.

Those wandering earthmen at first tended to be in the John Carter mold, cardboard heroes with brains and brawn but no gonads. There were no bathrooms on the early spaceships, either, but they were normally well-equipped with blasters, death rays, and other paraphernalia of the twenty-second century. This was the "space opera" phase of science fiction when anything was possible, especially if it seemed impossible.

For example, there was the matter of interstellar flight. Einstein's cosmic speed limit of the velocity of light was blithely ignored by many writers. Others, who felt inhibited by the narrow confines of our own solar system, resorted to such devices as hyperspace, space warps, "jumps," "jaunts," n-space, folded space, and "transitions" in order to get their heroes out into the Galaxy, where the action was. But the difficulties involved in leaving the solar system led many writers to concentrate on planets closer to home.

Mars was the favorite choice largely because it seemed to be the most nearly earth-like planet. The outer planets were too cold or too big, and Mercury was too hot, so that left Mars and Venus as the most likely homes for extraterrestrial civilizations. Venus, though, was mainly a mystery because of its cloak of clouds. Scientific opinion was divided as to whether Venus would be cold because the clouds reflected the sun's heat, or hot because the clouds trapped the heat. Most science-fiction writers went for the second hypothesis. Also, the clouds seemed to suggest a high water content in the Venerian atmosphere. So Venus was hot and wet—a planet of steaming tropical oceans and swamps, populated by huge reptiles and slimy creatures from the depths of the lagoons. It made a nice contrast to cold, dry Mars. There was an apparent continuum: young, volatile Venus, temperate middle-aged earth, and ancient and dying Mars.

If Mars was, indeed, older than the earth, then it stood to reason that any Martian civilization would be advanced far beyond that of earth—perhaps to the point of decay. That was in line with Lowell's theories, which were popular with fiction writers long after they had been discarded by most scientists. Lowell's canals, in particular, were as real and tangible to the science-fiction writers as the Erie Canal.

The Flash Gordon-Buck Rogers School of science fiction

continued to be popular throughout the thirties, but hard scientific realism gradually crept into the literature. One of the first—and best—of the "real" Mars stories was written in 1934 by Stanley G. Weinbaum. "A Martian Odyssey" was an account of the first expedition to Mars, a theme which was to become a science-fiction staple. Weinbaum's Mars was definitely Lowellian, but not in the least Burroughsian. The earthmen had to endure the dry, cold climate and the thin air, and the low gravity may have helped them move about, but it didn't turn them into supermen, as it had John Carter. They found plant life and canals, but not any signs of fantastic civilizations. There were interesting inhabitants, however, including an ostrich-like creature which was friendly and intelligent. More interesting, there was also a "pyramid creature" whose chemistry was based on silicon rather than carbon.

The question of silicon-based life has intrigued science fiction writers and, to a somewhat lesser extent, scientists themselves. All earthly life is tied to the carbon atom, and as far as we know there are no alternative examples of biochemistry. But silicon can take the place of carbon in numerous chemical activities, so it is not too farfetched to suppose that some sort of life form could be silicon-related. Since silicon is a major constituent of rocks and sand, fictional silicon creatures usually tend to be very rock-like, as were Weinbaum's. Even during the *Viking* mission to Mars in 1976, there were persistent questions from the press about *Viking*'s ability or inability to detect any hypothetical silicon–based life forms. Scientists now think it highly unlikely, but are not willing to exclude the possibility that silicon-based life might exist somewhere in the universe. Silicon, by the way, should not be confused with "silicone"—a mistake which was made by a Los Angeles TV newswoman during the *Viking* mission. Her reference to "silicone" on Mars was, perhaps, revealing, but not accurate.

In 1940, Robert A. Heinlein began writing science-fiction

stories. Heinlein, frequently referred to as "the dean of American science-fiction writers," was an Annapolis graduate and brought to his stories and novels a solid background in science and engineering. The emergence of Heinlein (and, at about the same time, Isaac Asimov, Arthur C. Clarke, and a number of others) marked a turning point in the history of the genre. The old space operas were supplanted by generally plausible, scientifically accurate tales that featured believable characters involved in action that was fantastic yet still credible.

Heinlein, more than any other modern writer, concentrated on Mars. He created a consistent, highly structured Martian civilization which carried over from book to book; thus, he was able to portray the pitfalls and problems of human interaction with an alien society in a variety of thought-provoking and entertaining ways. The same Martians we meet in *Red Planet* are present in *Stranger in a Strange Land* and several other books, including *Double Star, Podkayne of Mars, Space Cadet, Between Planets,* and *The Rolling Stones.*

Heinlein's Martians are the sort that might have been imagined by Percival Lowell (one of the earth colonies on Heinlein's Mars is called Port Lowell). They are an incredibly ancient civilization, older and wiser than men can truly comprehend. They had space travel once, but gave it up eons ago, finding meditation and contemplation more agreeable pursuits. The Martians are in constant contact with The Old Ones—dead ancestors who have passed on to another plane of existence. They are willing to put up with the minor inconvenience of having their planet colonized by earthmen, for they don't consider human beings to be very important in the overall scheme of things.

Physically, Heinlein's Martians are huge, somewhat over twelve feet tall. On earth biology works in twos, but on Mars, it works in threes. The Martians have three legs, three eyes—three everything. Young Martians, however, look totally un-

82

like their elders, and at first the earthmen don't even suspect the relationship. The youngsters are roughly the size and shape of bowling balls, except that they have three retractable stalks with eyes on them, and three retractable all-purpose appendages. They also have the ability to mimic human speech and other sounds. The earthmen think they are cute and keep them as pets.

The colonists on Heinlein's Mars tend to be, like almost all of his characters, independent, abrasive, intelligent, principled, and quick on the draw. That causes occasional trouble with the natives, who have the ability to "discorporate" anyone or anything that bothers them to the point of action. One of Heinlein's most memorable characters, Valentine Michael Smith, was born on the first Mars expedition and raised by the Martians after the other humans died. Smith naturally learns all of the Martians' marvelous mind techniques, and creates something of a sensation when he is eventually returned to earth. *Stranger in a Strange Land,* Smith's story, became Heinlein's most successful novel, reaching the status of "cult book" among counter-culture types in the late sixties. Smith, in the book, became the focal point of a new religion that preached sexual openness, meditation, and cannibalism. Actual attempts to imitate the life-style of Smith and his followers failed, however, due mainly to the fact that no one really had the powers possessed by Smith.

Stranger in a Strange Land added a word to the language—grok. The verb "to grok" is a Martian word that means "to understand fully, to have complete empathy with," as in, "I really grok the Beatles," or, "I grok it, man." The book also introduced the concept of water-sharing, a custom of highest importance on arid Mars. To share water with someone, Martian or human, was to bestow the greatest possible honor. This, too, was adopted by many hippies; on not-so-arid earth, it usually meant communal bathing, although for some it became a sort of love ritual with roughly the same meaning on earth as on Mars. In David Crosby's song "Triad," there is a warm reference to "water brothers."

That Heinlein should have been taken to heart by the counter-culture was one of the stranger things in the strange land that was America in the late sixties, for by then Heinlein himself had become an ultra right-winger. In his later books he denigrated democracy, extolled the virtues of a military society, and suggested that it should be no crime to gun down a pacifist. His fascination with genetics and "clean" gene charts, for some of his readers, smacked of Nazism.

But whatever Heinlein has become in his old age, in his prime he was one of America's greatest science-fiction writers. His books, particularly his "juvenile" novels of the fifties, were directly responsible for a great many young people's turning to science for a career. Like Burroughs, he made us want to get to Mars, but unlike Burroughs, Heinlein showed how it could be done.

Heinlein was one of over 1,800 guests at the Jet Propulsion Laboratory in Pasadena on the night of the *Viking* landing on Mars. Unfortunately, through some slip-up, he was denied admittance to the press area because he lacked the proper set of credentials. Another science-fiction writer, there as a newspaper correspondent, was angry over the incident. "Hell," he said, "Heinlein's the guy who started all of this. Half the people here got into science because they read his books. Short memory, I say."

Perhaps. But perhaps it was just another indication that today's science has already caught up with the science fiction of yesterday. Now, you need a pass to get into the future.

Even more than Heinlein, Arthur C. Clarke is known as a writer of "scientific" science fiction. He has written extensively about science fact, and even his fiction is, for the most part, securely grounded in science. Among his many accomplishments is his "invention" of the communications satellite. He first proposed that artificial earth satellites could be used for communication relays in an article written in 1945 for *Wireless World,* a trade magazine.

Clarke had his vision of Mars, too, and in many respects it has held up remarkably well. *The Sands of Mars,* Clarke's first novel, was published in 1952 and was one of the first attempts to present the "real" Mars in fictional form. There are no beautiful princesses or strange silicon creatures running around on Clarke's Mars; as the title implies, mostly there is just sand.

But there are some plants. In the fifties, it was still widely believed that the dark areas of Mars consisted of vegetation. Scientists were much less certain about the existence of canals by then, so Clarke neatly sidestepped the issue by simply failing to mention canals. He may have been the first science-fiction writer *not* to write about them.

Clarke presents us with a highly believable picture of the first permanent earth colony on Mars. The atmosphere is too thin to breathe, so anyone venturing outside the inflated domes of the cities must wear breathing gear. It is expensive and difficult to bring supplies from earth, so the colony, like any colony, places top priority on attaining self-sufficiency. The colonists themselves are young, intelligent, multitalented, and dedicated to making a go of it on Mars.

But back on earth, the powers that be are not convinced that the Martian venture is worthwhile. It has been a tremendous drain on earthly resources, and there is no immediately obvious benefit for the folks at home. With uncanny foresight, Clarke predicted the backlash against space exploration even before the Space Age was properly under way. The following passage, written in 1952, might have come from an editorial written in 1976:

> You've got to realize that from the point of view of Earth, Mars is a long way away and costs a lot of money, and doesn't offer anything in return. The first glamour of interplanetary

exploration has worn off. Now people are asking, "What do we get out of it?" So far, the answer's been, "Very little." I'm convinced that your work is important, but in my case it's an act of faith rather than a matter of logic. The average man back on Earth probably thinks the millions you're spending here could be better used improving his own planet—when he thinks of it at all, that is.

For Clarke's colonists, the answer to the problem is to make Mars more like earth, make it a less expensive, less dangerous place to live. To that end, they set off a nuclear device that turns Phobos, the inner moon, into a small star. The added warmth makes possible the extensive cultivation of a local plant known as *oxyfera,* an oxygen-giving plant that will someday make the Martian atmosphere thick and breathable. When the domed cities are no longer needed, the colonists will be able to spread out and make the planet truly their own.

It is an exciting vision, and one that might actually be possible someday. We know now that there are massive quantities of oxygen and water locked up in the same sands of Mars that Clarke wrote about a quarter of a century ago. If those sands could be induced to give up their bounty on a large scale, then Mars might someday become a second home for man. No one alive today is likely to see it happen, but when it finally does happen, one hopes that in addition to a Port Lowell, there will also be a Clarkeville on Mars.

Possibly the finest book ever written about Mars was Ray Bradbury's *The Martian Chronicles*—if you concede that *The War of the Worlds* was mainly about *earth.* Bradbury, in contrast to Heinlein and Clarke, is one of the least scientific writers of science fiction. He is often described as "the science-fiction writer for people who hate science fiction."

Bradbury himself is not particularly at home with technology. He has never flown (a trait he shares with Isaac Asimov, who is one of the most scientific writers of science fiction—or anything else), and he refuses to learn to drive a car. He confesses that he is also afraid of the dark; in fact, he is "afraid of the universe." It is not surprising, then, that there is a dreamlike (or sometimes nightmarish) quality about his writing. His books are like the elaborate fantasies of a nine-year-old boy. Science fiction critic Brian Aldiss has claimed that Bradbury's work deals with "a prepubertal world," and that "his stories read like translations of Ukrainian folk tales." Which is true enough, for *The Martian Chronicles* is basically a collection of Martian folk tales.

The book is pieced together from a series of short stories Bradbury wrote in the late forties. Taken together, they are like an epic poem about the rise and fall of two civilizations.

Bradbury's Martians have fair, brownish skin and eyes like golden coins. Their voices are soft and musical, and they are artistic and imaginative. They are an altogether attractive race.

The first Martian to know that the earthmen are coming is Ylla, a housewife. She has strange dreams and finds herself singing songs she has never heard before, songs like "Drink to Me Only With Thine Eyes." She becomes fascinated with her dream creatures, tall men with blue eyes. But her husband is not so enraptured by it all; when the earthmen finally land, he kills them.

The second expedition from earth arrives, hoping to discover what happened to the first expedition. But instead of being either welcomed or shot, they are simply accepted matter-of-factly. The earthmen can't understand it—until eventually they are herded into a Martian insane asylum. It seems that when Martians go crackers, they assume odd shapes; the astronauts are simply presumed to be unbalanced locals.

The third expedition finds another surprise: Hometown, U.S.A. It is Grinnell, Iowa, or maybe Green Bluff, Illinois, circa 1909, and it is populated with friends and relatives of the crew. It is unbelievable, but so seductive that they are willing to accept it. The Martians kill them in their sleep.

The earthmen finally succeed with their fourth expedition to Mars, but by then it is too late to meet the Martians. They are all dead. In a switch on H. G. Wells, the earthmen of the previous expeditions have brought chicken pox with them, and it reduces the entire population to piles of dead autumn leaves. Only their crystal cities remain, and they are soon desecrated by the earthmen, who use the spindly towers for target practice.

So the earthmen come to Mars, and they come to stay. They build their cities and their roads and they begin to turn it into a suburb of their home planet. The atmosphere problem is solved by a Johnny Appleseed who plants trees that grow to overwhelming size in a single night, releasing fresh, pure oxygen.

But the Martians are still around them, like ghosts. In a marvelous scene, one of the colonists encounters a Martian in the desert, but each is like a phantom to the other. The Martian is on his way to a festival in one of the crystal cities; the earthman is on his way into the newly built town. Neither can see the Mars that the other sees:

". . . See the broken pillars?"

"Broken? Why, I see them perfectly. The moonlight helps. And the pillars are upright."

"There's dust in the streets," said Tomás.

"The streets are clean!"

"The canals are empty right there."

"The canals are full of lavender wine!"

"It's dead."

"It's alive!"

Ultimately, it is the earthman who is right, for the colonists have brought their own special brand of death with them. War breaks out on earth, and the colonists are drawn homeward, to share in the final agony. Mars is left to the ghosts.

Bradbury, the eternal optimist, ends his book on a note of hope, however. Characteristically, our last view of Mars is through the eyes of children. Two families escape the holocaust on earth and come to Mars for "a million year picnic." The children are excited, but they are eager, most of all, to see the Martians.

"I've always wanted to see a Martian," said Michael. "Where are they Dad? You promised."

"There they are," said Dad, and he shifted Michael on his shoulder and pointed straight down.

The Martians were there. Timothy began to shiver.

The Martians were there—in the canal—reflected in the water. Timothy and Michael and Robert and Mom and Dad.

The Martians stared back up at them for a long, long silent time from the rippling water. . . .

Bradbury's Mars was perhaps the least realistic since Burroughs', but it was also one of the most compelling. Bradbury freely admits the connection. "Without Edgar Rice Burroughs," he has said, *The Martian Chronicles* would never have been born."

And without the soaring imagination of men like Burroughs, Bradbury, Heinlein, Clarke, and a hundred others, the Space Age would never have been born. Scientific curiosity alone could never account for the incredible expense and effort involved in exploring the solar system.

On the eve of the *Viking* landing, at a symposium sponsored by the British Interplanetary Society, Bradbury suggested the real reason for space exploration. "We go to Mars," he said, "because it is in our genetics to go to Mars." Simplistic, perhaps, but probably true. Certainly, the Mount Everest syndrome ("because it is there") is at least as powerful as what Bradbury calls "the tupperware syndrome"—the benefits to be realized from space spin-offs. In fact, Bradbury has threatened to punch the nose of the next man he hears talking about spin-offs. We don't need such mundane reasons for going to Mars, according to Bradbury.

The expense doesn't bother him. "The big money is in the Pentagon," he told his appreciative audience. "That's where we go to grab it someday, okay?"

In Bradbury's phrase, man explores in order to "act out the universe." Bradbury's attitude may be at odds with some of the scientists and engineers, who see more pragmatic reasons for exploration, but no one could disagree with his conclusion: "We touch Mars so as to touch ourselves better." Or, to paraphrase another great philosopher of the age, Pogo, we have met the Martians, and they are us.

6

Other Voices, Other Barsooms—
Radical Visions of the Red Planet

The universe is not only queerer than we suppose, it is queerer than we *can* suppose.

—J.B.S. Haldane

Everything you know is wrong.

—The Firesign Theater

The difference between science and science fiction is not always clear-cut. There are many prominent scientists who have written science fiction in their spare time—Fred Hoyle, Isaac Asimov, and Robert S. Richardson, to name a few. Unfortunately, there are also a number of fiction writers who have been writing what they like to think of as science. But it is not necessarily a two-way street.

The fantastic success in recent years of books by Immanuel Velikovsky, Erich von Däniken, and their kindred spirits has been a source of concern to bona fide scientists. The public has seemed eager to accept the pseudoscience offered by such writers, often to the detriment of serious science. An astronomer or an archeologist may labor for years on a thoughtful, analytical, worthwhile manuscript, only to have it ignored by the general public; meanwhile, von Däniken makes millions and corrupts the masses with his fables.

Part of the problem has been the inability, and occasional

unwillingness, of the scientific establishment to come to grips with the issues posed by people like von Däniken. When scientists have attempted to take on the von Dänikens, the results have often seemed, to the general public at least, inconclusive or worse. The purveyors of ancient astronauts and ancient catastrophes, as science-fiction writer Theodore Sturgeon has suggested, tend to take an attitude that makes their "discoveries" impossible to tackle head-on. Sturgeon's example of a von Däniken-like argument is to say, "Nobody can disprove this statement: Somewhere in the middle of the asteroid belt there is a piece of chocolate devil's food cake."

Immanuel Velikovsky might not even want to disprove that statement. Food raining from the heavens is just one of the ancient events he claims to have uncovered.

Velikovsky was born in Eastern Europe and worked for a time as a psychoanalyst. He emigrated to Palestine during the thirties and became fascinated by the ancient cultures that had once thrived there. By 1939, when he moved to the United States, his studies of the ancients had convinced him that scientists had ignored the true significance of events described in the Bible and other ancient records.

Velikovsky set forth his theories in his first book, *Worlds in Collision*, which was published in 1950 and has since sold over a million copies. Despite the almost universal scorn of the scientific community, Velikovsky has continued to argue his case and win converts.

Basically, Velikovsky takes as literal truth many ancient stories and legends depicting cosmic cataclysms. He supposes that myths about the old gods are in fact metaphorical accounts of actual events. In the Greek myths, to take one example, Pallas Athena is born full-grown from the head of Zeus. Velikovsky uses this myth to support his contention that the planet Venus began life as a comet which was expelled from the planet Jupiter.

The event supposedly occurred in relatively recent times, which is why, according to Velikovsky, there are no records of observations of Venus before about 1500 B.C. As a comet, Venus was responsible for a lot of the more miraculous happenings recorded in the Bible. Sweeping through the earth's upper atmosphere, Venus blackened the skies, produced the famous plagues of Egypt during the Exodus, and even fed the fleeing Israelites with a rain of carbohydrates from its tail—manna from heaven. Gravitational disruptions and earthquakes associated with this encounter also produced the parting of the Red Sea and the storms covering Mt. Sinai. Venus eventually settled down and assumed its present orbit around the sun.

Meanwhile, Mars was behaving rather capriciously. Although it was not a comet to begin with, collisions with the comet Venus threw it out of its stable orbit. Velikovsky finds confirmation of these collisions in the *Iliad* which, he says, shows that this "cosmic drama was projected onto the fields of Troy."

We should be grateful to Mars, if Velikovsky is right. Venus had collided with earth in the fifteenth century B.C., wreaking considerable havoc. But during the eighth century B.C., Venus repeatedly collided with Mars. Although Mars is much smaller than Venus, it was able to disrupt the elliptical orbit of Venus and eventually push it into a tame circular orbit, where it resides today. Mars, however, was also thrown out of its orbit and had several near misses with the earth in the eighth and seventh centuries B.C. Velikovsky supposes that during these encounters, the atmospheres of the planets were intermixed; the argon and neon in our atmosphere, he says, may have come from Mars.

Prior to all these collisions, there were fireworks of another kind lighting up the solar system. Velikovsky believes that giant electrical discharges ("thunderbolts") were bouncing around between Jupiter, Mars, Venus, and the earth. These thunderbolts were responsible for zapping Sodom and Gomorrah.

It makes a dramatic picture, entertaining and more than a

little scary. Also completely wrong, said scientists. From the beginning, Velikovsky was assailed as a cosmic quack. Macmillan, the original publisher of *Worlds in Collision,* was faced with a general boycott of its scientific textbooks; rather than lose a profitable market, Macmillan signed the rights over to Doubleday. Velikovsky was too hot to handle.

Why such a vehement response if Velikovsky was wrong? It is a complex question, and it bears on problems that have bedeviled scientists down to the present day, including those involved in the *Viking* mission to Mars.

Velikovsky published his book in 1950, less than a century after Darwin wrote *The Origin of Species,* and only a quarter of a century after the famous Scopes trial. The theory of evolution was slow to gain acceptance, and is still under attack from many quarters. The attacks center around the fact that Darwin and evolution have decreed that man has descended from lower orders of life. That is hard for some people to swallow, for they believe that it somehow demeans humanity to be related to apes, lizards, and bacteria.

The most important aspect of the theory is that it deals with a continuing process, rather than an end result. The theory says that life—the life of organisms and, by implication, the life of the earth, the solar system, and the universe—proceeds slowly, according to definite rules of behavior. The universe is not a random, erratic pinball machine, as Velikovsky would have it. Or, as Einstein put it, "God does not shoot dice."

If there are universal rules of behavior, then it should be possible to discover what they are and try to understand them. That is what science does. If there are no rules, then the entire structure of science is meaningless.

Velikovsky did not completely ignore the rules. What he did, in the eyes of many scientists, was much worse: he distorted the rules. He built a castle in the air, then tried to support it with a substructure of scientific fact. But that isn't the way science works. Like evolution, it is a slow, methodical process that starts at the bottom and builds. A theory or hypothesis is no more than a proposed blueprint for the next floor of the structure; if the facts are found not to fit the suggested blueprint, then it must be the theory—not the facts—which is discarded. But Velikovsky ignored the facts that didn't fit; he substituted the cheap wood of supposition for the brick and mortar of scientific investigation.

It would have been easy to bring down Velikovsky's castle. But scientists, perhaps rightly, feared that in the process, their own building would be damaged. So rather than tackle Velikovsky head-on, most scientists preferred to ignore him and hope he would go away. Instead, Velikovsky's theories had time to take root and spread.

There is something to be said for Velikovsky's side of it, however. To continue the structure-of-science metaphor a little longer, Velikovsky argued that the scientific establishment had constructed its own castle, complete with moat, drawbridge, and battlements. If you didn't belong to the club, you weren't welcome. There was no room for the radical theorist who had new ideas about how the structure should be built.

There was enough truth in Velikovsky's charges to make the scientific establishment uncomfortable. It was a difficult situation. If they debated Velikovsky's theories in the same manner as they would the theories of a reputable scientist, they would be lending legitimacy to a man who had perverted the principles of science—principles which had been established only after a long, hard fight against the know-nothings and reactionaries. But if they refused to debate Velikovsky, it would seem that they were afraid of him.

The sensational aspects of Velikovsky's theories presented still another problem. Ever since the rather bloody public debate surrounding the existence or nonexistence of Lowell's canals, scientists—particularly astronomers—have been reluctant to get themselves involved in issues which are likely to appear on the front page of tomorrow's newspaper. During *Viking*'s search for life on Mars, even the most cautious statements by biologists tended to wind up as blaring headlines which, more often than not, badly distorted what they had said. The result was that the cautious remarks became super-cautious remarks.

It was not until 1974 that Velikovsky (by then seventy-nine) was given his chance to storm the walls of the scientific establishment. Largely at the insistence of Cornell astronomer Carl Sagan, Velikovsky was invited to speak at a forum of the American Association for the Advancement of Science. Sagan pointed out that the AAAS had managed to deal with the hot topic of UFOs and flying saucers without doing itself irreparable harm—it should be able to handle Velikovsky.

Indeed, the scientists actually seemed to relish the opportunity to dispose of Velikovsky once and for all. The forum was hardly a collision of worlds—it was more like shooting fish in a barrel.

Swiss statistician and Assyrian expert Peter J. Huber undermined the validity of all those ancient records Velikovsky relied upon. Velikovsky's arguments, said Huber, were based on "obsolete and erroneous translations." Velikovsky, he charged, "makes a complete muddle of texts, insights, periods, and places." For one thing, the ancient records showed that Venus was in its present orbit at least 1,500 years before it was supposed to have collided with earth.

Velikovsky was shown to be ignorant of some fundamentals of celestial mechanics, geology, biology, and chemistry. The hydrocarbons in the tail of the comet Venus, had it existed, could hardly have been responsible for the rain of "carbohydrates" that gave the Israelites their manna. Hydrocarbons and carbohydrates are not at all the same thing, as Velikovsky apparently assumed.

The coup de grâce was delivered by Carl Sagan in a 57-page paper. "Where Velikovsky is original," said Sagan, "he is very likely wrong; where he is right, the idea has been preempted by other workers.... There are large numbers of cases where he is neither right nor original." To take just one example, Sagan showed that if an object the size of Venus ever had been ejected from Jupiter, the force of the explosion would have vaporized the departing body.

Velikovsky refused to give up. He complained that he was being treated like Giordano Bruno, although there is no evidence that the AAAS had arranged for a bonfire. As for his chief tormentor—if Sagan keeps this up, vowed Velikovsky, "I will destroy him."

Coming from a man who had, in his time, moved heaven and earth, it was a formidable threat. However, to date, no planets have fallen on Sagan.

Despite overwhelming scientific evidence against him, Velikovsky continues to have a large following. But Velikovsky has been little more than a John the Baptist for the cult of Erich von Däniken, whose books have sold more than 12 million copies in 32 languages.

Velikovsky believed in ancient catastrophes; von Däniken believes in ancient astronauts. Of the two, von Däniken's claims hold up better simply because it is flatly impossible for anyone to *prove* that the earth was never visited by intelligent beings from other worlds. On the other hand, von Däniken has not even come close to proving that such visits did take place. But in the topsy-turvy universe of the cultists, the mere fact that he can't be disproved, according to von Däniken, means that he is right. Again, that is not the way that science works, but von Däniken and his readers seem to be blissfully unaware of scientific method.

Some scientists end their careers in jail, as did Galileo. But von Däniken *began* his career in jail. A Swiss hotelkeeper by trade, von Däniken was convicted of fraud and embezzlement. While serving his term, he became curious about some unexplained events in antiquity. After his release, he set about trying to explain them.

The earth, he says, has been visited repeatedly by beings from other worlds. The evidence is plentiful: wheels of fire and burning bushes in the Bible, Sumerian legends of fishmen, Babylonian batteries, landing fields in Peru, the Pyramids of Egypt, the Easter Island statues, and, last but certainly not least, the miracles performed by one Jesus of Nazareth. All of these, says von Däniken, are evidence of extraterrestrial visitors.

The Pyramids, for example, could not possibly have been built by mere earthmen. They are too big, and von Däniken can't figure out how they were constructed, unless by the use of some antigravity device. His historical research, he claims, shows that the absurd idea that the Pyramids were built with the use of ramps, wooden rollers, and rope is clearly impossible because the Egyptians didn't have enough trees for the wood. What von Däniken doesn't mention is that the Egyptians had a flourishing lumber trade going with Lebanon. Antigravity is not necessary to explain the construction of the Pyramids; all that is needed is time, slave labor, and fear, all of which the Egyptians had in abundance.

Von Däniken also claims that many ancient artifacts and paintings show the extraterrestrial visitors in action. He points to bits of jewelry which look like spaceships. Yes, they do look like spaceships; they also look like fish. That von Däniken chooses to see the resemblance to rockets is a sign of the times. Just as in an age of canal building, canals were seen on Mars, in an age of space exploration it is not surprising that spaceships should be seen in any ancient artifact that is the least bit streamlined.

We also have pictures of the aliens themselves, according to von Däniken. Many small sculptures from different cultures clearly show the visitors dressed up in their space suits. Von

98

Däniken seems never to have heard of ceremonial headdresses and the like.

Like Velikovsky, von Däniken insists on the literal interpretation of the ancient legends and artifacts. If something looks like a spaceship, it must therefore be a spaceship. Another thing von Däniken apparently never learned about in that Swiss jail is symbolism. If we accept von Däniken's literal interpretation, then we must believe that several different races of aliens visited the earth, and each race stopped in a different area: short, squat aliens with big mouths in Mexico, graceful six-armed aliens in India, huge-headed aliens at Easter Island, and so on.

Time and again, von Däniken has been exposed as a fraud. He has never even visited places which he claims to have explored. He cites sources which don't even exist. Nevertheless, his followers are legion, and von Däniken continues to rake in "gold from the gods."

The Velikovskys and von Dänikens represent a growing phenomenon in America and in the rest of the world. It is, perhaps, a sign that we have lost faith in ourselves—we feel the need for miraculous events and wise visitors to explain the things we don't understand. We want to believe in cosmic babysitters because the universe is dark and we are afraid of it.

The scientific establishment's distaste for dealing with the likes of Velikovsky and von Däniken is also apparent in its attitude toward UFOs. Unfortunately, the list of people who have seen UFOs includes not just wild-eyed visionaries, but also pilots, police officers, military men, meteorologists, radar operators, astronauts, and presidential candidates.

The fallout from the Orson Welles broadcast and all the jokes about Little Green Men from Mars have made it difficult to deal with the subject of UFOs in an objective manner. For many years, serious scientists were reluctant to get involved in the debate, leaving the field to the military, amateur investigators, and sensation seekers. In recent years there have been a few organized efforts to solve the UFO puzzle, but the question of whether or not the UFOs are spacecraft from other worlds remains very much open.

Although there are prominent exceptions, most scientists are of the opinion that there is no evidence to suggest that the UFOs are from other planets. Philip Morrison, of MIT, has written, "I have now, after a couple of years of fairly systematic listening and reading, no sympathy left for the extraterrestrial hypothesis. That does not mean that I know what is going on; I don't, at least not in every area. But the apparent strength of the evidence is not such as to make me regard the UFO phenomena as a matter of very high priority for myself."

On the other side of the fence is James E. McDonald of the University of Arizona. McDonald charges that the scientific investigation of UFOs has been superficial, at best: "In my opinion, the UFO problem, far from being the 'nonsense problem' it has been labeled by many scientists, constitutes an area of extraordinary scientific interest."

The vast majority of all UFO sightings can be adequately explained: weather balloons, birds, clouds, aircraft, satellites, reflections, planets, stars, hoaxes, and illusions. But there have been a few well-documented cases which don't fit neatly into any of those categories. The fact that they haven't been explained does not mean that they must therefore automatically be classified as true flying saucers; it does mean that more investigation is required.

There have been investigations in the past, but there is substantial disagreement as to their value. The Air Force Project Blue Book concluded that the UFOs were no threat to national security, but the military's obsession with secrecy has made it difficult for other investigators to check out their

100

records. The Condon Report, based on a federally funded study conducted by the University of Colorado in the 1960s, also concluded that UFOs were not worthy of further study, but the report has been criticized on a number of grounds, including shaky methodology and inadequate follow-through.

The American Association for the Advancement of Science did hold a forum on the subject of UFOs, and the book that came out of the forum, *UFOs, A Scientific Debate,* edited by Carl Sagan and Thornton Page, is far and away the best book on the subject. Yet even the AAAS report is inconclusive. The Unidentified Flying Objects remain unidentified.

Mars has always been closely linked to the UFO phenomenon. The number of UFO reports seems to rise during oppositions. That connection has led some, including Donald E. Keyhoe, to speculate that Mars might be the home, or at least the base, of the flying saucers. Keyhoe, a retired Marine major, has for many years been the leader of the "serious" UFO investigators. He discounts most of the "contact" stories, and his organization, the National Investigations Committee on Aerial Phenomena (NICAP), often checks out reported sightings more thoroughly than the Air Force.

The Air Force, to Keyhoe, is the chief villain in the UFO story. He charges that the Air Force has systematically censored UFO reports and has kept the truth from the public—the truth being that the UFOs are intelligently controlled vehicles from other planets. Keyhoe's allegations sounded like nothing more than paranoia for a long time, but in the wake of Watergate and the CIA revelations, Air Force censorship no longer seems so unlikely.

Whether or not the Air Force is covering up something, the central question remains unanswered; they may simply be covering up their own ignorance on the subject. There is compelling evidence to support both sides of the debate. The problem is that the evidence must be more than merely intriguing. On a question of such overwhelming importance, we must demand the best possible proof, either way, and so far, that proof does not exist.

We don't know if the earth has been visited by beings from other worlds. Some of von Däniken's theories may even be correct—although there is no way to prove it (and no reason to believe it) based on his books. We can be sure, however, that whatever the UFOs are, they don't come from Mars.

As late as 1973, Keyhoe tried to build a case for Martian civilization and flying saucers. In what must surely be the last gasp of the canal debate, Keyhoe charged that in 1965 *Mariner 4* had sent back to earth pictures of the canals, but that scientists at the Jet Propulsion Laboratory suppressed the photos. Unfortunately for his credibility, by the time Keyhoe made the charge, *Mariner 9* had already returned much more detailed pictures which proved once and for all that there were no canals on Mars.

In a sense, the story of Martian UFOs is just beginning. If there are any Martians, perhaps hiding underground, as Keyhoe suggests, they are certainly having a UFO debate of their own. Strange objects are unquestionably appearing in the Martian skies. And in this case, we can state with absolute certainty that the UFOs *are* intelligently controlled vehicles from another planet.

They are from earth.

PART THREE

Flights of Fact

7

The View from Earth

We *want* Mars to be like the Earth. There is a very deep-seated desire to find another place where we can make another start, that somehow could be habitable. ... It has been very, very hard to face up to the facts, which have been emerging for some time, that indicate it really isn't that way, that it is just wishful thinking.

—Bruce Murray
Mars and the Mind of Man, 1973

From the point of view of planetary astronomers, the Space Age happened at just the right moment. By the beginning of the 1960s, scientists were approaching a dead end in their studies of the solar system. Despite the introduction of new techniques, such as radio astonomy, and better equipment, there was a limit to how much could be learned about the planets from earth-based observations. The only way to find out more was to go to them.

Planetary studies had languished during the first half of the century, a situation that was at least partially the result of the controversy surrounding Percival Lowell's observations of Mars. Few astronomers wanted to get embroiled in heated debates over topics such as the canals; besides, another field of study was opening up. With modern telescopes, like the 200-inch Hale Telescope at Mt. Palomar, it was now possible to observe the farthest reaches of the universe; looking at nearby planets seemed rather parochial when, instead, you could be looking at galaxies a million light-years away.

Cosmological theories abounded. Was the universe finite or infinite? Did it begin with a loud bang, or had it always been there? Did it expand, contract, or remain the same? How were stars born? And how do they die? These grand questions seemed far more interesting than the comparatively trivial problem of how much water was on Mars. Anyway, the big questions looked easier to answer than the small ones.

But there were more than enough "small" questions to keep planetary astronomers busy. The mystery of the canals was only one piece in the jigsaw puzzle that was Mars.

There was, for example, the phenomenon of the "blue clearing." Astronomers normally photograph planets through various filters in order to bring out different details. Martian surface features are best seen through a red filter, since red and infrared light are not scattered by the atmosphere of Mars. But at the short end of the spectrum, it is a different story. Photographs of Mars taken through a blue filter generally reveal no surface detail at all; Mars presents a blank, featureless face, almost like that of Venus. There is something in the Martian atmosphere that scatters blue light.

But in 1937, E.C. Slipher of the Lowell Observatory found, to his surprise, that the "blue haze" had vanished. Photographs taken during opposition showed sharp surface detail around the region of Syrtis Major, even in blue light. At first, Slipher thought there might have been a mistake in the photo processing, but that proved not to be the case. Whatever the blue clearing was, it apparently was a real phenomenon.

During subsequent oppositions, Slipher and others again observed the blue clearing. For a time, it seemed that the blue clearing occurred *only* during oppositions. That suggested that the earth itself was somehow connected with the phenomenon, although no one could say just how. The clearings could occur within the space of a few hours, then disappear just as quickly. They might involve the entire planet, or only a small portion of it. Like the canals, the blue clearings were an enigma. And like the canals, astronomers who hadn't personally observed the blue clearings were inclined to doubt that they were real.

By the 1950s, the blue clearings had become a little less mysterious, but remained unexplained. They were observed several months before oppositions, so at least earth's involvement could be eliminated. More likely, the Martian seasons had something to do with the clearings. It was suggested that the blue haze was caused by crystals of ice or dry ice in the upper atmosphere of Mars—but that didn't explain why the haze should suddenly disappear. Astronomers needed to know more than what they were able to learn from beneath the thick blanket of our own atmosphere.

Earth's atmosphere also prevented astronomers from determining the composition of the Martian atmosphere. The device most commonly used to determine what elements constitute celestial bodies is the spectrometer. Isaac Newton was the first to observe that light from the sun could be refracted into a spectrum, but he failed to notice that included in the spectrum were a number of dark lines. The significance of those dark lines (known as Fraunhofer lines, after a nineteenth-century German optician) was not fully appreciated until about 1859, when Robert Bunsen (of burner fame) and G.R. Kirchhoff noticed that the dark lines in the solar spectrum corresponded with bright lines in the spectra of various gases. They reasoned that by matching up the dark lines with the bright lines, they would be able to tell what elements were present in the sun and the stars.

It should have been possible to use the same technique to determine the composition of planetary atmospheres, but here scientists ran into difficulties. The planets shine only by the reflected light of the sun, so whatever light they give off is heavily influenced by the solar spectrum. But if a planet's atmosphere contained gases which were not present in the sun, then it should be easy to determine which part of the spectrum was contributed by the sun and which part represented the planetary atmosphere. By using this method, ammonia (NH_3) and methane (CH_4) were discovered in the atmosphere of Jupiter.

Now a further complication comes into play. The reflected light of the planets must also travel through our own atmosphere, which, naturally enough, has its own spectrum. If a planet's atmosphere contained gases similar to those in the earth's atmosphere, their spectral lines would tend to be hidden by the same lines in the terrestrial spectrum. For planets like Jupiter and Saturn this was not too much of a problem, since ammonia and methane are not present in any quantity in our atmosphere; but for Mars, it was a major obstacle. If there were life on Mars, the Martian atmosphere would almost certainly have to contain significant amounts of oxygen and water vapor. But the high concentration of those two items in earth's atmosphere made it difficult to see their Fraunhofer lines in the Martian atmosphere.

There is a way around this problem, however. Back in 1843, Austrian physicist Christian Doppler became curious about the fact that the lines in the solar spectrum did not exactly match those of laboratory gases. If the gases were the same, what could account for the discrepancy of the lines? He reasoned that if light comes from an object which is approaching the observer, the spectrum would be crowded together, or shortened. Conversely, light from a receding object would be lengthened. Doppler's reasoning proved to be sound, and scientists had an important new tool—the Doppler effect.

By using the Doppler effect, it is possible to measure the speed and distance of almost any object in the sky. The amount of "red shift"—spectral displacement toward the longer wavelengths—or "violet shift"—displacement toward the shorter wavelengths—can be used to calculate the motions of planets, stars, or even galaxies. Because of the red shift, we know that the universe is expanding, and some distant galaxies are racing away from us at more than a quarter of the speed of light.

The Doppler effect is important to planetary astronomers because the shift toward violet or red in effect moves a planet's Fraunhofer lines out from behind the same lines in our own atmosphere. If an observation of Mars were to be made just before or after an opposition, it should produce a substantial shift that would allow the identification of the elements in the Martian atmosphere.

Unfortunately, in actual practice it is extremely difficult to prove out the theory. Because our own atmosphere is so dense, it is necessary to make observations from a high altitude, above most of the atmosphere, if any real benefit is to be derived from the Doppler effect. Such observations are difficult, and in any event, the Doppler shift of Mars is not large enough to make it easy to differentiate between Martian and terrestrial spectra.

Nevertheless, the method made possible at least tentative identification of some of the elements in the Martian atmosphere. In 1947, G. P. Kuiper found evidence of CO_2 on Mars, but in very low quantity, although still several times more abundant than it is in our atmosphere. In 1963, Audouin Dollfus obtained results which indicated that there was a tiny amount of water vapor present in the Martian atmosphere, barely enough to measure.

The CO_2 and H_2O apparently accounted for about one percent of the Martian atmosphere. That left astronomers guessing about the other 99 percent. They had found no sign of oxygen in the Martian spectra, so that important element seemed to be eliminated from consideration. The most likely candidate seemed to be nitrogen, which makes up about 78 percent of the earthly atmosphere. Unfortunately, nitrogen in its molecular state is almost impossible to identify in observable spectra. That is also true of argon, which constitutes about one percent of earth's atmosphere.

This combination of limited observation and educated guesswork led astronomers in the early 1960s to believe that the Martian atmosphere was composed of about one percent carbon dioxide, one percent argon, and 98 percent nitrogen. They also believed that at the surface of Mars, atmospheric pressure was about 85 millibars, as compared with about 1,000 millibars on earth. Taken together, these estimates suggested that it would be extremely difficult for any terrestrial life forms to survive on Mars.

And yet, it did seem that *something* was alive on Mars. The seasonal changes in the Martian dark areas which had been reported by Schiaparelli and Lowell continued to defy explanation. The theory that the changes were caused by vegetation was difficult for many astronomers to accept, but it was even more difficult to come up with a plausible alternative.

The wave of darkening, which starts in early spring at the polar caps and then proceeds southward (or northward) at the rate of about one mile per hour, is a recurring phenomenon on Mars. Lowell's explanation was that as the polar caps melted, water was released and Martian vegetation reacted to it. This was a rather simplistic explanation, but it seemed to fit all the observed evidence.

For a number of years, this theory was under attack because it was thought that the Martian polar caps might really consist of frozen CO_2 rather than water ice. However, in 1948 spectral analysis of the polar caps produced tentative evidence that they were, in fact, composed of H_2O. True, the total amount of water on Mars would not have been enough to fill up the Great Lakes, but it was reasonable to suppose that Martian organisms would have evolved to meet the arid conditions. Even a little water might be enough.

There were other reasons to believe the vegetation theory. E.J. Opik reasoned that since there was no evidence of mountains on Mars, the surface must be more or less uniform—yet, obviously it was not. There was ample evidence of periodic dust storms on Mars, which Opik said would eventually cover the entire planet with a thin layer of uniformly colored fine material, unless some other process were at work on the surface. That other process might be the growth of plants, which would be covered by the dust during the winter, but would grow above the dust layer in the spring.

Audouin Dollfus, of the Paris Observatory, theorized that the dark areas might be explained, not by vast Martian cabbage patches, but by simple microorganisms. He found that light reflected from the dark Martian maria tended to be polarized in much the same manner as light reflected from microscopic plants such as algae. More evidence for the vegetation hypothesis.

But if Martian plants were at all similar to terrestrial plants, they ought to contain chlorophyll. Chlorophyll absorbs red and blue light, but reflects green and yellow, which is why the grass looks green. Possibly chlorophyll was also the reason why the dark areas on Mars looked green. It is possible to test for the presence of chlorophyll (and thus, vegetation) on Mars because it does not absorb infrared light. The difference between a red and infrared photo of Mars ought to reveal the chlorophyll. The experiment was tried as early as 1924, but the results were consistently negative. There was little difference between the red and infrared photos. If there were plants on Mars, they must have found a way to operate without chlorophyll.

Some plants on earth do just fine without chlorophyll—lichens. Moreover, the lichens are among the hardiest of organisms. They can survive practically anywhere on earth except in cities, where the smog kills them. Assuming no smog on Mars, then, lichens would be a strong candidate for a Martian life form.

Whatever form of life was on Mars, it would have to be

composed of organic molecules—complex carbon-based compounds which are the building blocks of living systems. Organic molecules show up in the far infrared end of the spectrum. In 1956, William M. Sinton of the Harvard Observatory found evidence that there might be organics in the Martian spectrum. Further investigation with the 200-inch telescope at Mt. Palomar showed that the organic molecules seemed to be present only in the spectra of the dark maria, and not in the desert regions. That seemed to be strong evidence supporting the existence of Martian vegetation, but Sinton was careful to point out that organic compounds could exist without the presence of life; we might be looking at *dead* plants.

Or we might not be looking at plants at all. Almost as soon as Lowell proposed the vegetation hypothesis, alternative, nonorganic explanations were offered in opposition. Svante Arrhenius' theory of "hygroscopic salts" was popular for a time, and was even improved upon in later years. However, such an explanation would require almost as much water as the vegetation theory, and there just isn't very much water on Mars.

What water there is appears to be locked in the polar ice caps. The caps do release some water during the spring and summer, but that does not necessarily mean that the ice melts. The pressure of the Martian atmosphere is too low to permit much, if any, liquid water on the planet. Instead of melting, the ice would tend to sublime, that is, go directly from the solid to the gaseous state. Moreover, even if the water were to be released in liquid form, there is no mechanism to account for its spread from the poles toward the equator. As Robert S. Richardson has pointed out, if water naturally flowed toward the equator, then Hudson Bay would annually flood the eastern United States.

Since water was the major difficulty in all the theories of seasonal change, some scientists decided that it would be

112

necessary to come up with a hypothesis that excluded water. In 1956, Dean B. McLaughlin proposed that volcanos and wind might account for the seasonal changes. McLaughlin suggested that a number of dark features on the surface of Mars might be volcanic in nature. Assuming active vulcanism, the ash produced by the volcanos would be carried into the atmosphere by strong winds and deposited elsewhere on the surface. If the winds were seasonal and regular, then one set of winds might deposit the ash on the maria during the winter, making them appear somewhat dimmer; during the spring, different winds might lift the ash out of the maria, causing the observed wave of darkening.

It was an ingenious hypothesis, but it, too, had problems. First, it made very large assumptions about conditions on the surface of Mars. It presupposed the existence of active volcanos, but none had been observed. As for winds, it was impossible to be sure if they were seasonal in character. Also, the annoying problem of water surfaced again. On earth, one of the major constituents of volcanic eruptions is water, in the form of steam. If there were big, belching volcanos on Mars, then there ought to be more water in the atmosphere.

In the early 1960s, Carl Sagan and James Pollack suggested that volcanos weren't really necessary for a nonvegetative explanation for the seasonal changes. The surface of Mars was assumed to be composed of a hydrated iron oxide known as limonite. Hydrated iron oxide is also known as rust, and since the surface of Mars was rust-colored, it seemed like a good explanation. Sagan and Pollack proposed that Mars was covered with a layer of very fine, pulverized limonite, which produces a strong reflection. Beneath it, there was coarser limonite, which looks darker than the fine particles. If there were seasonal winds on Mars, they would remove the fine limonite from the maria in the spring, then redeposit it in the winter. As in McLaughlin's theory, this would account for the darkening of the maria in the spring. It was a neat theory because it totally avoided the necessity of water. However, it presupposed extremely regular Martian wind patterns, and opponents of the theory said that was assuming far too much.

By the early 1960s, astronomers were forced to make such assumptions because hard evidence was impossible to obtain from earth. They knew for sure that Mars was a cold, dry world with little or no oxygen. Beyond that, they knew almost nothing for certain. Of all the planets in the solar system, Mars was the only one, other than earth, which seemed likely to harbor some form of life, but there was no way to be sure if there really was life on Mars.

Extraterrestrial life had once again become an important subject, because if it existed and could be detected, it would tell scientists a great deal about the nature of life on earth. Stanford's Nobel Laureate Joshua Lederberg coined the word "exobiology" to describe the study of extraterrestrial life. Some scoffed that it was "a science without a subject," but if its subject could be found, the implications would be enormous.

Finding life on another planet would give us a new perspective about life on our own planet. As Carl Sagan has written, "We are like linguists on an isolated island where only one language is spoken. We can construct general theories of language, but we have only one example to examine."

Scientists think they have some clues about how life began on earth. Experiments by Stanley Miller, Leslie Orgel, and others have shown that amino acids can be produced by exposing a mixture of methane, ethane, ammonia, and water to ultraviolet radiation and electricity. We believe that earth's early atmosphere contained those compounds; and we know that they are present in the atmosphere of Jupiter. In addition, the "primordial soup" produced by these experiments is the same sickly brown color that is characteristic of some of the gaseous bands on Jupiter. Does that mean that the building blocks of life are being produced in the Jovian atmosphere?

114

We don't know for sure, because we haven't been there . . .
yet.

Numerous theories have been proposed to explain the birth
of the solar system, but more data is needed. We have a
general idea of when and how the earth was formed, but the
record is incomplete because the geological record of our first
billion years is missing. The weathering process has wiped out
much of our early history. But there are other worlds, such as
Mercury and the moon, where the lack of an atmosphere has
limited erosion. Mars seems to be an intermediate case, a
planet similar to what earth might have been if it hadn't
developed a thick atmosphere. Careful studies of the earth
and the other planets—how they differ and what they share in
common—has given us a new and important area of scientific
investigation: comparative planetology.

The earth, the sun, the moon, and the other planets and
satellites were all born at about the same time—4.6 billion
years ago. The galaxy itself is perhaps three or four times
older. A huge cloud of hydrogen gas slowly collapsed on itself,
raising temperatures and pressures at the center of the cloud.
The first stars were born there, and gravitational forces
brought them together in a rough, spherical shape. The
leftover gas collected in a thin disk around the sphere and
became the birthing ground for another generation of stars.
They clustered together and formed the spiral arms of our
galaxy.

In the fusion reactors of these new stars, heavy elements
were formed and ejected, creating tiny grains of interstellar
dust. The dust and gas formed new clouds which reached a
stable balance between the gravitational forces pulling them
together and the internal pressure pushing them outward. But
some disturbance—a nearby supernova, perhaps—upset the
equilibrium of one of those clouds, causing gravity to become
dominant over pressure. The cloud collapsed, breaking into

fragments. One of the fragments continued to collapse into a flattened disk, with very hot temperatures at the core and cooler material circulating around it.

That was us—four and a half billion years ago. Every atom inside us was born in that cloud. We are made of the stuff of stars. As Carl Sagan has written, we are all "Starfolk."

The theory that we were born from a primitive solar nebula is not a new one. The idea was first put forth by Descartes in 1644. In the nineteenth century Immanuel Kant and Pierre-Simon de Laplace elaborated on the nebular hypothesis, showing how the contracting cloud would shed cooler matter that would eventually form planets.

There were a number of competing theories which sought to explain the birth of the planets. Most of them postulated some sort of Velikovskian collision between the sun and another star or, possibly, a very massive comet. Matter thrown off by the collision condensed into the planets. The difference between the competing theories had important implications. According to the Kant-Laplace hypothesis, planets would be very nearly ubiquitous in the galaxy; but if the planets were formed by a rare event such as a collision, there would be very few planetary systems. And if planets were scarce, the odds were that we were alone in the universe.

The collision theories eventually fell into disfavor because they left too many things unexplained. Astronomers now believe that there may be billions of planetary systems within our galaxy—and perhaps as many as 100 million intelligent civilizations.

But it is no easy task to get from an inchoate lump of matter to a planet teeming with paramecia, porpoises, parrots, pumas, and people. Current theories suppose that the tiny grains of dust in the cooler regions of the nebula gradually gathered into clumps about a centimeter in diameter. These clumps settled into the midplane of the nebula and collided with one another, building up clusters. These tight-knit clusters in the nebula grew together into larger bodies, about the size of asteroids. Over an undetermined period of time, collisions between the bodies resulted in the accretion of planet-sized objects. Exactly how long the process took remains uncertain, although it probably happened fairly rapidly (six days, according to one widely held hypothesis).

Meanwhile, the sun had turned on. A lot of unconsolidated debris remained in the solar system, but at some point the sun went through what is known as the T-Tauri stage and swept the system clean with a powerful solar wind. This wind would have stripped the inner planets of any primitive atmosphere they may have accumulated from the hydrogen and helium in the cloud. In the outer part of the cloud, however, the gas giants (Jupiter, Saturn, Uranus, and Neptune) were strong enough to hold onto their gaseous shells. In a sense, Jupiter and Saturn were like mini-solar nebulae in their own right. They are like stars that failed.

Before the T-Tauri winds cleaned up the solar system, the newly formed planets were bombarded by the debris left over from the planet-making process. The face of the moon still bears the scars of that early episode. Earth, too, was heavily cratered, but unlike the moon the earth was capable of healing itself. An active geology and an evolving atmosphere eventually wore away the evidence of the era of bombardment, although there are still a number of visible features which suggest ancient crater basins. The famous Meteor Crater in Arizona, on the other hand, is of much more recent origin.

Because the moon hasn't changed much in the last four billion years, scientists studying it have been able to learn a great deal about what the earth must have been like at that time. The number of lunar craters, for example, gives us information about the rate of cratering during the history of the solar system, and thus makes it possible to calculate the magnitude of erosion on earth, or any other planet with an atmosphere. Astronomers expected that Mercury, with little or no atmosphere, ought to look very similar to the moon. But Mars, as usual, was something of a mystery. It had a thin atmosphere, enough to burn up small meteors, but perhaps not enough to erode any large impact craters. Earth-based observations had revealed no sign of cratering on Mars, but that didn't meant that there had been none. A few scientists predicted that there would be many craters on Mars; others didn't think there would be any.

The objects that cause the craters are also of interest, because they are the remains of the original solar nebula. It is difficult to obtain samples of meteorites because they tend to burn up in our atmosphere, or fall into the ocean if they survive the heat of entry. Some of them do fall on land, however, and studies of them have given us a better under-standing of the primitive solar system. The gases trapped inside meteorites are the same as those which were present in the solar nebula. The minerals that compose the meteorites give us information about temperatures and pressures in the nebula. The ratios of radioactive isotopes present in the samples provide accurate indications of the age of the meteor-ites.

Until the Space Age, meteorites were our only specimens of extraterrestrial material. They told us part of the story of the solar system, but left a lot unexplained. The meteorites had to have been formed in a particular region of the original cloud; conditions might have been vastly different elsewhere.

We know, for example, that conditions were different in the part of the cloud where Mars formed. The Red Planet is only about 70 percent as dense as the earth. That implies that Mars received less metallic iron than did our own planet.

Mars is also much less massive than the earth. As a smaller, less dense, less massive planet, Mars probably accreted rapidly, possibly in only about 100,000 years. As on earth, pressure and temperature rose in the interior of the primitive planet, resulting in the formation of a dense core, a differentiated mantle, and a light surface crust. The heating also resulted in the release of gases from the rocks, and it was here that Mars and the earth started down different roads.

The outgassing from the melting rocks created the atmospheres of both planets. Water vapor, carbon dioxide, methane, nitrogen, and ammonia were all released. Earth's gravity was strong enough to hold onto most of the gases, with only hydrogen and helium escaping into space. But Mars, with its much weaker gravity and lower escape velocity, lost more of its gases than the earth. Although earth did lose its hydrogen, the rate of escape was slower, allowing the hydrogen to participate in a number of chemical reactions. The early atmosphere was a reducing atmosphere, that is, one where the principal chemical reactions involve hydrogen—as opposed to our present oxidizing atmosphere, where oxygen is dominant. On earth, the hydrogen reduced most of the carbon dioxide to methane and water vapor.

It was in that early atmosphere of methane that the first amino acids and organic molecules were produced, probably by a process similar to the one involved in the experiments by Miller and Orgel. The massive amounts of water vapor in the atmosphere condensed out in a rain that may have lasted for thousands of years. The oceans were formed and became a rich incubator for the organic compounds. As early as four billion years ago, those complex molecules somehow combined to form the first living cells.

In the congenial environment of that primordial soup, life evolved, grew, and spread. The life forms released oxygen into the air; meanwhile, the rate of outgassing from the rocks slowed down. Gradually, over a period of hundreds of millions of years, the early reducing atmosphere evolved into an oxygen-rich atmosphere where life flourished.

Did the same process occur on Mars? It would have been much more difficult. Hydrogen escaped from Mars more quickly, making the production of organic molecules less likely. Mars is colder than the earth, so the free water vapor tended to freeze out at the poles, rather than create oceans in which life could form. The free oxygen on earth formed an ozone (O_3) layer which protected the surface from harsh ultraviolet radiation; but did Mars receive similar protection?

At the beginning of the Space Age, it was impossible to answer these and many other questions. Mars was enough like the earth to raise the hope that it, too, was a home of life. But it was sufficiently different to cast a very large shadow of doubt across that hope. One thing was clear: if there were answers to these questions, they wouldn't be found on earth. We would have to go to Mars and see for ourselves.

8

Mars from *Mariner*

In all the history of mankind, there will be only one generation that will be the first to explore the solar system, one generation for which, in childhood, the planets are distant and indistinct discs moving through the night sky, and for which, in old age, the planets are places, diverse new worlds in the course of exploration.

—Carl Sagan
The Cosmic Connection, 1973

When *Viking 1* landed on Mars, at least one man was not very impressed. "Mars? Hah!" scoffed Buster Crabbe, "I landed there forty years ago!" In his role as Flash Gordon, Crabbe had, indeed, landed on Mars, as well as Venus and a lot of places no one had ever heard of. He zipped around the universe in his smoky rocket ship with a speed and ease that made interplanetary travel seem like a snap.

At the same time Crabbe was so blithely bouncing around between planets, scientists back on earth were discovering that it was no mean task just to get a rocket off the ground. The Russian pioneer K. E. Tsiolkovsky and the American Robert H. Goddard had led the way with their liquid-fueled rockets, proving, at least, that rocket travel was feasible. But lack of money and interest hampered their studies, and by the mid-thirties, Flash Gordon to the contrary, interplanetary travel was still just a distant dream.

In Germany, there was money and interest. The German rocket experimenters were, for the most part, interested only in science, but the German leaders saw other possible uses for rockets. They poured money into rocket research, and the scientists gladly accepted it even though they must have known what was coming. Wars have a way of accelerating the growth of science.

At about the same time the Germans began testing their big rockets, ancestors of the V-2s which were to devastate London, a group of Cal Tech students started their own tests in a dry arroyo at the base of the San Gabriel Mountains north of Pasadena. Under the leadership of Dr. Theodore Von Karman, the group learned about the problems of putting theories into actual practice. This was the birth of the Jet Propulsion Laboratory.

After World War II, with the worth of rockets so graphically demonstrated, the Russians and Americans captured as many V-2s and German scientists as they could and then went back home to develop their own missiles. The Americans established a proving ground at White Sands, New Mexico, where the V-2 evolved into the Wac, the Wac-Corporal, the Redstone, and eventually, the Jupiter-C. White Sands was too small for the bigger rockets, so a new base was established at Cape Canaveral, Florida. By the mid-fifties, American scientists were confident that they were ready to put an artificial satellite in orbit around the earth.

The Russians beat them to it. On October 4, 1957, *Sputnik* beeped its way into orbit and launched a new era of exploration—and competition. The Americans, who had been stymied by a lack of funds, rushed to catch up with the Russians. At first they failed; tall, slender *Vanguard* rockets had a way of blowing up on national television. Finally, in February 1958, a Jupiter-C put a small *Explorer* satellite into orbit. National pride was at least somewhat restored. But in 1961, the Russians put Yuri Gagarin into orbit—another first for the Soviets and another headache for the Americans.

This was the era of all-out competition between the two superpowers. Every Russian success in space was hailed as proof of the superiority of the communist system. Each American success was a vindication of the free enterprise system and good old American know-how. But the Americans were trailing in the space race, as the press was calling the competition. Something had to be done—an American triumph was needed. President John F. Kennedy decided that it should be a national goal to put a man on the moon and return him safely to earth before the end of the decade. Congress responded by opening the fiscal faucets, and billions of dollars poured into space research.

Not all scientists were entirely pleased by this turn of events. Manned space flight was incredibly expensive and the scientific return, in the view of some, would not justify the cost. Much more could be learned, more cheaply, by unmanned probes. The money and energy that went into putting men into space could be better used developing automated instruments.

Although attention continued to be centered on the race for the moon, there was still some money left over for unmanned exploration of the planets. In 1961 the Russians launched a probe to Venus. It was a failure, but if the Russians were going to the planets, then of course the Americans had to go there, too.

Mariner 1 was launched in July of 1962. The booster rocket behaved erratically, and was destroyed by the range safety officer. *Mariner 2,* launched a month later, proved to be America's first clear triumph in space. It was the first successful flyby of another planet. Of more interest to the scientists than the political impact was the data returned from *Mariner 2.* Venus turned out to be much hotter than had been expected, about 400 degrees Celsius (centigrade). Venus also apparently lacked a magnetic field.

Attention next turned to Mars. The Russian probe, *Mars 1,* was launched in November of 1962. Unfortunately, contact with the spacecraft was lost after it was about 60 million miles out in space. America's first attempt at Mars also failed when the protective shroud around *Mariner 3* failed to jettison after launch.

Then came *Mariner 4.*

Before the launch of *Mariner 4,* Mars remained as much a mystery as it had ever been. Scientists debated whether the atmospheric pressure at the surface of Mars was as low as 25 millibars or as high as 85 millibars. The composition of the atmosphere was still unclear. Estimates of the amount of carbon dioxide were rising, but nitrogen was still believed to be the major component, even though none had been detected.

The surface of Mars was still not understood. In 1954 a new area about the size of Texas had suddenly turned dark—no one could explain it. A strange W-shaped cloud—or M-shaped, depending on how you viewed it: the M proponents thought it might have been a kind of global monogram arranged by the Martians; some W supporters thought it might stand for War—appeared over the region known as Tharsis, and no one could explain that either. The canals were still a subject of controversy, although few scientists were willing to talk about them publicly. Hardly anyone accepted the old Lowellian hypothesis, but it had never been completely disproved. Perhaps there really were Martians. Whether there were or not, *something* had caused the canals. Most scientists were willing to agree that there were some sort of long, linear features on Mars, but that was about as far as they could go.

The problem with Mars was the earth. Its atmosphere was still in the way. Even the largest telescopes were greatly limited in the amount of detail they could resolve on the Martian surface. In 1963, Project Stratoscope launched a 36-inch telescope aloft on two large balloons in an attempt to get above our turbulent atmosphere. It succeeded in getting above most of it (96 percent) and returned data that confirmed the presence of CO_2 and water vapor in the Martian atmosphere. But even 100,000 feet above the earth, Stratoscope was still 40 million miles from Mars. A closer look was needed.

Mariner 4 was designed to answer some of the questions that had been baffling earthbound scientists for centuries. The spacecraft weighed a mere 575 pounds, but it contained over 138,000 separate parts. The body of the probe was an octagonal box about 50 inches across. Extending out from the body like the arms of a windmill were four solar panels that provided power and increased the total length of the spacecraft to 22 feet 7½ inches.

The probe was equipped with six scientific instruments which were to conduct experiments en route and in the vicinity of Mars. There was an ionization chamber, which would provide an accurate count of cosmic rays. A "Trapped Radiation Detector" was designed to find out if Mars had belts of radiation surrounding it, similar to earth's Van Allen Belts. There was also a "Cosmic Ray Telescope" which was capable of detecting lower energy particles than the ionization chamber. Other subatomic particles, hydrogen nuclei which composed the solar wind, would be detected by a solar plasma probe. A fifth instrument aboard *Mariner 4* was a magnetometer which would measure the magnetic field of Mars—if it had one. Finally, the spacecraft was equipped with micrometeoroid detectors which would give a count of the number of times the spacecraft was struck by dust particles during its voyage. Since *Mariner 4* was headed out toward a region of the solar system where there were meteor swarms, it was expected that the probe would collide with a number of such particles. However, it seemed unlikely that it would encounter anything large enough to do it damage. Still, there was the nagging question of what had happened to the Russians' *Mars 1*.

The most intriguing item aboard *Mariner 4* was the camera.

The probe was scheduled to sweep by Mars at a range of about 10,000 kilometers (6,000 miles); during the brief two-hour encounter, the single vidicon tube television camera was to take 22 pictures of the Red Planet.

Normal television pictures on Earth consist of lines (545 of them), but the Mariner camera would take pictures composed of single dots. There were 200 dots in each line and 200 lines per picture, for a total of 40,000 picture elements, known as pixels. During the encounter, a "Mars sensor" would aim the camera at the planet. Each exposure was to last one-fifth of a second. The light from Mars would hit a light-sensitive, selenium screen which would translate the image into electrical charges. The charges, varying according to the brightness of the image, would be scanned by an electron beam.

On a terrestrial TV, that beam would be translated directly into a picture. But the great distance to Mars and the limited power available to *Mariner* (10.5 watts) made a direct picture transmission impossible. Instead, a system was designed to translate the signal from the electron beam into binary digits ("bits") on board the spacecraft. Each pixel would become a 6-bit number, coded to correspond to the brightness of the dot. Since *Mariner 4*'s transmission rate was only $8\frac{1}{3}$ bits per second, obviously a 240,000-bit picture couldn't be transmitted back to earth all at once. Instead, the bits representing each picture were to be stored on a 330-foot tape loop. After the encounter with Mars, the tape would be played back and broadcast to earth.

The signals from *Mariner* would be received by the giant antennas of the Deep Space Network, whose stations were located at Goldstone, California, Johannesburg, South Africa, and Canberra, Australia. The spacecraft would constantly be in view of at least one of the DSN stations.

By the time the *Mariner* signals reached earth, their relative strength would decline to a level that was barely detectable. But by using a liquid helium superconductor, it was possible

126

to amplify them to a usable strength. The data would then be sent to the Jet Propulsion Laboratory, where a computer would translate the numbers back into a picture.

Mariner 4 was, for its time, a highly sophisticated spacecraft which, its designers hoped, would be capable of sending back to earth a treasure trove of new information about Mars. The real problem lay in getting *Mariner to* Mars.

At its closest point, Mars passes within 35 million miles of the earth. Theoretically, a very powerful rocket could cut across that straight-line distance in a matter of weeks. Unfortunately, no rocket existed in 1964 that was capable of taking such a shortcut. Fuel requirements for getting the 575-pound package to Mars decreed that *Mariner 4* must take the most economical route.

That route had been calculated half a century earlier by a German mathematician named Walter Hohmann. For his own amusement, Hohmann plotted the possible varieties of orbits available for a spacecraft bound for Mars. The cheapest way to get there, it turned out, was to follow a long, curving orbit which would intersect with a point on the Martian orbit at the precise time when Mars itself arrived at that point. For *Mariner 4*, the voyage would mean traveling a total of about 325 million miles in order to encounter Mars at a straight-line distance of 134 million miles from Earth. The trip would last 228 days.

Mariner 4 began its journey from Cape Canaveral on November 28, 1964. The launch vehicle was an Atlas-Agena booster; the Atlas got it off the earth, and the Agena gave it a shove in the direction of Mars. The protective shroud, which had ruined the *Mariner 3* mission, jettisoned perfectly, and *Mariner 4* was off to a good start.

The initial flight path of the spacecraft would have caused it to miss Mars by a good 150,000 miles. That was more or less expected, and a mid-course maneuver was planned to reduce the encounter distance to about 5,000 miles. Before *Mariner*'s small rocket could be fired, however, the spacecraft had to be pointed in precisely the right direction. Otherwise, the mid-course burn would only make matters worse.

The spacecraft's attitude was controlled by a device known as a Canopus sensor. Canopus is a rather bright star, and *Mariner*'s sensor was supposed to search for it, identifying it by its intensity. When Canopus was found, *Mariner 4* locked onto it. As long as the Canopus sensor was aimed at the right star, the spacecraft would be in a correct attitude.

But there are a lot of stars. Early in the mission, the Canopus sensor displayed a marked preference for other stars than the one it was designed to find. First it locked on Markab, then Alderamin, then Regulus, then a small three-star cluster. Scientists at JPL kept sending up new search commands, and *Mariner* kept finding new stars. Finally, on November 30, it locked on Canopus.

On the day before the scheduled mid-course burn, *Mariner 4* began looking all over the sky again. It locked onto stars in places where there *weren't* any stars. The mission controllers finally concluded that the Canopus sensor was actually track-ing bright bits of dust which had shaken free from the Agena and were traveling along with *Mariner*. On December 5, Canopus was once again locked up long enough to conduct the course correction maneuver. An hour later, *Mariner 4* lost Canopus again.

More bad news came back from *Mariner*. The solar plasma detector was sending nonsense data. The experiment was written off, but in March, it mysteriously regained its senses and started returning meaningful information. But on the same day, the particle counter in the ionization chamber went haywire. Such "glitches" are not uncommon in the space business. They are expected, which is why most spacecraft systems are built with redundancy, or even "multiple redun-dancy." But even with backup systems, things tend to go wrong in space, and they can't always be fixed from earth. A

128

spacecraft such as *Mariner 4* which loses only one of its experiments is considered to have a pretty good batting average.

The crucial instrument was the camera, and for that, there was no backup. *Mariner 4*'s flyby of Mars would last less than an hour; during that time, the camera was scheduled to take its pictures from a range of about 8,000 miles from the surface of the planet. At that point, the spacecraft would be totally on its own. Its distance from earth was so great that it required twelve minutes for a signal traveling at the speed of light to reach the antennas of the DSN. If something went wrong, it would take at least half an hour for the controllers at JPL to learn of the glitch and get a corrective command back to *Mariner*. And by then, it would be too late.

In the evening hours of July 14, 1965, *Mariner 4* made its rendezvous with the Red Planet. As the spacecraft passed behind the planet, its signal was cut off. This was expected, and was the basis for one of the most valuable experiments of the entire mission. By studying the manner in which the signal was occulted by Mars, it was possible to make calculations concerning the thickness of the Martian atmosphere. Reacquisition of the signal as *Mariner* emerged from behind Mars provided similar data.

The day after the flyby, *Mariner 4* was commanded to begin the playback of its data. At 8⅓ bits per second, it took about eight and a half hours to transmit a single picture. In between the pictures, the data from the other experiments was transmitted. The whole story of *Mariner 4,* then, took over ten days to be told.

The first picture, taken from a range of 10,500 miles, showed a section of dark sky and a blurred image of the planet. It didn't provide much in the way of useful data, but it was nonetheless an historic photo—the first "close-up" picture of Mars. The early pictures were taken over a part of the planet where the sun was high in the sky. That meant that there would be little shadowing on the ground and therefore very little contrast in the pictures. Likewise, the pictures taken late in the run showed only the dark side of the planet. It was the pictures from the middle of the run, taken near the terminator, which were expected to be the best.

As expected, each succeeding picture was better than the one before. By the time the fourth picture was completed, it was possible to make out detail on the surface. But it was Frame Seven which provided the shock. It was the first clear, detailed picture of the surface of Mars. It showed craters.

A few scientists had predicted that Mars might be cratered in a manner similar to the moon, but the *Mariner 4* photos still came as a surprise. Later frames in the sequence confirmed that the Martian surface was distinctly lunar in appearance. To the disappointment of just about everyone, there were no canals.

The best of the *Mariner 4* pictures was Frame Eleven, which showed a large impact basin about 75 miles in diameter, with smaller impact craters inside it. After Frame Eleven, the quality of the pictures began to decline, but the later pictures did show evidence of what looked like ground frost or, possibly, low clouds. Frame Fifteen was the last of the usable pictures, taken near the terminator in the Southern Hemisphere. The rest of the pictures were taken over the night side, and the camera's exposure failed to adjust to the decrease in brightness.

The other experiments returned equally intriguing results. Mars, apparently, had no detectable magnetic field, and no radiation belts similar to earth's Van Allen Belts. The radio occultation results showed that the Martian atmosphere was even thinner than had been supposed. Calculations indicated that at the surface of Mars, the atmosphere was less than one percent as thick as the terrestrial atmosphere at sea level—about 10 millibars.

The combined data from the *Mariner 4* experiments added up to a very depressing picture of Mars. With a thin atmosphere and no magnetic or radiation fields, the surface of Mars was virtually unprotected against a bombardment of cosmic rays and ultraviolet radiation. Scientists thought it unlikely that any organism could survive in such an environment. In addition, the craters were evidence of another kind of bombardment; debris from the solar nebula and the asteroid belt had clearly slammed into Mars in great quantity. The fact that there were so many craters visible indicated that erosion processes were not very active on Mars. The implication was that there was little or no water on Mars, now or ever.

In response to the evidence from *Mariner 4, The New York Times* printed an editorial about Mars. Its title: "The Dead Planet." And if *The New York Times* said it, it had to be true.

But hope springs eternal. Optimists pointed out that TIROS weather satellite pictures of the earth showed absolutely no evidence of life, intelligent or otherwise, on Planet Earth. Why expect the *Mariner 4* photos to show signs of life, especially since we didn't know what to look for?

Canal enthusiasts noted the fact that *Mariner 4* had covered only about one percent of the surface of Mars, and had flown over a region where there weren't any canals, anyway. Furthermore, it was a bad season for seeing canals. They regarded the *Mariner* data as inconclusive.

One writer thought he *did* see a canal. Eric Burgess, of the British Interplanetary Society, had been writing about Mars since 1936, so he enthusiastically pored over the *Mariner* pictures. Frame Eleven revealed, to Burgess at least, clear evidence of a canal in the region of Mars known as Atlantis. "The canal," wrote Burgess, "appears as a rift valley 30 miles wide with the north and south escarpments recognizable as crater walls." Burgess charged that the *Mariner* scientists had been seduced by the craters into looking at Mars as they would the Moon. They had overlooked the canal because they hadn't expected to see it.

To say that Burgess saw a canal is not to say that he

believed in a Lowellian Mars. Canals as rift valleys constituted an entirely believable explanation of a phenomenon that had been observed from earth for nearly a century. Scientists generally wished that the canals would just go away, and at first glance, it seemed that they had. But Burgess forced them to look again at the *Mariner* pictures. Yes, there was a rift valley in Frame Eleven, but whether or not it corresponded with a classical canal was another story. So the question of the canals remained where it had always been: up in the air. The only way to resolve it was to go back to Mars and take another look.

Mariner 6 was launched February 25, 1969, and *Mariner 7* a month later. Both were flyby missions, similar to *Mariner 4*. These new *Mariners* were more sophisticated spacecraft, however. They weighed 847 pounds each, as compared with *Mariner 4*'s 575 pounds. The additional weight meant more experiments and more data.

Mariner 6 encountered Mars on July 31, 1969 at a range of about 3,400 miles. *Mariner 7,* following a slightly shorter flight path, reached Mars on August 5, 1969 and passed within 3,500 miles of the planet. Both spacecraft were equipped to make in-depth studies of the Martian atmosphere in the infrared and ultraviolet spectral ranges. Together, they returned 202 high quality pictures of the surface of Mars, concentrated in the equatorial and south polar regions. The two spacecraft sent back a total of two billion data bits, compared with around 200 million for *Mariner 4*. This order-of-magnitude increase was made possible by a transmitting system which upped *Mariner 4*'s 8⅓ bits per second to an awesome 16,200 bits per second (or 16.2 kilobits).

One of the first questions answered by *Mariner 6* was the size of Mars. Earth-based measurements had given the planet a diameter of somewhere between 4,200 and 4,220 miles. *Mariner 6* refined the measurement to a figure of 4,216 miles four degrees north of the equator. The *Mariners* also refined estimates of the Martian surface temperature. At noon on the equator, temperatures could reach above 60°F; at night, the temperature plunged to more than 100° below zero.

Near the south pole, the temperature reading was a chilly −193°F. That was an important observation because it implied that the polar cap was mainly composed of frozen CO_2. Frozen H_2O was not excluded, but it was clear that the Martian snow was considerably different than our own.

The *Mariner* evidence also seemed to clear up the mystery of the blue haze. Apparently, it didn't exist. Photographs taken through a blue filter showed no sign of the famous blue haze that had baffled earthbound astronomers. Unfortunately, the blue haze continued to be observed from earth, so there was still some controversy on the subject. Most scientists believed that the haze was inherent in the use of a blue filter, which reduced the contrast of surface markings, and was not a function of something happening in the Martian atmosphere.

Regarding the atmosphere, just five years earlier it was assumed to be mainly composed of nitrogen. But further data pushed the nitrogen level down and the CO_2 level up. Measurements from *Mariners* 6 and 7 continued that trend: no nitrogen was detected at all. The Martian atmosphere was apparently 99 percent carbon dioxide.

Mariner 4 had viewed about one percent of the Martian surface. *Mariners* 6 and 7 looked at an additional 19 percent. The new photos were much more clear and showed far more detail. The early indications of heavy cratering were confirmed, but at least two other types of terrain were observed. In Hellas, a large basin in the Southern Hemisphere, there appeared to be a great deal of featureless terrain. There were no observable craters, mountains, ridges, or anything else within the confines of Hellas. The existence of such a region implied that there must still be extensive erosional processes at work on Mars. Wind was the logical candidate.

The other type of terrain discovered by the spacecraft was what geologists call chaotic terrain. There were regions of "irregular, jumbled topography, reminiscent of the slumped aspect of a terrestrial landslide." Although the chaotic terrain showed up in just two *Mariner 6* frames, it was estimated that such topography might cover as much as a half of the Martian surface. One explanation for the "jumbled topography" was that there might be great quantities of subsurface water in the form of permafrost. If this permafrost were to melt, the surface above it would tend to collapse, causing the chaotic features that had been observed.

Also, it was apparent from *Mariner* photography that there were, indeed, mountains on Mars. Lowell and others had searched for mountains by looking for shining peaks on the dark side of the terminator; they found none and thus assumed that Mars was more or less level. But the close-up photos proved that there were large mountains on Mars, possibly comparable with some of the major mountain ranges on earth.

As for the canals, there was still no clear evidence of them. Clusters of craters and rift valleys might be invoked to account for some of the classical canals, but the intricate network described by Schiaparelli and Lowell was simply nowhere to be seen.

Lowell's Mars was irretrievably gone, but a new Mars, no less interesting, was beginning to emerge. The *Mariner 4* pictures showed the lifeless, lunar aspect of Mars. But *Mariners 6* and *7* gave hints of another, more terrestrial face of the Red Planet. Mars, it seemed, was a bit like the moon and a bit like the earth, but mainly, Mars was like Mars.

The year 1971 saw one of the closest oppositions of the century, and both the Russians and the Americans took advantage of it. Early in the Space Age, optimists had hoped that '71 would be the year of the first manned mission to

Mars. That turned out to be an unrealistic expectation, but 1971 did see four unmanned probes launched toward the Red Planet, and three of them made it. In the meantime, there *had* been successful manned missions to the moon. Astronauts brought back a valuable collection of moon rocks, and for the first time, scientists were able to make direct measurements of the composition of another world. The knowledge gained helped to fill in some of the blank spaces in theories about the origin of the solar system.

The United States planned a twin *Mariner* mission to Mars in '71. Unlike earlier missions, which had been flybys, *Mariners 8* and *9* were to be put in orbit around Mars. Once there, they would be able to return data for months, instead of just hours. Unfortunately, *Mariner 8,* launched on May 8, 1971, malfunctioned and crashed into the Atlantic Ocean. It was a costly accident; *Mariner 9* would have to be reprogrammed to do the work of both spacecraft.

Mariner 9 was launched without a hitch on May 30, 1971. The Russians, meanwhile, had launched two probes of their own, *Mars 2* and *Mars 3.* But although they beat *Mariner 9* into space by over a week, the American spacecraft, following a slightly shorter flight path, beat the Soviet probes to Mars by more than two weeks. *Mariner 9* thus became the first spacecraft to be put into orbit around another planet. After a 167-day flight, a fifteen-minute rocket burn inserted *Mariner 9* into Martian orbit on November 13, 1971.

By comparison, *Mariner 9* made the earlier *Mariners* look like Model T's. *Mariner 4* had weighed just 575 pounds; *Mariner 9* arrived at Mars with a weight of 2,150 pounds, although nearly half of that weight resided in the fuel necessary for the orbital insertion burn. The new spacecraft also had a miniature on-board computer, which allowed mission controllers at JPL to update instructions and carry out a highly adaptive mission.

The most vital element of *Mariner 9* was its camera system.

While earlier *Mariners* had only one camera, *Mariner 9* had two, and both of them functioned perfectly. With two cameras, *Mariner 9* was able to take a wide swath of overlapping pictures at the periapsis (low point) of each orbit. From a minimum distance of 862 miles above the surface of Mars, the cameras achieved a resolution of 100 to 300 meters, using their 500mm lenses. Using their 50mm lenses, resolution of 1 to 3 km was achieved. Because of the failure of *Mariner 8,* *Mariner 9* was forced to cover a larger surface area than had originally been planned, so it was necessary to use the wider-angle 50mm lens the major part of the time. By the time the mission ended, *Mariner 9* had transmitted 7,329 pictures. Virtually the entire surface of the planet was mapped to a resolution of 1 to 3 km, and about 2 percent of the surface was mapped at a resolution of 100 to 300 meters.

When *Mariner 9* first arrived at Mars, however, it couldn't even see the surface. During September and October, earth-based astronomers had noticed the steady obscuration of the Martian surface by what appeared to be a gigantic dust storm. By late November, when *Mariner 9* was put in orbit, the entire surface of the planet was hidden. Mission controllers were forced to content themselves with ultraviolet and infrared observations. For anything more, they would simply have to wait until the dust settled.

By the beginning of January, 1972, the dust storm had subsided enough to reveal some surprising details on the surface of the planet. While the rest of the surface was still obscured, four dark spots poked through the dust cloud in the Tharsis region. Three of the spots were arranged almost in a straight line running from southwest to northeast. The fourth and largest spot was off to the northwest, and corresponded with a telescopically observed dark region known as Nix Olympica—the Snows of Olympus.

With nothing else to look at, *Mariner*'s cameras were focused on the mystery spots. High resolution photos showed that each spot had a roughly circular center and terrace-like features around the center. They were clearly craters, but the question was, what kind of craters? Impact craters were by now a familiar sight on Mars, but no one had yet seen definite evidence of volcanic craters. If they were volcanic, then scientists would have proof that Mars, at one time, had had a very active geology, unlike the moon.

As the dust settled and more details became visible, it was obvious that the four spots were volcanic, and not the result of meteoric impact. There were signs of relatively fresh lava flows on the slopes of the volcanos, and there were very few fresh impact craters on top of the lava. The implication was that the Tharsis volcanos were geologically young, probably less than a billion years old, possibly less than half a billion.

Nix Olympica, the largest of the volcanos, was estimated to be about 27 kilometers above the mean surface level of the planet (Mars, of course, has no convenient "sea level"). By comparison, the highest mountain on earth, Mt. Everest, is a mere 9 kilometers high. Nix Olympica was not only high; it was also massive. According to Harold Masursky of the U.S. Geological Survey at Flagstaff, Arizona (where much of the *Mariner* photo analysis was done), "This single volcanic edifice is about twice as wide as the largest of the Hawaiian volcanic piles and is about equal in volume to the total extrusive mass of the Hawaiian Islands chain." Thus, the planet that Lowell believed to be devoid of mountains turned out to possess peaks that were higher and more massive than any that existed on earth.

The three other Tharsis volcanos were also in the 20 km range. They were named, for convenience, South Spot, Middle Spot, and North Spot. Later, in keeping with the classical nature of Martian names, they were rechristened Arsia Mons, Pavonis Mons, and Ascraeus Mons, and Nix Olympica became Olympus Mons. During the *Viking* mission, *Mariner* veterans were readily identifiable by their habit of using the original names. For those who first knew it as a dark splotch on an otherwise featureless planet, South Spot will always be South Spot.

The Tharsis volcanos were concentrated in a region that was known to be higher than the rest of Mars. Radar studies from earth had given indications of a definite equatorial bulge in Mars. But aside from these lumps and bulges, Mars proved to have gravitational inequities as well. The period of the *Mariner 9* orbit was 11 hours, 58 minutes, and 14 seconds—which was 34 seconds shorter than the predicted orbit. The difference was the result of subsurface concentrations of mass (mascons) which gave Mars an uneven gravitational field. Mascons had been discovered on the moon, but they hadn't been anticipated on Mars.

Mariner 9, which had been expected to function for about ninety days, performed beautifully and continued sending data until November 1972, when its attitude control propellant was exhausted. By any standard, it was the most successful unmanned space mission ever carried out, up to that time. In a sense, *Mariner 9* opened up an entirely new branch of science. It was no longer adequate to leave the study of the skies to astronomers; geologists, chemists, meteorologists, physicists, and, eventually, even biologists found fertile fields in the heavens. Rather than classify themselves as astronomers or geologists, many of those involved in the space program now prefer to think of themselves as "planetary scientists."

The geologists, in particular, were overwhelmed by both the quantity and quality of the *Mariner 9* data. As the Martian atmosphere cleared following the dust storm, *Mariner* sent back mind-boggling pictures of the surface. Earlier missions, by bad luck, had seen only the cratered regions of Mars. *Mariner 9* now revealed vast plains areas and a great deal of chaotic terrain. But the most significant discovery was that Mars was covered with thousands of small channels.

These were not the channels or *canali* of Schiaparelli; they

138

were something entirely new. There were perhaps four to six thousand channels more than a kilometer wide, and a few that were much larger. The smallest observable channels were sinuous and twisting and had obvious dendritic tributary systems. Some of the Martian channels were almost indistinguishable from orbital photographs of terrestrial rivers.

Rivers on Mars? The nineteenth-century mappers had confidently put entire oceans on the planet, but those had long since been discounted. After the results of the early *Mariner* missions had been digested, scientists had become accustomed to thinking of Mars as a dead, lunar-like world. But there are no rivers on the moon, and the *Mariner 9* photos unmistakably and unambiguously declared that at one time there were a great many rivers on Mars. The atmospheric pressure on Mars is too low to permit the existence of running liquid water, but the implication of the *Mariner 9* photos was clear. At some time in the past, Mars had possessed a thicker atmosphere and copious amounts of liquid water.

It was a startling revelation, rather like seeing a corpse blink. Some cautious scientists tried to make a case for the sinuous channels being the results of lava flows, but lava flows generally don't have elaborate tributary systems. The nature of the channels, according to Masursky, "requires rainfall" for an adequate explanation.

The larger channels also were a surprise. The dominant surface feature on Mars is a tremendous canyon about 3,100 miles long, 60 miles wide, and several thousand feet deep. The only terrestrial analog is the East African Rift Valley, which runs from southern Africa to the Dead Sea. This huge Martian valley, originally called the Coprates Rift Valley, was probably the result of the melting of subsurface permafrost, although the size of the feature implies that other erosional processes may be at work as well. The Martian Grand Canyon, incidentally, was later renamed Valles Marineris, in honor of its discoverer, although some purists objected, pointing out that the name could also mean "marinated valley."

While *Mariner 9* was still in orbit, it was joined by two other visitors, the Russian probes *Mars 2* and *Mars 3*. *Mars 2* ejected a capsule which made a hard landing on the surface and returned no data. A more ambitious lander from *Mars 3* made it safely to the surface and broadcast twenty seconds of featureless television before it mysteriously shut off. It was assumed to have been wrecked by the high winds of the dust storm which was still blowing when the probe landed.

The Russian spacecraft had been sterilized in order to avoid contaminating Mars with terrestrial organisms. Although *Mariner 9* was expected to remain in orbit for at least twenty years, it too had been partially sterilized. The sterilization was important because the *Mariner 9* results showed a Mars which might, after all, be the home of some form of life. Plans were already under way for an American lander on Mars, the 1976 *Viking* mission. *Viking* would be equipped with a highly sophisticated biological laboratory which might be able to determine if there were life on Mars. In the meantime, *Mariner 9* had provided a wealth of new and exciting information about the Red Planet. When *Mariner 9* was shut off, planetary scientists took the new data and retired to their laboratories to study, measure, quantify, theorize, and ponder the meaning of it all. And to wait for *Viking*.

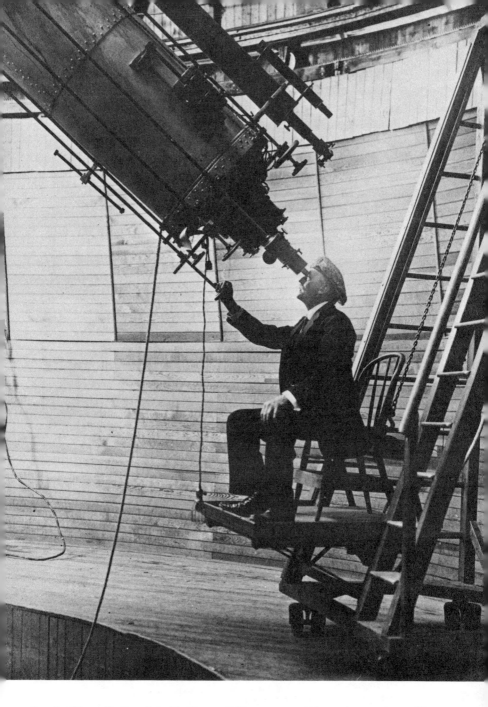

Percival Lowell at work in his Flagstaff Observatory: "At a telescope eyes differ surprisingly little, brains surprisingly much." (Lowell Observatory Photograph)

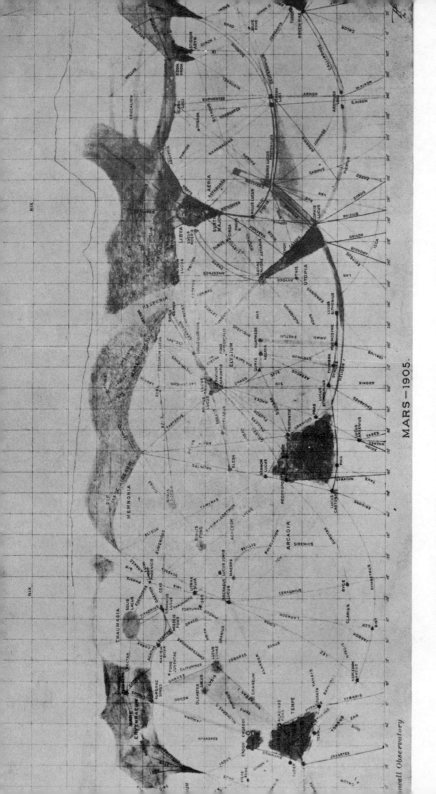

MARS — 1905.

Lowell confidently mapped over 400 canals on the surface of Mars, yet none of them correspond to real features. Note that in this telescopic map, north is at the bottom. (Lowell Observatory Photograph)

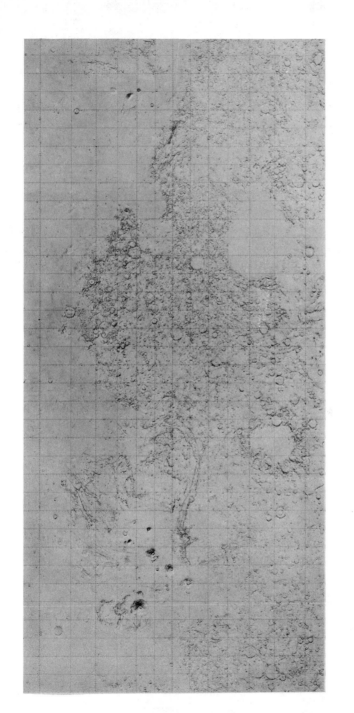

This map, prepared by the U.S. Geological Survey from *Mariner 9* photos in 1972, shows the surface of Mars as it really is, crater-pocked, mountainous, and devoid of canals. Valles Marineris is the horizontal feature running from about 40° West to 110° West, at about 10° South. To the northwest of it are the Tharsis volcanoes. North is at the top. (NASA/JPL)

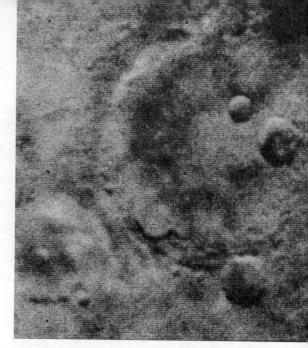

Even when seen through the best telescopes, from earth the surface of Mars (above) is splotchy and indistinct—"like a moldy tangerine," said one astronomer. The bright white spot on the planet is the Martian north polar cap. (Lowell International Planetary Patrol)

Mariner 4 provided the first close-up view of Mars in 1965. This picture, Frame 11, shows an impact crater 75 miles across in the region known as Atlantis. (NASA/JPL)

The *Viking* Lander (Martin Marietta Corp.)

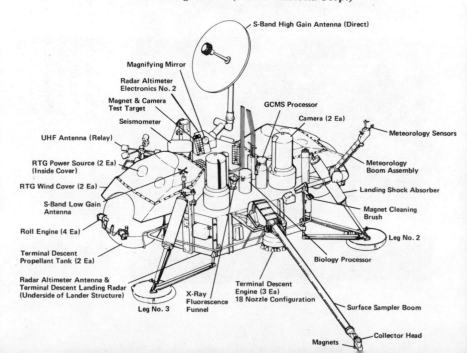

S-Band High Gain Antenna (Direct)

Magnifying Mirror

Radar Altimeter Electronics No. 2

Magnet & Camera Test Target

Seismometer

GCMS Processor

Camera (2 Ea)

Meteorology Sensors

UHF Antenna (Relay)

RTG Power Source (2 Ea) (Inside Cover)

RTG Wind Cover (2 Ea)

S-Band Low Gain Antenna

Roll Engine (4 Ea)

Terminal Descent Propellant Tank (2 Ea)

Radar Altimeter Antenna & Terminal Descent Landing Radar (Underside of Lander Structure)

Meteorology Boom Assembly

Landing Shock Absorber

Magnet Cleaning Brush

Leg No. 2

Biology Processor

Leg No. 3

X-Ray Fluorescence Funnel

Terminal Descent Engine (3 Ea) 18 Nozzle Configuration

Surface Sampler Boom

Magnets

Collector Head

The Argyre Basin, seen from a distance of 12,000 miles. A thin haze of carbon dioxide crystals, 15 to 25 miles high, can be seen above the horizon. In the Basin itself, there are long, meandering linear features which were once Martian rivers. (NASA/JPL)

The results of meteorite impact can be seen in the crater Yuty, which is about 11 miles in diameter. The ejecta blanket, formed from material thrown out of the crater following impact, is clearly visible.

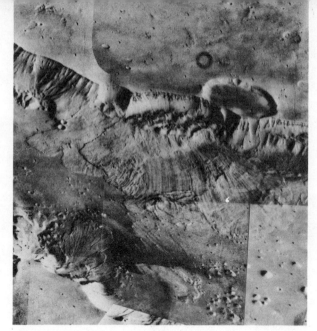

Another spectacular view of Valles Marineris, taken at a range of 1240 miles. At this point the canyon is over a mile deep. The dark circle in the picture (known to *Viking* scientists as "the Cheerio") appears in many Orbiter photos and is the result of a speck of dust on one of the cameras. (NASA/JPL)

The Plain of Gold. After a difficult search, this spot was chosen as the landing site of *Viking 1*. The ellipse, which indicates the expected area of landing, is 62 by 137 miles. Note the abundance of small channels and craters to the west of the ellipse. (NASA/JPL)

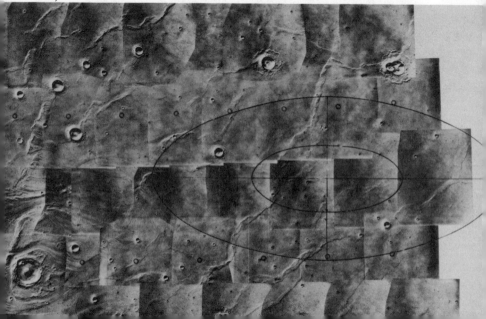

The first picture taken on the surface of Mars. The rock in the center of the picture is about 4 inches across. Some debris settled into the center of the concave footpad. (NASA/JPL)

The first panorama picture taken by *Viking 1*, covering approximately 300 degrees. The horizon is about 1.8 miles away. The layered appearance of the sky is caused by the camera itself. In the foreground, from the extreme left, one can see parts of the spacecraft: the meteorology boom, the surface sampler housing, the RTG windscreen (bottom), and the high-gain antenna. (NSA/JPL)

"Big Joe" dominates this VL-1 picture. The boulder is about 10 feet long and 3 feet high and is covered with red dust. To the right of the boulder are apparent sand "dunes"—actually semipermanent "drifts." The black and white dots in the picture are computer errors, known as "bit hits." (NASA/JPL)

This panorama from *Viking 2* revealed a vast sea of rocks, probably the result of a lava flow. The horizon is actually flat; the apparent slope is caused by the 8.2° tilt of the spacecraft. (NSA/JPL)

This high-resolution photo from *Viking 2* shows vesiculated rocks about 10 inches across. The vesicles, or small holes, are probably the result of bubbles formed by escaping gases when the rocks were molten. (NASA/JPL) *Viking* Orbiter 1 took these photos (below) of Phobos, the inner moon, from a distance of about 400 miles. As seen here, Phobos is about 75% illuminated and is about 13 miles across and 11.8 miles from top to bottom. North is at top. (NASA/JPL)

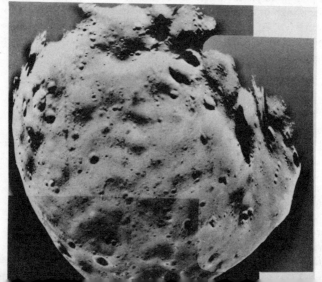

9

New Mars, New Moons—
The Mars of *Mariner 9*

Ten thousand times a hundred thousand
    dusty years ago,
Where now extends the Plain of Gold,
Did once my river flow;
It stroked the stones and spoke in tongues
    and splashed against my face,
Till ages rolled,
The sun shone cold
On this unholy place.
          —Jonathan Eberhart
          "Lament for a Red Planet"

A week before *Viking 1* made its descent to the Martian surface, excitement and anticipation were at a high pitch among the scientists gathered at the Jet Propulsion Laboratory. Every day brought some new revelation from the *Viking* Orbiter, and theories and speculations blossomed overnight. But in the midst of all the hubbub, Dr. Crofton B. (Barney) Farmer, Team Leader of the atmospheric water vapor investigation, provided a caution. Said Farmer, "We are now approaching the dangerous point where our judgment may be biased by some facts."

Mariner 9 had produced a similar situation. It had provided so many new facts (about 54 *billion* bits) that theories toppled like tenpins. As Carl Sagan wrote following the *Mariner 9* mission, "Now we have moved from a data-poor, theory-rich situation to one that is data-rich, theory-poor." The task faced by the planetary scientists was formidable: integrate the mass of *Mariner 9* data into a coherent picture of the planet Mars.

The Mars seen by *Mariner 9* was a marvelously heterogeneous place, teeming with surprises and mysteries. It showed the absolute necessity of looking at the whole of the planet rather than just individual features. A theory that might explain one phenomenon could be totally inadequate to account for many other features. It was impossible to explain the channels in terms of the present-day atmosphere; the atmosphere seemed to be closely related to temperature; temperature could be affected by the amount of dust in the atmosphere; the dust could be the product of a number of processes, including vulcanism; the volcanos implied an active geology and a hot interior ... and so on, seemingly forever.

The nine planets were formed by the accretion of matter in the solar nebula. The four inner planets and the earth's moon probably formed at about the same time. After the planets had accreted, there was still a great deal of debris left in the nebula. Inevitably, there were collisions. Both the moon and Mars were heavily cratered by such impacts, and much of the evidence has survived. When *Mariner 10* took the first pictures of Mercury in 1973, it was revealed to be another crater-pocked world. Earth, too, was subjected to the bombardment, although most traces of it have been erased.

If one assumes a uniform rate of cratering on the terrestrial worlds (that is, rocky planets, as opposed to the outer gaseous planets), then it is possible to build up a rough chronology of events on the individual planets. It is by no means certain that the rate of cratering was uniform, however; Mars, near the asteroid belt, may have had a higher cratering flux. On the other hand, crater counts on the moon, Mercury, and Mars show similar densities, so if the absolute rate of cratering was not the same, some other process has to be invoked to account for the similarities. For argument's sake, then, postulate a relatively uniform cratering rate that is isotropic, that is, equally from all directions—a planet is as likely to get hit at the poles as at the equator.

Working from this theory, it is immediately apparent that Mars has undergone extensive erosion. *Mariner 9* showed that approximately half of the Martian surface is "ancient cratered terrain." Over the rest of the surface, the craters have been either eroded or covered up. Even in the cratered terrain, erosion is evident. There are two basic types of impact craters, one caused by the meteorite itself, and the other produced by the secondary impact of matter ejected by the primary impact. The "rays" of large lunar craters, such as Tycho, are actually made up of thousands of smaller secondary craters. But on Mars, there are very few examples of "rayed" craters. The secondary craters exist, but for the most part they have been heavily eroded. It is thus possible to come up with relative dates for the Martian craters. Younger craters are sharp and distinct, while the older craters have been degraded by erosion.

Finding absolute ages for the craters is more difficult. The *Apollo* missions to the moon provided firm radiometric data on the age of some of the lunar craters, but that data may not be directly applicable to Mars. Still, it is likely that the Martian cratering was occurring at about the same time as the lunar cratering, so we have at least a rough yardstick. The ancient cratered terrain on Mars, then, must be older than three billion years.

Overlying the cratered terrain in many areas, there is a mantle. The mantle material is, in many cases, composed of lava, but *Mariner 9* also provided evidence of other depositional processes. In any case, at some point less than three billion years ago, extensive tectonic and erosional processes began to obliterate much of the ancient cratering. The process has continued at least until relatively recent times, as evidenced by the Tharsis volcanos. Very low crater densities on the slopes of Olympus Mons imply a relatively young age for the mountain, perhaps less than half a billion years.

Huge volcanos such as Olympus Mons and South Spot must have expelled massive amounts of gas into the Martian atmosphere. The pressure of the atmosphere must have been raised, and the temperature must also have risen.

To Dr. Bruce Murray, one of the principal *Mariner 9* investigators (and now the Director of the Jet Propulsion Laboratory), the relative youth of the volcanos implied that Mars was in a state of transition. He theorized that Mars had a lunar-like early history, but a much more terrestrial future. In recent times, according to Murray, internal pressures may have brought Mars to a "boil," touching off the vulcanism.

Murray's picture of Mars constituted a complete reversal of the old Lowellian version of a dying Mars, cooling off and losing its atmosphere. To Murray, the *Mariner 9* evidence suggested that Mars might actually be heating up and developing an atmosphere. He speculated that the present Martian atmosphere "may be a relatively late arrival on Mars— late in a geological sense, as within the last 1 or 2 billion years."

If Murray's theory was correct, then life on Mars would have been highly improbable. But other scientists have looked at the same *Mariner 9* pictures and come to an opposite conclusion. They point to the Martian channels as evidence that sometime in the past, possibly more than a billion years ago, Mars had a much denser atmosphere and a climate that permitted liquid water. Life, they say, could have evolved in such an environment.

The channels may be the key to understanding what has happened on Mars. Unfortunately, they provide no clear answers. It is possible to interpret them as both life-supporting and life-denying. If they are very old, then life may have had time to get started on Mars. But if they are old, there is also the implication that the lack of younger channels means that conditions in the last billion years or so have been too harsh to support life. If the channels are young, Murray's argument against life may be true. But young channels may also imply that conditions have been clement in recent times and may still allow some form of Martian biology.

The age of the channels has been the subject of considerable debate. There are craters on the floors of some channels, which would indicate great age. But other channels go around craters, implying that the craters were there first.

Carl Sagan thought it significant that most of the Martian channels were concentrated in the equatorial region. That seemed to indicate that they were somehow temperature related. Sagan and William Ward postulated a cyclical variation in the Martian climate, possibly related to the planet's inclination. At the present time, Mars is tilted about 23 degrees from the plane of the ecliptic, about the same as earth. But like the earth, Mars wobbles slightly, and in the past Mars may have been tilted as much as 35 degrees. Such a shift might have drastically altered the ambient Martian temperature.

Most of the volatile gases (mainly CO_2) on Mars seemed to be locked up in the polar caps. Sagan suggested that eolian (windblown) dust deposits, perhaps in a period of active vulcanism, might have raised the temperature at the poles by absorbing more of the sun's heat. The heat circulates through the atmosphere, setting up an "advection" system which brings warmer equatorial air up to the poles. The heat melts much of the polar cap material, releasing gases into the atmosphere and raising the pressure. Eventually, pressures and temperatures are high enough in the equatorial regions to permit rainfall and the formation of the channels. The process also works in reverse. Long dust-free periods would bring about a lowering of temperature, the atmosphere would partially freeze out at the poles, pressure would drop, and Mars would come to look as it does today.

If the Sagan theory is correct, it has important implications for our own planet. The deposition of dust on the polar caps of Mars may have raised temperatures. The abundance of pollutants in earth's atmosphere may have the same effect, and the result could be a runaway situation similar to what might have happened on Mars. Earth could be turned into a hothouse.

Sagan's theory has been at least partially undermined by one of his own students. David Pieri, working with Larry Soderblom of the U.S. Geological Survey at Flagstaff, mapped the small sinuous channels and found evidence that they are not limited to the equatorial regions. Pieri believes that a great many nonequatorial channels have been covered up by lava flows and eolian deposition. If the channels have been covered, then they must be very old, surviving only in terrains which have not been overlain with lava or sediments. That argues against recent cyclical variations being responsible for channel formation. On the other hand, if the channels are ubiquitous, they must have had a ubiquitous source, possibly rainfall. According to Pieri, cyclical variations may have been possible on the order of three billion years ago, but on a "rubber ball" basis, with the amplitude of each bounce decreasing with time.

This disagreement between Sagan and Pieri, a Cornell graduate student, is illustrative of the state of the study of Mars. Pieri's work at Flagstaff came to Sagan's attention and sparked an exchange of letters which resulted in Pieri's coming to Cornell to pursue his doctorate. There are no true "experts" on Mars; the field is wide open. The conclusions reached by someone like Pieri may be as valid as those reached by a man of Sagan's stature. Or, they may not be valid. The wealth of *Mariner 9* data encouraged theory formulation, but they can't all be right. Eventually, after all the evidence has been sifted and analysed, one theory, or a combination of theories, may emerge as the most likely explanation of what has happened on Mars. Until that happy day, the Sagans and Murrays will continue to disagree and graduate students will go on challenging their professors. That is the way science works, and in the planetary sciences it appears to be working overtime.

Whatever processes may have been at work in the Martian past, *Mariner 9* clearly established that eolian deposition and erosion are continuing in the present. The planet-wide dust storm that greeted *Mariner 9* on its arrival provided graphic evidence of high winds and dust deposition on the Martian surface.

Vulcanism may still be active, as well. Over the years many astronomers have reported seeing bright flares on the surface of Mars, suggestive of volcanic eruptions. Although spacecraft photos have not yet shown any evidence of current volcanic activity, the possibility has certainly not been excluded.

Water erosion is another story. Conditions prohibit liquid water on Mars in any great quantity, yet the *Mariner 9* photos strongly suggested that at some time in the past there was quite a lot of water. The question now is, where did all that water go? Some of it may be locked up in the polar caps, along with frozen CO_2. If it is in the caps, there is the possibility that it could once again be released.

The water may also be trapped in the form of permafrost beneath the surface. The chaotic terrain observed in *Mariner* photos is characteristic of surface collapse caused by the melting of permafrost.

A third possibility is that the water has become chemically bound in the soil and rocks. If that is true, the water is no longer available for recycle into the atmosphere.

What happened to the water is a crucial question because the possibility of life on Mars revolves around it. Water is indispensable to virtually any form of life we can imagine. It is conceivable that our imaginations are too limited in this regard; Carl Sagan warns against what he calls "Earth chauvinism." Life elsewhere may not necessarily conform to terrestrial rules. Nevertheless, Mars is an earth-like planet in many respects, and if life exists there, in all probability it is at least chemically similar to life on earth.

Mariner 9's orbital photos offered tantalizing hints about the possibility of life on Mars, but showed absolutely no evidence that it actually does exist. If nothing else, the *Mariner* photos finally ruled out the possibility of an advanced Martian civilization. The *Mariner* "B Frames" (500mm photos) had a resolution of 100 to 300 meters. At the same resolution, photos of the earth clearly show evidence of civilization: geometrical fields of crops, cities, stadiums, parking lots, harbors, and at least one mountain with faces carved on it. No such artifacts were observed on Mars. Conspiracy theorists may point out that the Martians may have arranged the dust storm to hide from Mariner while they camouflaged everything, or that there are great Martian cities underground, but realistically, all those glorious visions of Barsoom must now be consigned to the realm of pure fiction.

The canals also suffered a deathblow at the hands of *Mariner 9*. The early *Mariner* missions observed nothing that could be definitely identified as a canal, but they did not cover most of the planet. *Mariner 9* mapped the entire planet and found nothing that even remotely resembled the canals of old.

Carl Sagan and Paul Fox tried to correlate the old Lowellian maps with the *Mariner 9* mosaics, but came up with a blank. A few of the classical canals did seem to correspond with prominent surface features. The best example was the canal Agathodaemon, which turned out to be Valles Marineris. There were a few other near matches, but Sagan and Fox concluded that the vast majority of classical canals didn't correspond to any real features: "Indeed, there are many canals where there are no real surface features, and there are many real surface features where there are no canals."

In the end, it seemed that those who came closest to

explaining the canals were Maunder, with his schoolboy experiment, and Antoniadi, who thought they were really disconnected surface detail. The canals were optical illusions, but, as Sagan and Fox put it, they were "self-generated by the visual observers of the canal school, and stand as monuments to the imprecision of the human eye-brain-hand system under difficult observing conditions." It was a rather ignominious conclusion for such a grand illusion.

Another intriguing life-on-Mars hypothesis was scotched by *Mariner 9*. This one, in its way, was even more farfetched than the canals, yet it had its roots in solid scientific research.

In 1944, B. P. Sharpless of the U.S. Naval Observatory collected a mass of observations of the two Martian moons, Phobos and Deimos, and attempted to calculate their orbits. He found that the orbit of the inner moon, Phobos, appeared to be decaying. Phobos was gradually getting closer to Mars and was moving faster. This is known as secular acceleration, and it is what happens to artificial earth satellites. Eventually their orbits decay to the point where they collide with particles in the upper atmosphere, producing friction, heat, and ultimately, a fiery death. It seemed that Phobos was headed for the same fate.

In 1960, Russian astronomer I.S. Shklovskii tried to explain why Phobos behaved as it did. He looked at a number of possible explanations, such as solar pressure, tidal forces, and interaction with Mars' magnetic field (if any), but none of them seemed to fit the observations. Shklovskii then examined the possible influence of atmospheric drag on Phobos, and found that it might be an acceptable explanation, depending on the density of Phobos. His calculation of that figure resulted in a wildly improbable answer: Phobos had to be about one thousandth as dense as water. No known object is that light. Shklovskii reasoned that Phobos must therefore be hollow.

149

If Phobos were hollow, it couldn't possibly be a natural satellite. It had to have been put there by someone. Martians, perhaps? Shklovskii thought that it was possible that Phobos, and perhaps Deimos, had been launched by some ancient Martian supercivilization thousands of years ago. The civilization had since disappeared, but its satellites survived.

Another possibility was that Phobos was of relatively recent origin. Why hadn't the Martian moons been discovered before 1877? Herschel and others had looked for them, but they remained undiscovered until Asaph Hall found them. Perhaps the reason was that they had not been launched until shortly before the opposition of 1877.

The scientific community was not exactly eager to embrace Shklovskii's hypothesis. It smacked of Lowell's canal theory. But Shklovskii was a renowned scientist, and his calculations were not simply optical illusions. It was a difficult theory to accept, but also difficult to ignore.

For a time, it seemed as if it were Sharpless who had been mistaken. Some astronomers challenged the notion that Phobos had a secular acceleration. Sharpless' data was open to interpretation, and it was by no means certain that the orbit of Phobos was in any way abnormal.

When *Mariner 9* reached Mars, it soon became clear that the only artificial satellites in orbit around the Red Planet were those that had been launched from earth. With the dust storm obscuring the surface of Mars, *Mariner*'s cameras were shifted toward the only thing around which was worth looking at: Phobos. The original mission plan had not included an examination of the Martian satellites, but mainly at the insistence of Carl Sagan, Phobos and Deimos were put on the program a month before *Mariner* reached Mars. The dust storm made Phobos that much more attractive, although, as Sagan's Cornell colleague Dr. Joseph Veverka put it, "The Mars program is mostly interested in Mars, and not very interested in the satellites."

Sagan, Veverka, and a JPL technician stayed up till the small hours of the morning of November 30, 1971, to get their first look at Phobos; in fact, it was the first time *anyone* had ever seen it up close. As the picture was assembled on a television screen, it was soon apparent that Phobos was not a gleaming, stainless steel space station. But for a moment, a single white spot appeared in the middle of Phobos. To Sagan, it looked like a star, though Veverka later admitted, "We were all pretty slaphappy by that point." If it was a star, then Phobos must have had a hole in it. Perhaps it was not hollow, but doughnut shaped.

The "star" turned out to be a computer error (or "bit hit"), and when the error was corrected, the white spot went away. When the picture was computer-enhanced, Phobos didn't look particularly exotic anymore. As Sagan put it, Phobos looked like "a diseased potato." It was a misshapen hunk of rock, heavily cratered, and very dark. Shklovskii's artificial satellite joined Lowell's canals in the limbo of fascinating theories that just didn't work out.

Phobos and Deimos are nonetheless intriguing. *Mariner 9* proved that Phobos does, indeed, have a secular acceleration. When aiming *Mariner*'s cameras at Phobos, it was first necessary to calculate where to look for the satellite. Calculations that ignored the secular acceleration factor resulted in aiming the cameras at the wrong place.

When *Mariner 9* discovered the mascons that were responsible for Mars' lumpy gravitational field, the mystery of Phobos' orbit was at least partially solved. Evidence from the Tharsis volcanos suggested that the interior of Mars was molten. The combination of mascons and a fluid interior made it possible to explain the secular acceleration purely in terms of tidal action. However, the amount of fluid material necessary may be greater than the amount present in the Martian interior.

The solution to the secular acceleration problem may lie in the manner in which Phobos and Deimos were formed.

Following *Mariner 9*, two major theories emerged concerning their origin. One held that the two small satellites are actually captured asteroids. They are about the size of many asteroids, and Mars is close to the asteroid belt, but it is difficult to explain how they arrived in their present orbits if they are ex-asteroids. Both satellites have very circular orbits in the equatorial plane; Phobos can't even be seen from high latitudes on the surface of Mars. For captured bodies to achieve such orbits, it is necessary to postulate very powerful tidal forces; but for bodies as small as Phobos and Deimos, the tidal effect would probably not be very large. It would work on a larger body, from which Phobos and Deimos might have been broken off after some sort of collision, but that is still just speculation.

The second theory about their origin is that they were simply left over from the original accretion of Mars, two chunks of rock that didn't quite make it. But there are problems here, as well. Phobos is uncomfortably close to Roche's Limit, the theoretical distance from a planet inside of which it is impossible for a large body to form. Deimos, on the other hand, is just outside another theoretical limit, beyond which a body's orbit will take it on a slow spiral outward. Just as Phobos will eventually (in about 100 million years) impact on Mars, Deimos will someday escape from it. If the satellites are leftover material from the solar nebula, it is odd that they should have formed so close to those limits.

Scientists are now closing in on an answer to the riddle of the Martian satellites. If it is assumed that Phobos and Deimos were originally part of the same body, then they should be made of the same material, and from *Mariner 9* observations, it appears that they are. Both moons are among the darkest objects in the solar systems, with albedos of about 6 percent; that is, they reflect only about 6 percent of the light that reaches them.

There are two logical candidates for the composition of the

152

satellites, both of which are cosmically abundant. One is a very dark basalt, similar to that found in the lunar mare areas. The other is the material found in meteorites known as carbonaceous chondrites. The chondrites are fascinating in their own right, for they have been found to contain organic molecules. There are a lot of chondrites in the asteroid belt.

If Phobos and Deimos could be determined to be made of either of these substances, it might be possible to deduce their origin. The chondrites, according to present theory, could form only in a cooler region of the solar nebula, out near the asteroid belt. Thus, if the satellites are composed of chondritic material, they are almost certainly fragments of a captured asteroid. If they are made of basalt, the answer is not quite as simple. They would have to have undergone melting as part of a far larger object. That could be consistent with either a big captured body or fragments of the proto-Mars of four and a half billion years ago.

The most likely way to determine the composition of Phobos and Deimos would seem to be by measuring their spectra, but unfortunately, that can't be done from earth. They are so small and so close to Mars that scatter light from the planet makes it impossible to distinguish their spectra telescopically. *Mariner 9* had a spectrometer on board, but it was not sensitive enough for observations of the satellites. The *Viking* spacecraft were also unable to measure the spectra of the tiny moons, but fortunately, an alternative means of determining their composition was available.

Carbonaceous chondrites are about twice as dense as water, basalt three times as dense. The denser an object, the greater its gravitational pull. If a spacecraft could be maneuvered into close proximity to one of the Martian moons, the gravitational effect on its orbit would be great enough to permit calculation of the moon's density, and thus, by inference, determination of its composition. *Mariner 9* was unable to perform the necessary maneuver, but scientists looked forward to the

Viking mission, when one of the *Viking* Orbiters was scheduled to be jockeyed to within 100 km of Phobos.

Phobos and Deimos are also worth studying because they provide a calibration of the cratering rate in the vicinity of Mars. With no atmospheres, their craters have not been eroded significantly with time, so careful crater counts on the two moons will increase our understanding of events which occurred on Mars.

The observations of *Mariner 9* catapulted the study of Mars forward a significant distance. Some old questions were finally answered, but many new ones were raised. The new questions, though, won't have to wait centuries for their answers. *Mariner 9* had merely scouted the War God from a safe distance; the next mission was to be an outright invasion.

PART FOUR

Visit to a Small Planet

10

Viking: Portrait of a Spacecraft

I felt all along that we had good hardware. . . .
—James Martin,
Viking Project Manager
August 18, 1976

It cost half a billion dollars and it looks like a cross between a Volkswagen and a hermit crab. No one ever accused the *Viking* Lander of being beautiful. It is said that a camel is a horse designed by a committee; *Viking was* designed by a committee, and looks it.

Ugly though it may be, there are those who love it.

Viking was born in the mid-sixties when NASA planners began to look at the possibilities for post-*Mariner* missions. Although the early *Mariners* had only given preliminary indications about what the surface of Mars would be like, the long lead time necessary to develop and build a spacecraft decreed that planning for a Martian landing must begin nearly a decade before the event was to take place. *Viking* was thus conceived and designed long before *Mariner 9* revealed the true nature of its destination.

There is a school of thought at NASA which holds that planetary missions should be staggered—Mars this year, Venus next year, then Jupiter and Saturn, and finally back to Mars again. By spacing the missions in such a manner, it would be possible to design each succeeding mission to a planet, using the knowledge gained from previous missions to that planet. Ideally, this would be the best way to run a planetary program.

Unfortunately, there are other factors that have to be considered. One of the most important is what football announcers call momentum. If there were to be a ten-year hiatus between Mars missions, most of the engineers and scientists involved in the Mars program would probably wander off and find other things to do. After assembling a competent and experienced Mars team, you don't want to see it fall apart between missions. So *Viking* followed close on the heels of *Mariner,* and many of the same people were active in both projects.

Originally, plans for a Mars Lander had called for a larger and more expensive spacecraft. Known as *Voyager,* the spacecraft was to have weighed a hefty 20,000 pounds, and would have been launched aboard a *Saturn V* rocket, the same booster used in the *Apollo* program. The *Voyager* mission was given a projected price tag of 1.6 billion dollars, but more realistically, it probably would have cost 2 to 3 billion. Congress looked at those numbers and didn't like what it saw; *Voyager* was canceled in 1967.

NASA began looking for a cheaper way to get to Mars. A study group was set up at the Langley Research Office in Hampton, Virginia to examine the alternatives. James Martin was chosen to head the team, and later became *Viking* Project Manager. Martin, a brawny 6'4", 225, was an ideal choice. As one *Viking* engineer put it, "I'll never work on another project with Jim Martin, but there'd never have been a *Viking* without him." With his military-style crewcut, he reminded some of a paratroop commander, and others of a Prussian general. Although he is easygoing and affable, Martin leaves no room for doubt that he is The Man in Charge.

Jim Martin brought to *Viking* a practical background in the roll-up-your-sleeves kind of engineering that is essential in so visionary a project. Burroughs to the contrary, you don't get to Mars just by dreaming. Martin was born in 1920 and was fascinated by airplanes as a boy—he once hitchhiked two days to get to the National Air Races. After graduating from the University of Michigan with a degree in aeronautical engineering, he went to work for Republic Aviation, and had a hand in the design of the P-47, the almost legendary World War II fighter plane, as well as the F-84, one of America's first operational jets. He joined NASA in 1964 and was involved in the Lunar Orbiter program, *Voyager,* and then *Viking.*

Martin's team at Langley spent all of 1968 looking at Mars Lander options. From a field of twenty alternatives, including hard landers, short-lived landers, and direct-entry vehicles, they selected *Viking* as the best combination of science, engineering, and economy. The decision to go with *Viking* (then known as *Titan-Mars '73)* was made by NASA in November 1968. By January 1970, it was apparent that *Viking* would not be ready on time, and the launch was postponed to 1975.

As with *Mariner, Viking* was to be made a twin mission. Each flight included an Orbiter and a Lander, so in reality *Viking* was not one spacecraft, but four. The Orbiter was a kind of super-*Mariner,* very similar in design, but larger and more versatile. Design and construction were carried out by the Jet Propulsion Laboratory. The prime contractor for the Lander was Martin-Marietta, of Denver.

The Orbiter was relatively easy to build, since it included very little that was really new. The Lander, however, was a spacecraft of another color. Except for the unmanned *Surveyor* missions to the moon, NASA had no experience in

159

landing robot probes on other worlds. The Russians had tried several planetary landers, but without much success. *Venera 3* had reached the surface of Venus in 1966, but had failed to send back any data. *Venera 4* landed the following year and returned atmospheric data, but apparently did not survive on the surface itself. In 1969, *Veneras 5* and *6* reached the surface and were more successful, but neither craft lasted very long.

But Venus has a thick atmosphere, making possible a parachute descent. Mars, with its very thin atmosphere, would not permit such an easy maneuver. Of the first two Russian *Mars* landers, the first crashed and the second was destroyed after just 20 seconds on the surface. Clearly, it was no easy task to put down a spacecraft safely.

There were additional problems. A treaty signed in 1967 guaranteed that any spacecraft sent to Mars for the next 50 years would be sterilized. Scientists were afraid that if a probe carried terrestrial microbes to Mars, the native life forms, if any, would be contaminated. Also, there was the fear that any life-seeking instrument sent to Mars might merely detect earth-grown microbes instead of actual Martian life forms. The only way to be sure that Mars would be kept safe for the Martians was to sterilize visiting spacecraft.

The sterilization procedure had to be foolproof and effective beyond any question. Spraying the spacecraft with Lysol would not do the trick. The entire Lander had to be heated to 254°F for a total of 200 hours prior to launch. Electronic systems and delicate instruments tend to break down when subjected to such heat. So the *Viking* Lander design problems were compounded; the instruments not only had to function on the surface of Mars, they also had to survive the rigors of sterilization on earth.

There is some disagreement among *Viking* people as to how big a hurdle sterilization represented. According to Jim Martin, "Sterilization presented a lot of problems in many areas." But Dr. Frederick S. Brown, the Biology Project Scientist, maintains that sterilization was "probably one of the biggest myths in the whole program." There was plenty of reason to be worried about the sterilization procedure. The only spacecraft which had undergone sterilization prior to *Viking* were the early *Ranger* hard-landing moon shots, and they had not worked very well; once the sterilization was omitted, the *Rangers* performed better. Despite the worries, though, *Viking* came through sterilization in fine shape. "Once you know you've got a big problem when you start out," said Brown, "you can work it out."

For Brown and the biology team, sterilization may have seemed like a small problem in comparison with others they faced. *Viking* was to be the first spacecraft ever equipped with a functioning, automated biochemical laboratory. The hope was that *Viking* would be able to find and identify Martian microbes on or just beneath the surface of Mars. The complexities involved in the conception, design, and operation of the *Viking* biology package were enormous. As late as 1974, the biology experiments were six months behind schedule, and serious consideration was given to flying *Viking* without the biology investigations. However, leaving off the biology package would have had some profound, nonscientific consequences for *Viking*. "It would have been tougher to sell," said Jim Martin. "The glamor of looking for life had a lot to do with the support *Viking* has had." The decision was made to wait for the biology, and it turned out to be the correct choice. The experiments were delivered to Cape Canaveral in early 1975, slightly ahead of schedule.

The biology investigation was certainly the most glamorous experiment planned for *Viking*, but it was just one of a total of thirteen separate experiments included in the mission design. *Viking*, by all odds, was the most sophisticated spacecraft ever flown; it is arguable, in fact, that the *Viking* Lander was the most complex machine ever built. A close examination of *Viking* may prove the point.

The *Viking* Orbiter is a linear descendant of the *Mariner* series of spacecraft. Like the *Mariners,* the heart of the *Viking* Orbiter is contained in an octagonal box, with windmill-like solar panels attached to it. The box is eight feet across and 18 inches high, and consists of eight alternating long (55″) and short (22″) panels. There is a total of 16 bays, or compartments inside the box, three on each of the long sides and one on each short side. Complete with rocket engine, propellant tanks, and extended solar panels, the entire Orbiter measures 10.8 feet high and 32 feet across. The four solar panels have a combined surface area of 161 square feet.

The solar panels provide the Orbiter with its power. *Mariner* missions to Venus, closer to the sun, had only two solar panels. For Martian missions, going away from the sun, four panels are necessary. In Mars orbit, the panels produce a total power output of 620 watts.

When the sun is not in view, during launch or when the Orbiter is occulted by Mars, power is provided by two 26-cell nickel-cadmium batteries, which are charged by the solar panels. Each battery can supply up to 30 amps per hour at 27.4 volts, and each is capable of operating independently of the other. During the launch and cruise phase of the mission, the Orbiter supplied power to the Lander, as well as itself.

The propulsion system of the Orbiter consists of a single 300-pound fixed-thrust rocket engine, mounted on a movable gimbal. Two helium-pressurized tanks provide the rocket with fuel (monomethylhydrazine) and oxidizer (nitrogen tetroxide). Although the rocket burns more fuel than oxidizer, both tanks are the same size, in order to keep the spacecraft balanced. The combined capacity of the tanks is 3,137 pounds of liquid propellant, bringing the total launch weight of the Orbiter to 5,125 pounds.

The Orbiter's rocket was designed for a minimum of four

mid-course correction burns. As it turned out, the navigation was so accurate that neither mission required that many mid-course burns. The major task of the rocket is to perform the Mars Orbit Insertion (MOI) burn, which puts *Viking* into orbit around Mars. Following MOI, the rocket is capable of a minimum of 20 Mars Orbit Trim (MOT) maneuvers. Because of the mascons buried inside Mars, rather frequent MOT burns are necessary just to keep the spacecraft in its proper orbit. Additional burns are used to change the plane or period of the orbit.

The *Viking* guidance system is very similar to *Mariner*'s. In addition to a sun sensor, there is the familiar Canopus sensor. "Canopus sensor" has become a kind of generic name for any star tracking device; aboard *Viking 2,* the Canopus sensor was actually a Vega sensor.

The attitude control electronics subsystem (ACE) keeps the spacecraft locked on its proper reference points. The ACE automatically fires small nitrogen jets in order to correct any drift. Two of the jets control pitch, and the remaining two are responsible for roll and yaw maneuvers. The nitrogen gas is stored in a pressurized tank contained in the Orbiter body, and is delivered to the jets through a series of pressure regulators. *Mariner 9* had a similar system, and the mission was finally terminated when the nitrogen tanks ran dry. To extend the life of the *Viking* Orbiter, an auxiliary set of pipes can be used to divert oxidizer or fuel from the rocket propellant tanks to the attitude control jets.

The Orbiter's primary post-landing task is to act as a communications relay station between the Lander and the earth. Although the Lander is capable of direct communication with the earth, the Orbiter relay link allows a much higher data rate. A small antenna mounted on one of the solar panels receives data from the Lander during the periapsis (low point) of each orbit. The data is then recorded for rebroadcast to earth.

163

The Orbiter maintains communications with earth via a high-gain S and X Band subsystem. A 59-inch parabolic dish antenna, motor driven, constantly tracks the earth to keep the link intact. The antenna receives S-Band signals from earth, and transmits both S and X Band signals. In addition, an omnidirectional low-gain antenna, a tubelike structure mounted on the side of the spacecraft, is capable of maintaining communications even when the high-gain antenna is not pointed directly at the earth. High-gain S-Band transmissions can send from 2,000 to 16,000 bits per second; the low-gain antenna transmits mainly engineering data at 8.3 or 33.3 bits per second.

The Orbiter's data storage system consists of two eight-track digital tape recorders. The tapes record data from the Orbiter and relay data from the Lander. Tracks one through seven handle the science data and can simultaneously record up to 301,712 bits per second. The eighth track is used for engineering data at rates of four and sixteen kilobits per second. This awesome recording capacity is made necessary by the short duration of the Lander-Orbiter relay link. The Orbiter is in position over the Lander for only a short time each day. The "nominal" mission design called for a minimum relay link of seventeen minutes. Actual performance turned out to be considerably better: about 42 minutes for *Viking 1* and 34 minutes for *Viking 2*. Since the Orbiter data storage system has a total capacity of 640 million bits, the extra time was put to good use.

The brain of the Orbiter is a redundant computer system; if something happens to one computer, the other automatically takes over. Each has a 4,096-word capacity. The first, 2,048 words are a permanent part of the system, protected from erasure. The second 2,048 words are changeable, and can be erased to make room for new commands from earth. Since a signal traveling at the speed of light would take nineteen minutes to cover the 212 million miles separating the spacecraft and the technicians in Pasadena, the Orbiter computer was designed to be able to take care of the spacecraft without any help from earth. When unforeseen problems arise, the computer simply shuts itself down and waits for new commands from earth. The importance of this feature was demonstrated during the landing of *Viking 2,* when communications were cut off for more than an hour.

Aside from its duties as a bus and relay station for the Lander, the Orbiter is a highly sophisticated spacecraft in its own right. Photographs taken from the Orbiter have been of generally higher quality than those taken by *Mariner 9,* and the water vapor and thermal detection experiments have provided important new information. The overall performance of the two Orbiters has been at least as impressive as that of the two Landers.

ORBITER IMAGING SYSTEM

Properly speaking, spacecraft like *Mariner* and *Viking* do not "take pictures"—they "image," a word that the *Viking* scientists insist on using as a verb. Since the imaging systems differ dramatically from ordinary cameras, it is not technically correct to talk of "taking pictures." Moreover, some of the scientists tend to take offense at such loose usage, since it carries with it the connotation of being able to drop off the film at the nearest Fotomat.

Each Orbiter is equipped with two television-type cameras mounted side by side on a movable scan platform. The cameras operate in the same manner as the *Mariner* imaging systems, using an electron beam to read off electrical charges on a vidicon tube. The information is then recorded on the seven science tracks of the tape recorder and played back to earth one track at a time.

The Martian scenes are focused onto the vidicon by a

475 mm Cassegrainian telescope. Resolution at periapsis is about 40 meters. Each pixel thus represents a field of view about the size of a baseball infield. The complete images consist of 1,056 lines, with 1,182 pixels per line. The pixels are translated into the computer as seven-bit words, so the total number of bits per image is about 8.7 million. A single *Viking* Orbiter image contains more bits than were returned by the entire *Mariner 4* mission.

Between the telescope and the vidicon, there is a filter wheel with six divisions: blue, minus blue, violet, clear, green, and red. By shooting the same scene three times in succession, using the red, green, and blue filters, it is possible to assemble color pictures of Mars. The accuracy of the color is good, though not perfect. The Image Processing Laboratory (IPL) at JPL receives the raw data and works to "color balance" the image. The final result may be heavily dependent upon the judgment of the technician who does the balancing. Unlike the Lander, the Orbiter has no convenient color test chart to use for comparison.

The cameras are mounted with slightly nonparallel sighting. The shutters also operate with a half-second offset. As a result of this slightly nonsynchronous operation, during each periapsis pass at the planet the cameras produce images of a long swath of adjacent territory. With an image taken every 4.48 seconds, there is quite a lot of overlap, which is good because it makes the construction of orbital mosaics easier.

The job of assembling those mosaics and interpreting the images belongs to the Orbiter Imaging Team, headed by Michael Carr of the U.S. Geological Survey at Menlo Park, California. Carr, a veteran of *Mariner 9,* is a diminutive Englishman with a keen sense of humor. In fact, nearly all of the British Empire scientists involved in *Viking* are notable for their wit. Not all of the members of the *Viking* press corps thought they were so funny; a disgruntled British reporter referred to Carr as "another bloody brain-drainer." That may be, but in the absence of a vigorous British space program, scientists such as Carr are a welcome addition to the American space community; they add an appropriately transnational flavor to the exploration of other planets.

The primary task of the Orbiter Imaging Team is to find a safe spot for the Lander to touch down. On a planet as heterogeneous as Mars, that is no easy task. Areas which looked relatively safe from *Mariner 9* photography turned out, under the keener eyes of *Viking,* to be strewn with craters, channels, mesas, and sand dunes. In terms of finding a good landing site, such observations were depressing. But since most of the Orbiter Imaging Team members are geologists, few long faces were in evidence when the first Orbiter images were returned.

The Orbiter also views Mars at different times of day. Careful study of early morning and late afternoon images can result in information about the formation and disappearance of clouds and ground frost, neither of which is normally visible during the middle portion of the Martian day.

MARS ATMOSPHERIC WATER DETECTOR

The *Mariner 9* pictures gave the first clear indication that Mars, at one time, possessed substantial quantities of running water. The major question posed by these observations was (and is), what happened to all that water? Some of it may be locked in the soil, some of it is certainly frozen in the polar caps, and *Mariner* data indicated that some of it is escaping into space in the form of free hydrogen and oxygen molecules. But earth-based observations revealed that there is still at least a small amount of water vapor present in the Martian atmosphere.

The Mars Atmospheric Water Detector (MAWD) was designed to find out exactly how much water remains in the atmosphere. MAWD is mounted on the Orbiter scan platform to the right of the cameras. The instrument is bore-sighted with the cameras, so it is possible to coordinate images of a particular patch of the Martian surface with data on the atmosphere above it. That capability is important because water vapor should be most abundant in low areas where the pressure is high; the MAWD readings thus give an accurate indication of the elevation of surface features.

MAWD is basically an infrared spectrometer, set to measure the diffuse reflection of sunlight through the Martian atmosphere at 1.38 micrometers—the characteristic wavelength of water vapor. At periapsis, the instrument examines a "footprint" 1.80° by 0.92°, or about 1.9 by 12.4 miles. A mirror at the aperture of the instrument sweeps through 15 smaller rectangles within the footprint in the space of 4.48 seconds, the same time interval that is used by the cameras between images.

Water vapor is normally measured in terms of precipitable microns, that is, the thickness of the layer of water or ice that would be produced on the surface if all the water vapor in the atmosphere were to be condensed out. MAWD has a sensitivity of less than one precipitable micron. On earth, the atmosphere generally holds between 1 and 2 precipitable centimeters of water, or about half an inch. The highest reading for Mars prior to *Viking* was about 50 microns (.002 inches).

At first glance, the figures indicate that Mars is an extremely dry world, but that is a somewhat misleading statement. Since the Martian atmosphere is so thin, all of the water vapor in it must be concentrated within the bottom kilometer or so. In terms of relative humidity, the Martian water vapor concentration may be quite high in certain places at certain times.

MAWD's job is to determine what places, what times. The leader of the MAWD team is Dr. Crofton B. (Barney) Farmer, another British member of the *Viking* community. With his neatly trimmed black beard and salt-and-pepper hair, Farmer would be a Hollywood casting director's ideal choice to play the Sheriff of Nottingham. Farmer is an accomplished pianist and is the owner of a uniquely English "dry" wit—so dry that even MAWD would have problems with it. When asked, for purposes of comparison, to give the normal amount of precipitable microns of water in the air over southern California, Farmer replied that in comparison with his native land, he would say that it was a figure approaching zero. Ironically, while Farmer was searching for water on Mars, and despairing about its general absence in southern California, England was experiencing its worst drought in a thousand years.

INFRARED THERMAL MAPPER

IRTM sounds like a spur to a New York subway line, but the IRTM, mounted to the left of the Orbiter cameras, measures thermal radiation from the Martian surface and atmosphere. Like MAWD, the IRTM is bore-sighted with the cameras. It scans the image area in a series of circles 8 km in diameter, arranged in an inverted V formation, known as the "IRTM chevron."

The instrument consists of four small telescopes, each with seven sensitive antimony-bismuth infrared detectors. The detectors measure infrared brightness, which varies with heat, in a range between 0.3 and 24 micrometers. With 28 separate detectors, the IRTM can measure a range of infrared "colors," and has a sensitivity of less than one degree Celsius (1.8°F).

From the heat measurements of the IRTM, it is possible to deduce the nature of the Martian surface. Walk along a beach at night, and the first thing you notice is that the sand which was too hot to walk on a few hours earlier is now much cooler than the air and water. Fine-grained material gives up its heat quickly. Large rocks, on the other hand, tend to maintain a more constant temperature. IRTM data obtained during the course of a Martian day measures the temperature gradient of the surface, and the shape of the resulting curves gives information about whether the surface is sandy or rocky. The best time to measure is just before the Martian sunrise, when the difference between the temperatures of the rocks and the sand is greatest.

One of the IRTM detectors is set to measure temperatures in the upper atmosphere. That information, combined with meteorology data from the Lander, permits the construction of models of wind circulation patterns in the Martian atmosphere. Atmospheric measurements can also be used to determine the height of clouds seen in the Orbiter pictures.

The IRTM scans Mars for 57 seconds in each sequence. A three-position mirror in the telescope then shifts the view to deep space for a few seconds in order to establish a zero level. The entire instrument cycle lasts 1.25 minutes.

The Thermal Mapping Team is led by Dr. Hugh H. Kieffer of UCLA. Except for a hint of gray in his hair, Kieffer could easily be mistaken for one of the many undergraduate interns who were working at JPL during the *Viking* mission. He sometimes attended *Viking* press briefings clad in shirt, tie, and cut-off khakis. The press, usually attired in about the same manner, appreciated the informality.

VIKING LANDER

One of the most popular arguments for manned versus unmanned space exploration is that men are smarter than machines and can do things that machines can't. While this is undoubtedly true in some cases, it is also true that machines can do things that men can't, and do them better and more economically. As for intelligence, smart men ought to be capable of building smart machines. Exhibit A: the *Viking* Lander.

Perhaps the most amazing thing about the *Viking* Lander is that anyone ever tried to build it in the first place. Consider the enormity of the task; the Lander requirements sound like a set of instructions from *Mission Impossible*. The mission, should anyone decide to accept it, is to design and build two spacecraft, weighing less than a ton each, deliver them to the planet Mars across 400 million miles of space, land them safely on the surface of that planet (the nature of which is unknown), and have them survive in a hostile environment for a minimum of 90 days, all the while returning billions of bits of data. Each spacecraft is to be equipped with a sophisticated computer that can operate independently of instructions from earth. Room must be found on the spacecraft to include four completely automated biochemical laboratories, two cameras, an inorganic analysis chamber, a meteorology station, a seismology station, a number of smaller experiments, and reliable communications equipment. To top it off, the spacecraft must be able to collect samples of the Martian surface material and deliver them to the on-board laboratories. All this must be done in less than five years at an expense of less than a half billion dollars.

Somehow, the mission was not only accepted, but accomplished.

On first viewing, the Lander looks like something that was assembled from leftover Tinkertoy parts, but taken piece by piece, the whole thing makes sense and even has a certain beauty about it. The body of the Lander is a hollow, six-sided aluminum-titanium box, measuring about ten feet across and 18.2 inches deep. Three of the sides are 43 inches long, and the remaining three are 22 inches long, making the box look like a truncated triangle.

The landing legs are mounted on each of the short sides. The decision was made to have three legs (instead of four, as on the Lunar Module) because a three-legged structure will always rest on all three legs.

The interior of the body is insulated with spun Fiberglas

and dacron fabric, in order to prevent heat loss. Located inside the box are the biology package, the molecular analysis experiment, the x-ray fluorescence experiment, the data storage memory, the computer, the tape recorder, and a number of radios, batteries, and control units. Everything else on the spacecraft is mounted on the top or sides of the box. All the external components are painted a drab battleship gray, which reflects solar heat.

Everything aboard the Lander was sterilized before launch. To avoid contamination following the assembling of the vehicle, the Lander was placed in a large, egg-like capsule known as the bioshield. A two-piece dome constructed of woven Fiberglas and an aluminum support structure, the bioshield protects the Lander during the launch phase. Following launch, the cap of the bioshield is ejected by explosive bolts; the base of the shield travels along to Mars.

Inside the bioshield is the aeroshell. One side of the aeroshell is a heat shield made of glass beads and cork embedded in silicone. During entry into the Martian atmosphere, the heat shield protects the Lander from temperatures as high as 2700°F.

The opposite side of the aeroshell holds the Lander's eight de-orbit engines, which burn following separation from the Orbiter and slow the spacecraft enough for it to be captured by the Martian gravity. The engines also control the Lander's attitude during entry. Also contained within the aeroshell are the upper atmosphere mass spectrometer, the retarding potential analyzer, and an array of temperature and pressure sensors, all of which record data during the brief encounter with Mars' upper atmosphere.

The Martian atmosphere is too thin to allow a parachute-only descent. But there is some atmosphere, so a parachute is utilized to help slow the Lander on its way down. At an altitude of about 21,000 feet, the aeroshell is jettisoned and a 15-inch mortar fires out a 53-foot diameter parachute. The chute slows the Lander's speed from about 560 miles per hour to about 138 miles per hour.

At 4,000 feet the parachute is jettisoned and the descent rockets take the craft the rest of the way down. Mounted on the sides of the Lander body are three throttleable rocket engines. The engines are controlled by the Lander's computer, and provide between 62 and 638 pounds of thrust, supplied as needed. An inertial reference unit and a radar altimeter return landing data to the computer, which then decides how much thrust to apply.

An important consideration in the design of the descent engines was the effect they would have on the surface immediately around the Lander. The biologists didn't want the sampling area to be contaminated by rocket fuel, and the geologists hoped that the engine exhaust would not disturb the surface material too badly. (They didn't mind a little disturbance, however; rocks rolling around and dust blown away from bedrock provided useful information.) In order to disperse the exhaust plume, each engine has 18 small nozzles, pointing in various downward directions.

The rockets slow the Lander to about 5 miles per hour. Anyone who has ever bashed in a bumper while trying to park knows that 5 miles per hour is enough to give a not insignificant jolt. That final shock has to be absorbed by the Lander's footpads and legs. Switches in the base of each footpad automatically shut off the rockets, so that the first footpad to touch the surface will terminate the descent sequence. The footpads are 12 inches in diameter and are mounted at the end of A-frame aluminum legs equipped with aluminum honeycomb crushable shock absorbers. Each leg can withstand a force of 2,500 foot-pounds. Stroke gauges, mounted at the top of the legs, pop out on impact; later, photographs are taken of the stroke gauges to measure the amount of compression of the legs.

The Lander is supposed to come down feet first. But even

the sturdy footpads may not be enough to protect the Lander's sensitive body. Ground clearance from footpad to the bottom of the body is slightly less than 9 inches. If the Lander comes down on top of a 10-inch rock, the footpads won't help at all. In the days before the landing of *Viking 1,* those unseen 10-inch rocks caused many a sleepless night among *Viking* personnel. There was simply nothing that could be done about them.

About eight days after landing, *Viking* begins the first of its biological and chemical experiments. Martian soil is collected for the investigations by the surface sampler, a kind of robot arm mounted between the two cameras. The sampler boom is made of two layers of thin stainless steel foil, welded together along the edges. In its stowed position, the boom simply rolls up inside its mounting. When extended, the boom tends to stiffen, much like a steel tape measure. The boom can reach out about ten feet from the Lander body. It can rotate through 302 degrees of azimuth and from 35 degrees above the horizon to 50 degrees below it.

At the end of the boom is the collector head, which resembles a rather sophisticated gardening tool. The shovel-like head scoops up soil and deposits it in its collector. When the sample is acquired, the boom reels itself in and brings the collector head to a position over the soil hoppers for the various experiments. The head then rotates and the sample falls into the hoppers through a screen in the top of the collector head. There is also a backhoe attached to the bottom of the collector head; as the sample is being dug up, the backhoe scrapes out a long trench in the Martian surface. Photos of the trench can give added information on the nature of the surface material.

The Lander keeps in touch with earth through a UHF relay link with the Orbiter and a direct S-Band link from the Lander to the earth. The UHF link can operate at 1, 10, or 30 watts and transmits up to 16 kilobits per second to the Orbiter, which records the data for later rebroadcast to earth.

Through the S-Band link, the Lander can both send and receive data. Transmission rate is as high as 1,000 bits per second; reception of command data is at 4 bits per second.

The S-Band antenna is a 30-inch parabolic dish mounted on top of the Lander. It is motor-driven and tracks the earth through the Martian sky. There is also a stationary low-gain antenna. The low-gain antenna serves as the primary command receiver.

If, for some reason, the Lander were unable to receive commands from earth, it would still be able to carry out a 60-day mission. An Initial Computer Load (ICL) is stored in the Lander's computer before separation from the Orbiter, and it contains all the information necessary for the Lander to complete its basic mission. If communications are not impaired, the ICL is periodically updated by commands from earth. These "uplinks" are prepared in three-day cycles and contain specific instructions to the Lander which override the ICL.

The data storage memory unit in the Lander gathers all the scientific and engineering data acquired by the Lander's instruments. The data is stored there until the next relay or direct link, at which time the information is transmitted. In the meantime, data can be fed to the computer's bulk storage memory.

Lander data is processed through the data acquisition and processing unit (DAPU), which digitizes information from the instruments, making it possible to transmit the data.

The digital tape recorder aboard the Lander stores data which cannot be transmitted immediately. Because of the high-temperature sterilization requirements, the recorder uses a tape made of a phosphor-bronze base, coated with nickel-cobalt as a recording medium. The tape is 650 feet long and records on four tracks. Ten million bits can be stored on each track. Recording is at 4 or 16 kilobits, and playback can be at any one of five different speeds, up to 16 kilobits.

Everything on board the Lander is controlled by the guidance, control, and sequencing computer. The GCSC is about the size and shape of an automobile battery, consistent with the overall junkyard appearance of the Lander. But this rather unimpressive-looking black box is the most sophisticated computer ever flown on a spacecraft.

The GCSC is actually two computers, like a brain with two lobes. Each lobe is identical. Before separation from the Orbiter, the computers are given a test; the one which performs the best and has "forgotten" the least is made the primary computer, and the other one is put to sleep. If the primary computer should falter, the secondary is automatically activated.

The computer contains a 25-bit, 18,432-word-plated wire memory. Its stored commands are sufficient to run every instrument on the Lander and process the data it produces. This broad computer capability would be necessary even if the Lander were in constant communication with the earth. The twenty-minute time lag between the two planets makes real-time operation from earth a physical impossibility.

The Lander draws its power and heat from two radio-isotope thermoelectric generators (RTGs). Each generator contains a bank of thermoelectric elements which convert heat from decaying plutonium-238 into 35 watts of power. Excess heat is funneled into the Lander body to keep the instruments at the proper temperature. Windscreens surround the RTGs and prevent heat dissipation into the cold Martian air. For periods of maximum power use, the RTGs are supplemented by four nickel-cadmium batteries. Because of the long-term nature of nuclear power, a Lander could theoretically continue to operate on the Martian surface for years.

ENTRY SCIENCE

On its way down, the *Viking* Lander must pass through the entire Martian atmosphere, top to bottom. Since the overriding philosophy of the *Viking* mission is that nothing should be wasted ("Indian use whole buffalo," explained one scientist), naturally enough, there are instruments attached to the aeroshell to collect atmospheric data.

The composition of the Martian atmosphere remained a mystery right up until the moment *Viking 1* plunged into it. The high-nitrogen atmosphere of the fifties and early sixties was gone; nitrogen had never been detected in the Martian atmosphere. And yet any reasonable model of atmospheric development implied that there ought to be at least a little nitrogen. If nitrogen turned out to be completely absent, the chances of there being life on Mars would be extremely remote, since on earth the nitrogen cycle is an important factor in the life process.

Argon was another puzzler. The Russian probe *Mars 6* had returned data in 1973, before it crashed, that indicated a high argon content, perhaps as much as 35 percent. The data was suspect because the argon value was derived by a failure analysis of one of the probe's instruments. It malfunctioned in such a way as to indicate the presence of high concentrations of some inert gas, most probably argon.

If the Russian data was correct, it implied that Mars at one time possessed a much denser atmosphere than it now has. All the argon-40 in earth's atmosphere has been produced by the radioactive decay of potassium-40, which is present in rocks. A 35 percent argon content in the Martian atmosphere (it is about one percent in our own) would mean that over the course of time, the Martian rocks outgassed tremendous quantities of gas, of which argon-40 was just one. If so, what happened to all those gases?

Since there was a definite chance that the *Viking* Landers could crash when they reached the surface, atmospheric measurements taken during descent were doubly important. To make those measurements, two instruments were attached to the aeroshell. One, the retarding potential analyzer, looks for charged particles in the upper atmosphere. The other, an

177

upper atmosphere mass spectrometer, counts neutral particles.

The retarding potential analyzer is a series of electrified wire grills which filter out particles streaming in during entry. The current in the grills is variable, and only particles of specific energy and charge are allowed past the filters at any given moment. By knowing the range in which the analyzer is working when a reading is taken, the presence and concentration of various ions can be measured.

The upper atmosphere mass spectrometer measures the amounts and concentrations of molecules in the atmosphere above an altitude of about 60 miles; below that altitude, the pressure is too great for the UAMS to operate. During entry, gas molecules pass through an opening in the aeroshell and are bombarded by electrons, turning the molecules into positively charged ions. The ions then pass into a detector. By varying the current, it is possible to accept only certain ions into the detector.

Each element or molecule has a specific mass-to-charge ratio. For nitrogen, it is 28, oxygen, 32, and CO_2, 44. The UAMS is sensitive in a range from 1 to 50, and sweeps through that range once every five seconds. By measuring the number of ions detected at each number, the composition and density of the atmosphere can be determined.

The Entry Science Team leader is Dr. Alfred O. C. Nier of the University of Minnesota. Since the entry phase is over very quickly, Dr. Nier and his colleagues had to wait years just to collect five minutes' worth of data.

For Nier, one of the frustrations of *Viking* was that design requirements had frozen his instruments several years before launch. In the meantime, better instruments were developed. In fact, even at the time of the design freeze, his instruments were not "state-of-the-art." Although Nier was pleased with the data he eventually got, he felt that even better data might have been obtained. "I have instruments sitting in my laboratory gathering dust that are a thousand times better than

178

what's on *Viking,*" Nier commented following the landing of
Viking 2.

LANDER IMAGING

Rising above the body of the *Viking* Lander are two stubby
appendages which look like the eyestalks of an arthropod. The
comparison is appropriate, because these are the eyes of
Viking.
The Lander Imaging System works on a different principle
than the Orbiter Imaging System. The cameras on the Orbiter
are similar to traditional television cameras; the Lander cameras are more like the facsimile photo reproduction systems
used by newspapers and wire services. The Orbiter vidicon
system scans the entire scene simultaneously, while the Lander
system scans consecutively, one pixel at a time.
A nodding mirror reflects light into the camera's optical
system, where it hits one or more diodes. The signal is then
digitized as a six-bit word and is either recorded or transmitted directly. On earth, a laser-computer system converts the
data back into pictures, which build up gradually on television
monitors.
The camera scans each line vertically, top to bottom, with
512 pixels to a line. After the line is completed, the entire
camera rotates to the right and scans the adjacent line. Each
camera can rotate nearly 360°, so it is possible to build up
panorama images in the space of about ten minutes.
There are twelve separate diodes in each camera, each one
designed to portray a particular spatial or spectral quality.
One diode is used to acquire black and white panoramas.
Three are filtered in red, blue, and green for color imagery.
Three others have infrared diodes for "false color" pictures.
Four diodes are placed at different focal positions to obtain
high resolution black and white pictures. The twelfth diode is

179

of very low sensitivity and is used for taking pictures of the sun. Following the landing of *Viking 1,* when there was intense competition among the various experimenters for Lander bit allocations, the members of the Lander Imaging Team hinted darkly about the existence of a mysterious thirteenth diode—a laser diode that could vaporize any other experiment whose investigators got too greedy for extra bits. The threat was hollow, but the problem was real. Each picture uses several million bits, reducing the amount of data transmission available to the other experiments.

Fortunately, the Lander Imaging Team is headed by an immensely likable man, Dr. Thomas (Tim) Mutch, of Brown University. Mutch's easygoing personality was an asset to the mission; although there were many squabbles among the experimenters, full-scale warfare never developed.

Mutch, like most of the Lander Imaging People, is a geologist. He is also a frustrated jazz clarinetist. His father once bought him a clarinet, but soon sold it when it became apparent that young Tim Mutch was tone-deaf. Music's loss was geology's gain. In preparation for *Viking,* Mutch spent a lot of time looking at rocks in Antarctica, the most Mars-like place on earth. He never tired of talking about Antarctic ventifacts, wind-shaped rocks which look as if they've been carved and polished by a modern sculptor. Mutch warned that such rocks might be commonplace on Mars, and should not be taken as evidence of intelligent life on that planet.

If macroscopic life of some sort did exist on Mars, the *Viking* cameras ought to be able to detect it. One indication that an object is alive is that it may move, and the Lander Imaging System has a unique method of observing motion.

The *Viking* cameras have a slow scan rate because of early design problems. It was thought at one point that pictures would have to be fed directly to earth because *Viking* was not going to have a tape recorder on board. *Viking* eventually got its tape recorder, but the cameras retained their slow scan rate. This possible disadvantage was turned into a definite asset. The cameras can be set on what is known as a single-line rescan: the camera records a single line and then, instead of rotating, scans the same line over and over again. The resulting picture is a series of parallel horizontal lines. If, during the course of the rescan, something moves across the field of view, its motion will be detected as a blur or slanting of the horizontal lines. Any passing Martian animal would be recorded in the rescan; a more likely phenomenon would be the motion of dust particles through the air.

The two cameras on the Lander are mounted 39 inches apart. By recording images of the same scene from slightly different angles, stereo pictures can be produced. Also, with two cameras it is possible to scan virtually everything in the vicinity of the Lander, even though each camera has part of its field of view obscured by various pieces of the spacecraft itself.

The Lander cameras were built by the Itek Corporation at a cost of twenty-seven-and-a-half million dollars.

BIOLOGY

How do you go about finding life on another planet? The easiest method is to sit back and let it find you—as it did in *War of the Worlds*. Aside from the obvious drawback of that strategy, there is also the fact that life elsewhere might not be intelligent enough or close enough or interested enough to come looking for us.

A more difficult but probably more productive way to go about it is to actively search for extraterrestrial life. If there are intelligent civilizations elsewhere in the galaxy, radio telescopes may be able to pick up signals from them. But it's a big galaxy and there are a lot of stars to listen to.

The most difficult method is to go out into space and try to find a sample of alien life. That is the primary mission of *Viking*, and it is even more difficult than it might seem. The major problem is, simply, how do you recognize life when you find it? Life on earth, viewed in one light, is incredibly diverse. There are anerobic microbes and blue whales, viruses and sequoia trees, sharks and tulips, a collection so vast and varied that they might all have come from different planets. But from the point of view of a biologist searching for life on Mars, all life on earth is virtually identical. Every terrestrial organism is made of the same basic chemical material, and at that level, the differences between an ant and an antelope are simply superficial.

But will life on another planet look like life on earth— chemically, or any other way? Is there any reason to suppose that separate evolution would produce similar biologies? And if extraterrestrial life is fundamentally different from our own, how do we detect it?

No one knows the answer to any of those questions. But for the purposes of *Viking*, certain assumptions have to be made. Bearing in mind Carl Sagan's warning about "earth chauvinism," one can still argue that terrestrial life is "the most probable case." Life *did* develop on earth, and it developed in a particular manner, for what we may suppose were very good reasons. Some of the chemical and physical constraints which affected evolution on earth must certainly apply elsewhere. Life here is carbon-based, and carbon is a cosmically abundant element. So it seems likely that extraterrestrial organisms may also operate on a carbon-based chemistry.

Having said that much, there is not a great deal more that can be said without jumping into the realm of pure speculation. Yet *Viking* biologists were forced to speculate, and to build experiments based on those speculations. Imagine: someone tells you that you are going to be taken to some unspecified location anywhere on the planet earth, and you can only take three items with you. What do you take? A fur

182

coat? An aqualung? Snowshoes? Hiking boots? Golf clubs? That is roughly the situation that confronted the *Viking* biologists.

Ultimately, the *Viking* Lander carried three biological experiments. Each was based on a different set of assumptions about the nature of Martian life, and each operated on a different set of principles.

The Pyrolytic Release (PR) or Carbon Assimilation experiment assumed that Martian life would be, above all, Martian. It would be comfortable and at home in Martian conditions, so the experimental environment must be as close as possible to actual Martian conditions.

For the Gas Exchange experiment (Gex), the assumption was that Martian life is similar to terrestrial life. The possibility of cyclical variations in the Martian climate might mean that Martian life has adapted to long-term changes. During the long, dry winter, the Martian organisms might simply go into hibernation and wait for the coming of a wet, warm spring.

The Labeled Release experiment (LR) assumed that Martian life might be somewhere between the two extremes of PR and Gex. The organisms would be reasonably well adapted to the present Martian environment, but might prefer more earthlike conditions.

The leader of the *Viking* biology team is Dr. Harold P. Klein, of the Ames Research Center. The principal investigators are Dr. Norman H. Horowitz, of the California Institute of Technology (PR), Dr. Vance I. Oyama, of Ames (Gex), and Dr. Gilbert V. Levin, of Biospherics, Inc., in Rockville, Maryland (LR).

In order to understand the results produced by the three biology experiments, it's necessary to understand how the experiments function. Although the basic principles behind them are relatively straightforward, the actual operation of the instruments is quite complex and posed almost (but not quite)

183

insurmountable problems for the engineers at TRW, Inc., who built them.

The Pyrolytic Release experiment takes its soil sample and exposes it to the Martian atmosphere and an injection of radioactive carbon-14 in the gases CO_2 and CO. The Martian soil incubates in the cell under a xenon arc lamp, which simulates the sunlight received on the surface of Mars, with the significant subtraction of the ultraviolet end of the spectrum, which is filtered out by a glass plate. The experiment can also be run "in the dark," with the xenon lamp turned off.

After the soil sample has incubated for a few days, the gases in the test chamber are flushed out, resulting in a "first peak"—the number of radioactive counts per minute produced by the labeled carbon gases. If there are microbes in the soil sample, during the incubation period they may have assimilated some of the radioactive carbon. To test this, the chamber is heated to 625°C, at which temperature organic molecules are broken down. The carbon is released and forms CO_2 again. The chamber is flushed again, and if there is any radioactive carbon remaining, it will produce a "second peak." If the second peak is very low, it means that no carbon has been assimilated into the soil, implying an absence of life. A high second peak implies that some of the carbon has been assimilated—possibly by microorganisms. Before any definite conclusions can be drawn about this or any other experiment, a control cycle must be performed. In the control cycle, the sample is sterilized by heat before the beginning of the experiment. If the results from the two cycles are different, it may be an indication of biology.

The Gas Exchange experiment, in Dr. Klein's phrase, "goes whole hog toward terrestrial biology." It works from the assumption that any living system alters its environment by the chemical processes of its metabolism—it eats, breathes, reproduces. The Gex looks for evidence of those processes.

And to promote them, it feeds the putative Martian organisms. Chicken soup, it feeds them.

The Gex soil sample is suspended in a porous cup. A nutrient solution is introduced into the test cell, but not allowed to come into contact with the soil. After incubating in this "humid mode" for a week, 2 cc's of nutrient are injected into the bottom of the cup—the "wet mode." During the incubation, a gas chromatograph samples the gases in the test cell, looking for metabolic products such as hydrogen, oxygen, nitrogen, CO_2, and methane (CH_4). The presence of those gases might indicate that something is alive in the soil sample.

The nutrient in the Gex experiment is generally known as chicken soup, because, as Dr. Fred Brown of TRW put it, the nutrient is "the microorganisms' version of a good Jewish mother's brew." Developed by Vance Oyama, the soup contains virtually anything and everything a terrestrial organism might like to eat—amino acids, vitamins, minerals—"a virtual smorgasbord of organic goodies," says Klein.

This "super-nutrient" is actually about as dilute as seawater. The hope was that Martian organisms would like it as much as their terrestrial counterparts. Unfortunately, one microbe's chicken soup may be another microbe's poison. Even among earthly microbes, some would thrive on some of the components of the brew, and others would choke on the same stuff. Nevertheless, the chicken soup is about as close as anyone has come to creating a universal medium for earth organisms.

The Labeled Release experiment also contains a nutrient solution, but compared to the chicken soup, it is a weak broth. The LR nutrient is composed of seven different carbon compounds in distilled water. All of them are synthetically produced and contain labeled carbon-14 atoms.

In the LR, the soil sample is barely moistened by the nutrient. If there are microbes in the soil, they may want to eat and/or breathe the nutrient. After the nutrient is metabolized, some of it should be released in the form of gases, such as carbon dioxide or methane. A Geiger counter monitors the gases, looking for signs of the radioactive carbon-14.

All three biology experiments are contained in a single box, about a foot square, weighing 34 pounds. Getting them into that box may have been one of the greatest technological achievements of all time.

Originally, the engineers at Martin Marietta, *Viking*'s prime contractor, said that the biology package would weigh about ten pounds and could be built for around two million dollars. NASA scientists said eight million was a more likely figure. At TRW, where the package was to be built, the estimate was more like eighteen million—although TRW signed a contract for eleven million. In the end, the biology experiments cost just under sixty million dollars. A TRW administrator close to the biology program later admitted that if the job had been done properly from the beginning, the cost would have been around thirty million.

The problem was that no one was quite sure what instruments should be built, or how to build them. Nothing similar had ever been attempted by anyone.

At one point, the bio package was to contain four experiments. The fourth, known as "Wolf's Trap," was a light-scattering experiment which would detect reproduction of microorganisms. Dr. Wolf Vishniac, who designed the experiment, was killed in a fall in the Antarctic in 1973. Although the instrument was farther along in its design than any of the others, it was dropped from *Viking* because it required the presence of much more water than was likely to be available in the natural Martian environment.

By 1972, the biology package was way behind schedule. The LR experiment, although the simplest in concept, was very rudimentary. The PR was still in a manual setup; the soil was incubated in one room, heated in another room, and the radioactivity was detected in a third room. The Gex was

186

pretty well developed, but the gas sampling was still being done by hand.

There was a real danger that *Viking* might have to fly with only one biological experiment, and maybe even none. NASA administrator James Fletcher made the decision to go with all three, despite the cost. In November 1973, NASA agreed to a complete redesign of the bio package, and TRW pledged that it would deliver the experiment to the Cape by April 1975, instead of six months earlier, to Martin Marietta, as had been originally planned. TRW came through, and delivered the package a month early.

Even after the design problems had been resolved, the actual construction phase was one long headache. *Viking* was to be the first spacecraft ever to physically move liquids around (if you exclude Tang on the *Apollo* missions), and the problems involved were enormous. The package contained 39 miniature valves, each with flow restrictors the size of a human hair. The valves tended to jam very easily. In the end, a new kind of rubber had to be invented in order to build the valves.

Things were to be moved around inside the experiment by pressurized helium gas. But helium can leak through literally anything, even solid steel. TRW had to develop a new double-vacuum-melt steel-making process that would minimize the leakage.

The xenon lamp in the PR was one of the worst problems. It was very high-intensity, and if its arc became too big, it shut itself off. The problem was eventually solved, by what a TRW manager referred to as "black magic." He didn't elaborate.

Even the chicken soup was a worry. Like real chicken soup, there was the possibility that it could spoil if it sat too long on the shelf. Would it survive an eleven-month space flight? Tests indicated that it would, but just to be sure, several control ampules were sealed at the same time as the nutrient on *Viking*. When *Viking* reached Mars, the control ampules were

187

broken open and given a quality test; happily, they passed.

In the end, the *Viking* biology package resulted in advancing the "state-of-the-art" in 47 different areas. The final product was one of the most sophisticated machines ever built, and *Viking* scientists were confident about its performance. "No matter where you put down the box on earth," says Fred Brown, "it would detect life." The nagging question was, would it do the same on Mars?

MOLECULAR ANALYSIS

A positive signal from one or more of the biology experiments would not necessarily indicate the presence of life. For the *Viking* scientists to believe that they are looking at life, it is also necessary to have evidence of organic material in the Martian soil. Organic compounds are produced by nonbiological processes, such as photochemical or radiation-induced reactions, as well as by living systems. It is possible to have organic material and no life (as in carbonaceous chondrites), but without organic material, there can be no life.

Finding organics is the task of the Gas Chromatograph Mass Spectrometer (GCMS). The GCMS receives soil in the same manner as in the biology experiments. The sample is heated to 200°C (392°F) while a carrier gas (CO_2) sweeps through the test chamber to carry off any vaporized substances. The gas enters the gas chromatograph column, which separates out the various materials in the gas. Carried by a hydrogen stream, the gas then moves into the mass spectrometer, which works on a principle similar to the Upper Atmosphere Mass Spectrometer. There, a spectrum from mass 12 to mass 200 is produced once every ten seconds for a period of 84 minutes. The more analyses that are done, the better the reliability of the data, and the greater the detection limit.

188

The sample can also be heated to 500°C (932°F). At that temperature, different types of organics are broken down, and they are also measured. The GCMS has three different ovens, which can only be used once, limiting the number of analyses that can be done.

The GCMS can also do an analysis of the atmosphere at the surface of Mars in order to confirm the UAMS data. For the atmospheric analysis, no heating is necessary.

Dr. Klaus Biemann of the Massachusetts Institute of Technology is the leader of the Molecular Analysis Team. The GCMS was built by Litton Industries at a cost of 41 million dollars.

OTHER INVESTIGATIONS

The curiosity of the *Viking* scientists doesn't stop with the question of life. They want to know about the planet itself— what it's made of, how it behaves, how it got to be the way it is. To answer those and other questions, an array of instruments aboard *Viking* provide geological, mineralogical, magnetic, and meteorological data.

The X-Ray Fluorescence Spectrometer (XRFS) analyzes the composition of the Martian soil. It receives a soil sample that may be more coarse-grained than the samples received by biology and GCMS; pebbles up to a half-inch in diameter may be included. The sample is placed in a chamber and bombarded with x-rays from radioactive iron and cadmium. The elements in the sample are "excited" by the x-rays and shoot out x-rays of their own. Each element has its own characteristic x-ray signature. The emitted x-rays hit detectors, which send out a series of electrical pulses in proportion to the energy of the incoming particles. The pulses are counted over a period of time, and the data digitized. As with the GCMS, the more counts, the better the data.

The XRFS can identify individual elements between magnesium and uranium. Elements lighter than magnesium appear as a group, but their individual abundances can be determined indirectly.

The X-Ray Fluorescence investigation is headed by Dr. Priestley Toulmin III, of the U.S. Geological Survey in Reston, Virginia.

One of the most intriguing experiments—and possibly the most beneficial—is the meteorology investigation. Mars is a planet without oceans, but it does have weather. In a sense, Mars is like a huge control experiment to determine the effects of oceans on global weather. Knowledge gained from *Viking* about Martian weather may lead to a better understanding of terrestrial weather.

Viking is equipped with a meteorology boom, which unfolds after landing (and is visible in many of the Lander photos). Temperature is measured by three thin wires in the tip of the boom which act as thermocouples. When these bimetallic wires are heated or cooled, an electric current is induced; the amount of the current determines the temperature. A wind velocity sensor on the boom works on a similar principle. Wind cools the sensor, and an electric current is passed through it to warm it. By measuring the amount of current necessary to maintain a constant temperature, wind velocity can be deduced. The velocity sensors measure wind coming in perpendicular to them, so two sensors are mounted at a 90-degree angle. Wind direction is partially determined by which of the sensors is cooling faster. But since winds from opposite directions would give the same reading, there is also a quadrant sensor, which has four temperature-sensitive thermocouples mounted at right angles.

Atmospheric pressure is measured by a sensor inside the body of the Lander, vented to the outside. The sensor consists of a thin metal diaphragm, with a vacuum maintained on the inside of it. The atmosphere presses against the diaphragm,

190

and the amount of movement determines the atmospheric pressure.

The Meteorology Team leader is Dr. Seymour L. Hess of Florida State University.

The evidence of *Mariner 9* photography suggested that Mars is, or has recently been, geologically active. The moon, which seems geologically dead, has been found to have a few moonquakes still in it, as measured by *Apollo* mission seismometers. Mars ought to be considerably more active than the moon. To measure just how active it is, each *Viking* Lander is equipped with three miniature seismometers.

The seismometers are mounted along three different axes, perpendicular to one another, in order to sense motion in any direction. They consist of a seven-ounce weight attached to a coil which projects toward a magnet. The motion of the coil relative to the magnet produces an electrical current that measures the intensity of the disturbance. The seismometers can be "tuned" to search for specific frequency ranges characteristic of different types of geological activity. The seismometers, when tuned to maximum sensitivity, are capable of detecting a Marsquake of 6.0 on the Richter scale anywhere on the planet.

The Seismology Team leader is Dr. Don L. Anderson, of the California Institute of Technology.

Probably the cleverest—and certainly the cheapest—experiment aboard *Viking* is the Magnetic Properties investigation. The surface of Mars was assumed to be red because of its composition, which was suspected to be limonite, an iron oxide. But iron oxidizes in a number of different ways, and some of the oxidation products are nonmagnetic.

An array of magnets was placed aboard the Lander, two on the back of the backhoe on the surface sampler head, and one on a photometric target used to calibrate the cameras. The magnets have a characteristic bull's-eye pattern, and any surface material attracted by them should duplicate the pat-

191

tern. Depending on the intensity of the attraction, and the color of the material, it should be possible to deduce the exact form of oxidized iron that is present on the surface of Mars.

The Magnetic Properties investigator is Dr. Robert B. Hargraves of Princeton University. The Hargraves experiment is beautiful in its design, since it involves no elaborate gadgets or complicated procedures, but can return highly useful information. Taxpayers might also appreciate the fact that *Viking*'s magnets cost only $25 to $50 each. "We bought them in bulk," Hargraves explained. According to Viking Mission Director A. Thomas Young, Hargraves' experiment "is probably the most cost-effective thing we have. I think the most expensive thing about it is the paper."

"We're sometimes called 'The Everything Else Experiment,'" said Dr. Richard W. Shorthill of the University of Utah, principal investigator of the Physical Properties experiment. Shorthill's group is concerned with the size, shape, and behavior of the particles on the Martian surface. They examine things such as the footpads' indentations on the surface, the characteristics of trenches dug by the sampler arm, and the cohesiveness of the surface material. The Physical Properties people also had hopes that during the extended mission they would be allowed to bang rocks together, dig deep trenches, drop dirt on a grid atop the Lander, and perform any other interesting experiment which might come to mind. There was even talk of using the sampler arm to shove the entire spacecraft a few inches away from its original landing site.

One final experiment is inherent in the *Viking* communications system. The Radio Science investigation, led by Dr. William H. Michael, of the Langley Research Center, uses the S and X Band communications from *Viking* (Lander and Orbiter) to measure a number of phenomena. Among them are: the surface reflectivity of Mars in the microwave range; the orbit and mass of Mars; the electronic density of the

Martian ionosphere; and a relativity experiment, which measures the sun's effect on radio signals sent when Mars is in conjunction with the sun.

The *Viking* Orbiters and Landers and support equipment cost a total of 930 million dollars. Throw in two launch vehicles at 35 million dollars apiece, and you get a *Viking* price tag of one billion dollars, give or take a few million. Although relatively cheap by the standards of manned space flight, *Viking* is the most expensive unmanned mission ever flown. And the most dangerous. Two multimillion-dollar vehicles were to be landed on the hostile surface of another planet, and what awaited them there, no one could say.

11

The Plain of Gold

I now know how Lewis and Clark must have felt when they began exploring the West. It's fantastic!

—Gerald Soffen
Viking Project Scientist
June 23, 1976

In the television series *Star Trek,* Captain Kirk would routinely tell the navigator, Mr. Sulu, "Set a course for Star Base Twelve." Sulu would punch a few buttons, and the *Enterprise* would be on its way. Perhaps in the twenty-third century, interplanetary navigation will be as simple as that, but back here in the twentieth, it is an enormously difficult and complex operation. Just getting *Viking* to Mars was a major hurdle.

Merely getting *Viking* off the earth turned out to be more of a problem than anticipated. The *Viking* spacecraft, all four of them, arrived at Cape Canaveral early in 1975, with lift-offs planned for August. The Orbiters and Landers were mated for the first time and put through a rigorous series of tests. Then the pair of assembled spacecraft were mated with the launch vehicles, Titan III-C missiles. Following more tests, the *Vikings* were removed from the Titans and subjected to final sterilization—forty hours at 235°F.

While all this was happening at the Cape, tests of another kind were being conducted at JPL in Pasadena. The *Viking* spacecraft are smart as machines go, but they still need human beings to run them. During the spring of 1975, training exercises were carried out for the *Viking* Flight Team. Using computer simulations, the team members learned their jobs in real-time tests. Procedures were worked out, computer software rewritten (when necessary), and, in general, the human component of *Viking* was checked out as thoroughly as the spacecraft themselves.

Back at the Cape, problems developed. *Viking 1* was scheduled to lift-off on August 11, but 115 seconds before ignition, a thrust vector control valve on the Titan malfunctioned. The launch was scrubbed for that day. The valve was replaced, and launch was rescheduled for August 14. But on the thirteenth, a battery in the Orbiter was found to have fallen from a normal charge of 37 volts down to 9 volts. The cause turned out to be a switch that was left in the "on" position following the postponement on the eleventh. The decision was made to remove the A spacecraft and replace it with the B spacecraft.

Finally, at 5:22 P.M. EDT, August 20, 1975, *Viking 1* began its journey to Mars. Lift-off was flawless, and the first planned mid-course maneuver put the craft into the proper trajectory on August 27. The initial aim was toward a point a considerable distance away from where Mars would be at the time of encounter. This bias was necessary in order to comply with planetary "quarantine" standards. If *Viking* had been aimed to hit Mars right on the nose, an Orbiter engine failure might have resulted in the entire spacecraft impacting on the surface of Mars. Since only the Lander was completely sterilized, contamination might have occurred. To avoid that eventuality, the trajectory was not corrected until it was certain that the Orbiter was operational after separation from the launch vehicle.

Viking 2 had more problems back on earth, but finally got going at 2:39 P.M. EDT, September 9, 1975. Despite the delay in the two launches, trajectory corrections allowed the mission to proceed more or less along the original time-line. Although launched nine days late, *Viking 1* would arrive at Mars just one day late; *Viking 2* would get there exactly as planned.

Like *Mariner 9,* the *Vikings* flew a Hohman transfer function. Basically, they were launched into a long, elliptical orbit around the sun; at aphelion, they would be precisely at the orbit of Mars, at the moment when Mars itself was at the same point. Since the spacecraft would be at the slowest point of their orbits at the time of encounter, Mars would actually overtake them, instead of the reverse.

The job of calculating *Viking*'s trajectory belonged to the Flight Path Analysis Group (FPAG), headed by Dr. William O'Neill. The computer programs necessary for navigating *Viking* took nearly three years to develop; O'Neill estimates that 150 man-years were consumed in the effort. It might have taken even longer but for the addition of a new piece of Space Age wizardry—pocket calculators. Complicated calculations which formerly had to be set up on the big computers could now be done quickly and cheaply with the new hand-held computers. "We wonder how we ever got along without them," said O'Neill.

Most people think of space as being empty, and if it were, calculating trajectories would be relatively straightforward. As it happens, space is far from empty. There are nine planets in the solar system, dozens of moons, and innumerable asteroids. Each exerts its own gravitational pull on all the others. Their effects had to be taken into consideration when plotting *Viking*'s path.

Even more important was the effect of the solar wind and the pressure of light itself. The solar panels of the Orbiters collected energy, but they also acted like sails in the solar wind. "If we ignored the effect of solar pressure," said O'Neill, "we would have missed by the order of tens of thousands of kilometers." Mission requirements stated that the aim should be off by no more than hundreds of kilometers; actual performance was at the level of tens of kilometers.

Viking was tracked primarily by radio. The Doppler effect was the main tool for measuring the motion of the spacecraft. Actually, the Doppler was caused not by the motion of the spacecraft, but by the motion of the earth itself— "That's where the 150 man-years come in," O'Neill explained. The FPAG people had to compute what they thought they would see, and then compare the results with what they actually did see. The differences had to be refined and eventually corrected by mid-course maneuvers.

Radio tracking was hampered by the presence of charged particles and plasma that streamed out from the sun. As a backup, *Viking* also used a visual navigation system. As the spacecraft approached Mars, the Orbiter cameras photographed Mars and its background star field to provide additional navigational information. "Without the optical system," said O'Neill, "we would have been in trouble."

During the cruise phase, periodic checks were made on the condition of the Landers. Minor glitches were discovered and dealt with successfully, but a major problem did develop in the Gas Chromatograph Mass Spectrometers on each spacecraft. One of the three ovens in each instrument failed to heat properly. Since the GCMS performs its organic analysis at 932°F, the loss of an oven was a serious blow. Rather than conducting three analyses, as planned, the GCMSs would be limited to two.

In Pasadena, the *Viking* science teams were assembled. Altogether, there were over 80 principal investigators and many more graduate students and undergraduate interns. Each of them had to know his job, and know it well, long before *Viking* reached its destination. During a four-month training period in the early part of 1976, numerous tests were performed at the team level. Then the various science teams were brought together and the entire flight team, with over 700 people, was put through a series of six simulations, one of which lasted twelve days. Several times during the simulations, the overloaded computers "crashed," leaving the scientists and engineers without a spacecraft for a few hours. Occasionally data would be lost in the computers. Unplanned anomalies developed. "The real spacecraft has behaved much better than the 'sim' system," commented Project Manager Jim Martin following the successful landing of the real spacecraft.

The simulations were complete down to tiny details, including press conferences. Several simulated press briefings were held in order to familiarize some of the scientists with the nonscientific problems they would be facing.

Another nonscientific consideration that weighed heavily on the *Viking* team was the choice of a landing date. *Viking 1* was scheduled to be inserted into Martian orbit on June 19. After a couple of weeks of orbital observations and landing site selection, the Lander would descend to the surface on the almost inevitable date of July 4, 1976. There was no good reason why the landing could not take place equally well on the third or the fifth, but there was strong pressure from Washington to give America something extra to celebrate on Bicentennial Day. The converse was that while a crash would be bad under any circumstances, it would be downright awful if it happened on the Glorious Fourth.

On May 1, from a range of seven million miles, the cameras on *Viking* Orbiter 1 took their first pictures of Mars. These were simply calibration pictures and showed no surface detail, but at least the destination was in sight. The journey of 420 million miles was approaching its conclusion.

By this point in the mission, the time lag between earth and *Viking* had become significant. At the time of orbital insertion, the one-way time was eighteen minutes. To avoid confusion, all mission events were given in Earth Received Time. An event which, in reality, took place at, say, 2:00 P.M., would occur in ERT at 2:18 P.M.

In the last week before Mars Orbit Insertion (MOI), a serious problem developed in the spacecraft's propulsion system. The mission policy had always been that no single part failure would prevent a landing; but the rocket engine was the one thing which could not be replaced. If the engine failed to fire, *Viking* would miss Mars completely and fall back into an orbit around the sun.

The fuel and oxidizer in the rocket were kept pressurized by a tank of helium gas. An automatic flow regulator valve controlled the pressurization of the fuel. The helium itself was pressurized at 3,600 psi. A week before MOI, a leak was discovered in the helium tank. Although the leak was tiny, with all that pressure behind it, the helium flowed into the fuel tanks, increasing their pressure by about 0.36 pounds per hour. If the leak continued, there was the danger of over-pressurizing the fuel, possibly resulting in an engine malfunction.

If the engine failed to fire, the mission controllers still had one last-ditch maneuver they could perform. As the Orbiter swept past Mars, the Lander could be detached and sent on a direct-entry trajectory. No choice of a landing site would be possible. "We'd just aim at the planet," said Martin.

That extreme option was available, but a better solution to the problem was worked out. To relieve the overpressure, a burn was conducted on June 10. Spacecraft burn maneuvers are usually expressed in terms of Delta V, or change in velocity. The June 10 burn had a Delta V of 50 meters per second. The maneuver slowed the spacecraft, but did not solve the problem of the helium leak. Another burn was needed on June 15, slowing *Viking* by another 60 meters per second. O'Neill compared the two maneuvers to "pumping the brakes."

The result of the maneuvers was that the overpressurization problem was neutralized, but *Viking* was now traveling slower than had been planned. The original mission profile called for a single MOI burn to place *Viking* into an orbit with a period of 24.6 hours. Due to the change in velocity, *Viking* would now achieve an initial orbit with a period of 42.6 hours. Following MOI, an orbital correction maneuver would put *Viking* into its proper orbit.

Achieving the original orbit was important because *Viking*'s potential landing site had already been chosen. Ideally, the landing site should be directly below the periapsis of the *Viking* orbit. With an orbital period of 24.6 hours, the orbit would be synchronous with the Martian day, and the Orbiter would be in proper position for relay links from the Lander. Unfortunately, at the time of MOI, the landing site would be 90° away from periapsis. The orbital correction maneuver would then be necessary to line up the periapsis with the landing site.

On the afternoon of June 19, *Viking* was put through a series of roll and yaw maneuvers to align it properly for the MOI burn. At 3:38:10 PDT (ERT), *Viking* was in position, and its engine ignited. In order to achieve orbit, the burn had to last for at least 35½ minutes. The nominal burn would be 38 minutes.

The mission controllers waited tensely as data came in confirming that the burn was in progress. Everything was running perfectly; the only malfunction occurred when a fuse blew out in the press room, knocking out the TV monitors and the coffee machine.

As the 35½-minute milestone was passed, cheering erupted in the control room. Two minutes later, the engine cut off, fifteen seconds early, due to a slight overthrust of seven tenths of a percent. After eight years, *Viking* was safely in orbit. "I must admit, I'm relieved," said Jim Martin. At the press briefing following MOI, he looked very much like a man suppressing an urge to holler "Whoopee!"

Viking's initial orbit had a periapsis of 1,514 km—just 3 km higher than predicted. Its apoapsis (high point) was 50,600 km. Two days after MOI, the trim maneuver was performed by an 80-meter-per-second burn lasting 132 seconds. The apoapsis was lowered to 32,800 km, and the periapsis was unchanged.

The overall accuracy of the launch, cruise, and MOI phases of the mission was incredible. O'Neill compared it to shooting a basketball from the Forum in Los Angeles and having it go through the hoop in Madison Square Garden in New York. Later, O'Neill refined his figures and admitted that the shot would have missed; he had forgotten to calculate the width of the rim.

The Jet Propulsion Laboratory looks like a community college that ran out of funds halfway through a five-year building program. On its campus-like grounds at the base of the San Gabriel Mountains there are a number of attractive glass and steel buildings, but the unfinished look derives from an acre of "temporary" trailers used for additional office space. The trailers have been there for years now, and are usually filled to capacity during a mission such as *Viking*. The offices in the trailers belong to lower-level personnel, while the senior scientists are comfortably esconced in Building 264, an eight-story building that overlooks the trailer camp like a baronial manor above the homes of the serfs. For the engineers and mission controllers, home is the Space Flight Operations Facility (SFOF), located at the top of the first of a series of foothills leading up into the mountains. The press center, perhaps symbolically, is located at the bottom of the hill.

By June 1 most of the *Viking* personnel had arrived in Pasadena. The logistics of assembling such a large team were a major problem. Professors and graduate students had to take leaves of absence from their universities and relocate themselves in the Pasadena area; no one knew how long they would be staying. If both Landers crashed, most of the university people would be back home for the fall term. But if things went well, the extended mission could keep them in Pasadena for as long as two years.

In the days following MOI, JPL was bristling with anticipation. Some of the people in the project had waited eight years for the landing; others arrived at the last minute just to be on hand for the Big Event. All three American television networks brought in cameras for live coverage of the landing as part of their day-long Fourth of July Bicentennial extravaganzas. Television crews from Britain, Italy, Belgium, and Japan were there, too. Over the years, in fact, foreign television had given more and better coverage of unmanned missions than had NBC, CBS, and ABC combined. Twenty different nations ran television specials on *Mariner 9*, but the American networks did not.

The potential landing sites for *Viking* had been chosen before lift-off, based on studies of *Mariner 9* photography. The prime consideration for *Viking 1* was safety; the preselected sites were "safe but dull," as Carl Sagan put it. While it would have been interesting to try to land a spacecraft in the middle of Valles Marineris, the chances of success would not have been very high. If *Viking 1* was successful, *Viking 2* might be permitted an attempt at a more difficult but more scientifically attractive site.

The periapsis of *Viking*'s orbit around Mars was always at the same latitude, although the longitude could be changed. Changing the latitude of periapsis would have required a prohibitively large expenditure of fuel. Thus, both the prime and backup landing sites had to be at the same latitude. *Viking 1*'s prime site was in a region known as Chryse

Planitia, the Plain of Gold, at about 22° north latitude, 35° west longitude. The backup, or A-2 site, was near Elysium Planitia, at longitude 255°, halfway around the planet from Chryse. *Viking 2*'s prime site was in Cydonia, at 44° north, 10° west. The B-2 site was near Alba Patera, at the same latitude, 140° west longitude. A possible C site was also selected, in the Capri region, 40° west longitude, 5° south latitude. The Capri site was near the rim of the Valles Marineris canyon system.

There were a number of reasons for the choice of those landing sites. All are areas of low elevation, which was a plus for the biologists. Atmospheric pressures are greater in low areas, and water is more likely to be found there; and, of course, the presence of water would increase the chances of finding life on Mars. Except for the C site, all the landing areas are in the northern hemisphere, where it would be summer at the time of landing, and water is also more abundant in the summer hemisphere. The B sites, at latitude 44°, were expected to possess the most water, in the atmosphere and possibly even on the ground, although that was deemed unlikely.

Another factor was safety. The *Mariner 9* and *Viking* Orbiter photos of the landing areas were augmented by earth-based radar studies. Simply put, radar signals beamed to Mars from earth are reflected back toward the earth. The strength of the returning signal gives a measure of the smoothness of the surface from which the signals were reflected. A strong signal indicates a smooth surface, and a weak signal means an uneven surface. Compare it to bouncing a rubber ball off a wall. If the wall is perfectly flat and smooth, the ball will bounce true. If the wall is, say, stucco, the ball will take an occasional erratic hop. If you bounce it against an old New England stone fence, with many facets, more often than not the ball will take off in an unpredictable trajectory. The same applies to radar signals.

The radar wavelength is 13 centimeters. In order to get a strong return signal, it must bounce off a facet at least ten times that size. Since that is at the scale of meters—the size of the Lander—one would at first think that the radar studies could pick out an absolutely safe landing site. Unfortunately, the radar signals are not that precise. The return signals represent the average over a broad area; an area filled with mesas would return more or less the same signal as a smooth desert floor. But since the radar was the only means of getting at least some resolution of the surface of Mars at the scale of the Lander, it was considered to be a valuable tool.

Another problem with the radar studies was that they were confined to regions near the Martian equator. At the equator, the surface of Mars is more or less perpendicular to the incoming radar signals, so a strong return is possible. But as you go farther away from the equator, the angle of attack gets shallower, and the signals tend to skip off into space instead of returning to earth. Studies of the A latitude, 22° north, had been carried out with some success in 1967. The B latitude, 44° north, was a much more difficult target. At that latitude, radar was all but worthless. Yet the desire to land in a relatively wet place outweighed the lack of radar, and 44° north was chosen for *Viking 2*. The equatorial C sites were essentially a last-ditch alternative in case *Viking 1* crashed.

The primary tool for landing site selection remained the Orbiter imaging. The first pictures from *Viking* Orbiter 1 (VO-1) were returned the night of June 22, and caused an immediate sensation. At the moment they came in, a scientific meeting was in progress in Building 264, with Martian dust storms the topic. Dr. Conway Snyder, Orbiter Science Group Chief, looked up, saw the first picture on a television monitor, and shouted, "Here it comes!" The meeting abruptly adjourned as everyone ran to the tube to watch the pictures. According to B. Gentry Lee, Science Analysis and Mission Planning Director, Mike Carr, the head of Orbiter Imaging, "broke the world record for the number of 'wows' in a single hour."

The pictures were fantastically good, perhaps as much as three times better than anything received from *Mariner 9*. The chief reason for the improvement was the clarity of the Martian atmosphere. *Mariner 9* had arrived during a dust storm and had to wait for the dust to subside, but even then there were a great number of particles in the atmosphere. But *Viking* arrived at a quiet time, and the Martian skies, relatively speaking, were crystal clear.

The very first pictures almost immediately resolved one of the questions posed by *Mariner 9*. Many scientists believed that the sinuous channels observed by *Mariner* could only have been carved by water, but some held out for nonaqueous explanations, such as lava flows. But the *Viking* pictures of the channels in the Chryse region showed that, beyond question, water had once flowed in great quantities on Mars.

The photos showed an extensive channel system running from southwest to northeast through the Chryse basin. The water flow was apparently quite rapid, and may have been due to catastrophic flooding. There was clear evidence of water having flowed around large obstacles such as craters and mesas. The *Viking* geologists were excited and amazed by the pictures; they had expected some signs of fluvial action, but nothing like this.

The A landing site was certainly not dull; but the question remained, was it safe?

Safety is a relative thing. Landing a robot spacecraft for the first time on an alien world is bound to be risky, no matter what precautions are taken. *Viking*'s risks were compounded by the fact that it was impossible to select the precise point of landing. There was a built-in uncertainty in *Viking*'s descent procedure; the Lander could drift off course during the time it was on the parachute, for example.

Instead of pinpointing an exact landing site, the *Viking*

scientists looked for places to position a landing ellipse, 120 km by 50 km. If the Lander were aimed for the center of the ellipse, there was a 99 percent chance that it would touch down somewhere inside the ellipse. At the middle of the 99 percent ellipse, a smaller 50 percent ellipse, 47 km by 20 km, marked the most probable region for the landing.

The size of the ellipse meant that the Orbiter Imaging Team had to find a broad, smooth area and define the hazard potential within it. If, for example, you wanted to put a landing ellipse in Southern California, by analyzing aerial photographs, you could assign numerical values to the probability of landing in a city, on the desert, the mountains, or the sea. On Mars, the hazards were less familiar. The main problem was craters, both impact craters and secondary craters. The impact craters had characteristic ejecta blankets of large, blocky material that was thrown off by the impact. Since craters are so common on Mars, it was impossible to find an ellipse with absolutely no craters in it, but the hope was that the number of hazards within the ellipse could be minimized.

The Landing Site Selection Team, headed by Hal Masursky of the USGS, was under great pressure to find a safe ellipse, and find it quickly. The clarity of the Orbiter photos caught them by surprise; areas which had looked smooth in the *Mariner 9* pictures now appeared to be littered with craters. "We were probably somewhat naive," admitted Mike Carr. There was no elaborate system for handling the data from the Orbiter pictures. Everyone had more or less expected a hazard-free landing site. The LSS people drafted geologists from the Lander Imaging Team, who had little to do until the landing, and set them to work counting craters.

The crater counts were useful in eliminating obviously bad sites, but they couldn't really determine what the surface was like at Lander scale. The smallest craters that could be reliably

206

detected in the Orbiter pictures were about the size of the Rose Bowl—and a rock a foot in diameter could wreck the spacecraft. For that reason, some of the people involved in landing site certification felt that the whole procedure was worthless. There was simply no way to tell what was happening at the meter scale, and that was the only scale that really mattered.

The LSS Team met with Jim Martin and other project leaders on the night of Friday, June 25; the planned landing was just nine days away. The geologists told Martin that in the A-1 region there were many craters and apparent riverbeds which had scooped out cliffs as high as 1,500 meters. But there was no unanimity. Some of the scientists felt that the Chryse site was as good as any they were likely to find; others felt they should look elsewhere. "I did not feel comfortable with the situation," said Martin. The radar data was fairly good at the A-1 site, but not everyone was convinced that it was meaningful. "If all the radar in the world fell off the mounts," Martin said later, "we would still go ahead and land."

It was the pictures which were the deciding factor. If the terrain was so rough at a resolution of 100 meters, what might it be like at one or two meters? Martin bit the bullet, and announced on the morning of Sunday, June 27, that the Fourth of July landing had been canceled.

The delay removed a lot of the pressure associated with the Bicentennial Day landing, and seemed to be the prudent choice. Said Hal Masursky, "It's called seeing whether there's any water in the pool before you dive off the board." However, any further delay could cause severe complications. *Viking 2* was approaching rapidly, with MOI scheduled for August 7; *Viking* Lander 1 (VL-1) had to be on the ground by then. Earth support facilities were simply not adequate to run four separate spacecraft all at the same time. For navigational purposes, the latitude of the VL-2 site had to be chosen by

July 22, which made it highly desirable to know the *Viking 1* results before that date. If the first Lander crashed, *Viking 2* could be retargeted for a safer latitude than 44° north.

Another time problem lay in store at the other end of the mission. In early November, Mars would go into conjunction with the sun, and all communications would be lost for a period of about three weeks. In order to have time to carry out all the planned experiments, it was absolutely necessary to land VL-2 no later than mid-September. Since the VL-2 experiments could not begin until the first Lander completed its work and was put into its "reduced mission mode," a delay in landing VL-1 could shave time off both missions.

With the A-1 site discarded, the mission controllers had essentially two options. One was to perform a trim maneuver and look at the A-2 site, 5,000 miles to the east. The second option was to perform a smaller trim and examine an area about 150 miles to the northwest of the A-1 site. In either case, landing was unlikely to occur before July 20. If a site could not be found by then, they were faced with the possibility of having to delay the landing of *Viking 1* until after *Viking 2* was put into orbit on August 7. The effect of such a postponement would have been that both Landers would have drastically reduced missions, or else one of the Landers would have had to wait in orbit until after conjunctions and then try for a landing in December.

The A-1 northwest site looked attractive because the terrain appeared to get smoother in that direction. A number of channels originating to the east of the A-1 ellipse made the original site too rough, but Dr. Robert Hargraves, the magnet experimenter, suggested that if they didn't like the place where the channel deposits were coming from, why not look at the place they were going? That was to the northwest, and sure enough, it seemed that the fluvial plains in that area were a more hospitable spot to place an ellipse. On July 1, the decision was announced that *Viking 1* would land on July 17 in the Northwest Territory, as the new site was being called by the press.

Meanwhile, the Orbiter had acquired photos of the B-1 and C-1 sites. Neither one looked very good. B-1, in Cydonia, was rough and crater-riddled. The C-1 site was at the rim of Valles Marineris and looked far too risky, although it would have been a geologist's delight. "We're all agog," said Mike Carr after getting his first look at the spectacular canyon system. The photos showed massive slumping along the sides of the canyon, providing some indication of how the canyon-forming process worked. It appeared that the cap rock was underlain by less coherent material which slumped to the floor of the canyon after undermining, possibly by eolian erosion or the melting of permafrost. The geological value of a landing in such an area would have been enormous, but the geologists were somewhat more adventurous than Jim Martin. "We would have preferred landing in the summit caldera of Olympus Mons," said Masursky, "but Jim didn't give us that choice."

The Northwest Territory wasn't quite as spectacular as Valles Marineris, but it was proving to have its share of hazards. The initial radar observations of the site were not encouraging. Analysis of the photos revealed a large number of small craters. Counting the craters was a tedious but vital task, and it was left to a mere handful of workers. With a decision due the next morning, Dave Pieri, twenty-seven, a Cornell grad student, Win Farrell, twenty-three, a UCLA grad student, and Chris Heberspacher, nineteen, an undergraduate intern, spent an entire night counting and plotting craters. At three in the morning, Farrell threw up his hands and cried in despair, "We're just kids! Where are all the grown ups?" Home in bed, probably; the manpower shortage was acute. Aiding the "kids" was Ted Flinn, a NASA administrator and geologist who just happened to be in town at the time. Flinn was drafted into the crater-counting brigade.

The crater counts were discouraging, and the tension around JPL mounted. Everyone looked tired. Before a press briefing, at which he announced that all was well, Martin remarked privately, "As long as we keep it in orbit, we're safe." On July 8, Martin again postponed the landing. The Northwest Territory was not to his liking, and the decision was made to look at an area about 365 miles farther west. Not everyone was in agreement. "If our backs were to the wall," said Masursky, "we'd take a chance on landing."

If the delay continued, their backs would be to the wall very soon. *Viking 2* was getting close, and an interplanetary traffic jam was becoming a very real possibility. "We could see a big mess," Martin said later. "A lot of people were rather annoyed with me for not agreeing to land."

Part of the problem was the age-old conflict between scientists and engineers. Great pains were taken to minimize the disagreements between the two camps, or at least limit the public's awareness of the situation. Project Scientist Gerald (Gerry) Soffen, of Langley, was on hand at virtually every press briefing for the sole purpose (or so it seemed to some of the reporters) of making sure that no scientist said anything derogatory about the engineers. But since Martin, an engineer, was in charge of the project, grumbles were inevitable. For his part, Martin later commented mildly that, "Dealing with scientists all these years, you expect controversy."

From an engineering standpoint, the primary goal was to get *Viking* safely to the surface of Mars. The scientists were in agreement with that, but some of them felt that science was being sacrificed in the process. A number of scientists also felt that Martin was not really at home in discussions of a purely scientific nature. During press briefings, Martin sometimes appeared a trifle uneasy when the geologists started talking about craters and ejecta blankets in the middle of his landing ellipse. There was also the question of the value of radar observations. "There was a fair controversy as to whether the radar told you anything useful," said Martin. Yet some scientists, such as Carl Sagan, insisted that good radar results should be considered a necessity prior to selecting a landing site.

In the end, there was no way to be absolutely sure of any site. "This *is* exploration, after all," said Martin. *Viking* could crash on the only rock in the entire ellipse, or it could find the only safe spot in a field of boulders. There came a time when, after all the craters had been counted and all the radar signals evaluated, it was necessary to go ahead and shoot the dice.

The territory at the western edge of the Chryse basin looked promising. A trim maneuver had "walked" the Orbiter into position over the region, at about 22.5° north and 48° west. If it continued to look good, a landing was possible on July 20. If not, the Orbiter would be sent back to the original Northwest Territory to take another look. A landing there could take place on July 22. If that date was missed, very likely the first landing would be delayed until after the arrival of *Viking 2*. A further constraint was the dwindling fuel supply of the Orbiter. Extra fuel had been consumed on its two-stage orbital insertion, and each orbital trim maneuver expended additional fuel. After Mars Orbit Trim (MOT) #5, on July 8, the Orbiter was left with a total fuel budget of 138 meters per second, that is, enough fuel to alter the velocity of the spacecraft by that amount. Station-keeping requirements following landing would use up another 16 meters per second. For the extended mission, a fuel reserve of 100 mps was required. That left the Orbiter with about 20 mps for additional landing site searches, and since it would require 30 to 50 mps to go to the A-2 site, for example, there was simply no margin left. If *Viking* did not land somewhere in the Chryse region, there would be a negative impact on the plans for the extended mission.

Finally, on July 13, Martin announced, "Contrary to past expectations, we are going to land." The site chosen was on the western slope of the Chryse basin, at 22.5° north, 47.4° west. Landing would occur at 5:12 A.M. PDT (ERT) on July 20. It was, said Martin, "the best, we believe, of all the sites we have looked at." The radar was better than at the Northwest Territory, and the crater counters had found fewer fresh impact craters. Hal Masursky called the selection, "The end of a long march, our westward trek. It was manifest destiny, obviously."

With the landing site and date finally chosen, the Jet Propulsion Laboratory became a self-contained world. Back in the real world, Nadia Comenici, a fourteen-year-old Rumanian gymnast, was winning banner headlines with her flawless performances in the Montreal Olympics. Jimmy Carter was holding court in Plains, Georgia, after accepting the Democratic Presidential nomination. But at JPL, the only thing that really mattered was the landing. Some of the *Viking* people had spent most of their professional lives working toward this one event, and after nearly a decade of waiting, it was about to happen.

Preparation for the landing began on the night of Saturday the seventeenth as the mission controllers started their elaborate check-out procedures to make sure that everything on both Lander and Orbiter was in a "go" condition. The Lander itself had been in a state of suspended animation ever since November of the previous year, but now it was being brought back to life. Every electronic system aboard *Viking* was given a thorough test, and virtually everything performed nominally. During the Preseparation Checkout on Sunday night, the Lander's RTGs were brought on-stream, confirming the operation of the Lander's power source. A few minor commands were sent up to some of the Lander's instruments, but generally speaking, *Viking* Lander 1 was an exceptionally healthy spacecraft.

On Monday the nineteenth, JPL began to fill up with press and VIP visitors. Over 1,800 invitations had been issued for the landing (and each delay had cost over two thousand dollars in mailgrams to the VIPs), including politicians, scientists, engineers, science-fiction writers, and (it seemed) their wives, children and pets. The press contingent, about 400 strong, represented dozens of countries and about every conceivable kind of publication, from aviation trade magazines and scientific journals to *Rolling Stone* and the *Pasadena Shoppers' News*. The *New York Times* science writers Walter Sullivan and John Noble Wilford rushed back to Pasadena from Loch Ness, where the *Times* was sponsoring a monster hunt. Network camera crews and local TV teams tripped over each others' cables and battled for interviews with scientists and visiting luminaries such as Ray Bradbury and Gene Roddenberry. Scattered around the JPL grounds at strategic locations were red-white-and-blue Bicentennial portable toilets. An overloaded socket in the press room shorted out another coffee machine; a Public Information Officer shook his head and said, "I knew this mission would blow the coffee machine."

The only place that looked relatively sane was mission control. Closed-circuit television provided the press with a video-only glimpse of events in the SFOF building, where Jim Martin, Mission Controller Tom Young, and the rest of the *Viking* brass made the final "Go" decision at 11:00 P.M. on the night of the nineteenth. Landing was less than six hours away.

The actual "Go" command was delivered by Tom Young. As Spacecraft Performance and Flight Path Analysis Director Pete Lyman described it, the command then followed a rather circuitous route to Mars. The "Go" command consisted of a preprogrammed word for the Lander computer which resided on a "spool" in SFOF. Al Scott, the Command Operator, punched in entries (preloaded) on a keyboard, cuing up the spool. The computer command was then transmitted to the Deep Space Network station in Australia (the others were at

Goldstone, California, and Madrid, Spain), where it was put into the computer's "stack." When Tom Young issued the voice command, the Australian operators got the word and punched a button which transmitted the command to the Lander and Orbiter, some 212 million miles away. Although inquiries were made, no one at JPL knew the name of the man in Australia who actually sent the "Go" signal, but he remains the anonymous hero of the project.

At 1:51:15 A.M., mission controllers received confirmation of separation, which had actually occurred eighteen minutes earlier—the light-speed time lag meant that all time notations were in Earth Received Time. Three explosive bolts severed the connections between the two spacecraft and shoved the Lander away from the Orbiter at one foot per second. A small cheer was heard in mission control when separation was confirmed and the tracking station discerned two separate objects.

The Lander was allowed to drift away from the Orbiter for about six minutes, while the people at JPL monitored its position. Pitch and yaw were as expected, but if they weren't, nothing could have been done about it. From this point on down, the Lander was on its own. Direct control from earth would have been a physical impossibility.

At 1:58:16, the Lander's de-orbit engines burst into life. For an on-target landing, the Lander's velocity had to be reduced by 156 meters per second. Engineering data, flowing at the 4-kilobit rate, confirmed that the burn was going well; all the data points fell on or near the predicted curve. One controller calmly opened up a sandwich and munched with apparent unconcern as the burn progressed.

The engines shut off at 2:20:32, as predicted. The Lander was now coasting, and would continue to do so for the next two and a half hours. Separation had occurred at an orbital altitude of 5,000 km, about 3,500 km above periapsis. The

214

Orbiter continued on its path, while the Lander gradually fell toward Mars.

The point of entry into the Martian atmosphere was arbitrarily defined as 806,490 feet above the mean surface level of the planet. At the time of entry, the Lander would be traveling almost horizontally, about 1000 km from the landing site. The angle of entry was a shallow 16 degrees; if it came in more steeply, there would not be enough time for atmospheric drag to slow it down.

After engine cutoff came the worst time of the entire mission. For more than two hours, there was not much to do but wait and worry. In the press room, James Pearre of *The Chicago Tribune* had already filed a story headed *"Viking* Failure." Deadlines were such that there would not be time to write the story after the landing. The story made strange reading, since the Lander was still far above the Martian surface. It was pointed out to Pearre that the *Tribune* was the same newspaper which had declared, in banner headlines: DEWEY DEFEATS TRUMAN.

The press and visitors in Von Karman Auditorium followed the spacecraft's descent via closed-circuit television from "The Blue Room" in the SFOF building. Dr. Albert Hibbs gave the "play-by-play" account with expertise and a certain amount of fumbling good humor, like a local TV talk show host. After MOI, Hibbs received glowing reviews from the press corps ("better than 'Misterrogers,' but not as good as 'Captain Kangaroo' "), but on this night he presented an odd combination of grave concern and schoolboy excitement.

A dozen different interviews were being conducted in the auditorium during the wait. Roy Neal, of NBC, talked with Ray Bradbury for the *Today Show,* which was covering the event live for the Eastern Time Zone, where it was already morning. With Bradbury preempted, journalists besieged Gene Roddenberry of *Star Trek.* He imparted the intriguing information that Spock's ears had cost two thousand dollars per episode.

At 5:03:08, *Viking* officially entered the Martian atmosphere. The commotion in the press room subsided as everyone concentrated on the TV monitors. Data was flowing in rapidly. The entry science experiments were now collecting their data; whatever else happened, scientists would learn the composition of the atmosphere.

There was a strong element of surrealism in the final minutes before landing. Television, radio, and print journalists were covering a story 212 million miles away by watching a television account of the receipt of data in SFOF from a receiving station thousands of miles away, which in turn was getting its data from halfway across the solar system from a spacecraft which might already have crashed. That was the strangest part of all—knowing that, one way or another, *Viking* was already on the surface of Mars.

At 5:10:06.5, the Lander was 19,376 feet above the surface—in Earth Received Time, at least. A fifteen-inch mortar in the aeroshell fired, deploying the parachute and separating the aeroshell. A few seconds later the three Lander legs were deployed and locked. The Lander had now slowed from an entry velocity of about 2,500 miles per hour to 100 miles per hour.

The Lander spent only a minute on the parachute. At 5:11:09.4, 4,797 feet above the surface, *Viking*'s three terminal descent engines fired. "Well," said Hibbs, "we're coming down, we're coming down."

Viking's radar altimeter scanned the terrain below and fed the computer the information it needed to control the engine thrust. In mission control, Jim Martin stared intently at a monitor, watching the descent data come in. The first indication of touchdown would come when the data rate switched from 4 to 16 kilobits; that change would be triggered by a switch in the footpad.

The final seconds were agonizing. Years of work and decades of dreaming were about to be fulfilled—or smashed on an unseen Martian rock.

And then—at 5:12:07 A.M. PDT (ERT), July 20, 1976—*touchdown!*

Von Karman Auditorium erupted in an orgy of cheers, hugs, and tears. In mission control, the controllers shouted and whooped, tore off their headphones and danced by the light of their computers.

"I don't think we're going to get any sensible commentary for the next few minutes," said Hibbs.

It didn't matter.

Viking was on Mars.

12

The Search Begins:
The Mars of Viking

At this particular time I guess the thing I feel is pride; pride that,
number one, we were willing to accept the challenge as a nation;
pride, number two, that we were able to meet that challenge; and
pride, number three, in the thousands of people who have contributed in a highly dedicated, professional manner to make all this work.
I think truly, today the search begins, and I am proud to be a part
of it.

—A. Thomas Young
Viking Mission Director
July 20, 1976

It was early morning in Pasadena when *Viking* landed, but in
the Chryse Basin, it was 4:13 P.M., Lander Local Time. With
night coming on, the Lander got straight down to business. A
few seconds after landing, Camera No. 2 began to take the
first picture of the surface of Mars, a view of the ground
directly in front of the spacecraft. When that picture was
completed, the camera then began a long panorama of the
horizon, covering more than 300°.

Chryse was on the side of Mars facing away from the earth
at the time of landing, so a real-time direct link was not
possible. But at 5:47 A.M., data from the Lander-Orbiter relay
link arrived at JPL. The initial relay link included the first two
pictures from the Lander.

Tim Mutch, head of the Lander Imaging Team, joined

Hibbs on television and prepared to provide commentary as the pictures came in, not that it was really needed. "The neat thing about pictures," said Mutch, "is that everybody can do their own analysis. We're really quite superfluous here."

Pictures from the Lander are reconstructed on earth in the same way they are taken, left to right. The first piece of the picture to come in covered only the extreme left-hand side of the television monitors and revealed little detail, except for the important information that the camera was functioning properly.

The next section revealed a rock. Probably no other rock in history has ever inspired such an emotional reaction. In the auditorium, there were cheers and whoops, oohs and aahs. The clarity of the picture was astonishing. "I don't feel like talking," said Mutch. Indeed, there was not a lot that could have been said at that point. The rock said it all. It was an ordinary, unspectacular rock, a few inches across, but it was a *Martian* rock.

Gene Roddenberry, with his keen director's eye, recognized a good take when he saw it. "Okay!" he shouted. "Cut and print!" But better scenes were still to come.

As the picture unfolded, it became clear that the Martian surface near the Lander was strewn with pebbles and small rocks resting on a fine-grained surface material. At the left of the picture, there was a curious dark vertical streaking effect. At first, no one could explain it, but later Mutch and his cohorts decided that it was due to a shadow of some sort; the operational mechanics of the camera merely made the dark area *seem* streaky. What had caused the shadow was in dispute—some even thought it could have been the shadow of the parachute, still on its way down. In the end, the conclusion was that the streaking was due to fine dust particles kicked up by *Viking* as it landed. The left side of the picture was taken just a few seconds after landing, before the dust had settled. To the right of the picture, the air was clear.

"It's a geologist's delight!" exulted Mutch as he looked at the first Martian rocks. He saw signs of windblown dust and erosion, and a couple of rocks which appeared to be vesiculated, that is, volcanically formed rocks with a Swiss cheese texture due to gas bubbles that were trapped in the original magma.

Several minutes after the picture began, Footpad #2 came into view. It was resting on top of the surface and appeared to have had very little impact on landing. The surface seemed to be hard, yet some of the small particles were obviously mobile. There were sediments from the dust kicked up by the landing resting in the concave top of the footpad. Some of the sediments were the size of small pebbles.

After the first picture was completed, Mutch sat back and smiled. "We always knew it was going to be good," he said, with the confident air of a man who had just won a long-shot bet. In fact, the picture was of better quality than anticipated. The Science Test Lander, a mockup of the actual Lander which resided in a large sandbox in a room next to Von Karman Auditorium, had functioning cameras which were used for test purposes. Mission Director Tom Young said later that day that, "The quality of the pictures that we got back from Mars, I believe, exceeded the quality that we were getting from the next room."

The second picture was even better. The first section of the panorama revealed the Martian horizon, about 3 km (1.8 miles) distant, and a part of the spacecraft. It was the meteorology boom, properly deployed, and the meteorology team cheered at the sight of it. "The important point," said Mutch, "is that the spacecraft has landed top up."

For the next half-hour, everyone watched in fascination as the panorama built up. Mars was becoming a *place*, instead of just a light in the sky. There was a hint of sand dunes at the left of the picture. On the horizon, there were structures which might have been mesas or the rims of nearby craters. Between the spacecraft and the horizon there was a field of rocks, some of them relatively large. The sky had a layered appearance, but that was an artifact produced by the way the pictures were digitized. Nevertheless, as one journalist commented, it looked like a nice day on Mars.

The length of the panorama picture was to be determined by the quality of the relay link. By the time the RTG wind cover came into view, Mutch expected that the link was about to end. But surprisingly, it continued for another five minutes, giving a view of the high-grain antenna and some more dunes in the distance. Toward the end, the quality of the picture began to decline as the link deteriorated. There were numerous bit hits and a few dropped lines. The dropped lines resulted when a bit hit occurred at the beginning of a line. In almost every case, the missing pixels were later reconstructed from the raw data.

Shortly after the picture was completed, Jim Martin, NASA Administrator James Fletcher, and other *Viking* brass attended a press briefing. They were greeted with loud, sustained applause from the press corps. Dr. Noel Hinners, Associate Administrator for Space Science, produced the most quotable comment: "I had tears in my eyes this morning for the first time, I guess, since I got married."

Jim Martin was typically brief, but it was apparent that he, too, had been moved. "I just want to say that this has to be the happiest time of my life—I've lived a long time for this." Martin and the others all expressed their gratitude to the American people for making the Mars landing possible. Martin also commented on the irony of the fact that many of the ten thousand people who had built *Viking* were now jobless. Cutbacks in the space budget had been severe in recent years, and at the moment of its greatest triumph, America's unmanned space exploration program seemed to have a bleak future. It is no exaggeration to say that *Viking*'s success may have saved the entire program.

With just two pictures back from Mars, scientists and spectators alike examined them almost bit by bit (literally) and searched for answers to age-old questions. Carl Sagan noted that Mars was "marvelously heterogeneous," but that there were "no obvious trees, bushes, or anybody else ... the pictures do not suggest that the planet is filled pole to pole with large organisms."

In the absence of Martian flora and fauna, observers concentrated on the rocks. Names were given: there was the Volkswagen, the House on the Hill, and one intriguing rock known variously as the sewer pipe, the beer can, the mortar and pestle, and finally recognized universally as "the Midas Muffler Rock." Later stereoscopic views of the Midas Rock showed that it was none of the above.

Viking was sent to Mars for the purpose of obtaining hard scientific data about the Red Planet, but for the first few days after landing, science tended to be overshadowed by engineering considerations. In the beginning, there was general amazement at how well the landing had gone. The Lander touched down just 17 seconds late, after an eleven-month trip. In order to optimize the imaging, so that the Lander wouldn't be facing its own shadow, plans had called for leg #1 (behind the cameras) to face 320°, plus or minus 20°, azimuth. The actual performance was close to perfect—322° azimuth.

Soon after the landing, it was apparent that *Viking* had some problems. On the evening of the twentieth, one of the Seismometry Team members approached a Lander Imaging member and asked him if the cameras were sensitive enough to record a slight movement of the Lander, such as might be caused by a Marsquake. It seemed like a strange question. Well, the Seismometry man explained, our readings are a bit lower than we expected. In fact, the readings were dead zero. The seismometer was "caged" for the landing, so that a rough jolt wouldn't damage it. Following landing, three explosive bolts were supposed to uncage it and allow it to make measurements. The bolts had not blown and the seismometer was still caged.

The problem was analyzed by a team at Martin Marietta in Denver, where a duplicate Lander was kept ready for just such anomalies. The glitch appeared to be a broken wire. The seismometer bolts were on the same electrical circuit as the GCMS lid, which had deployed properly. The seismometer should have uncaged, but it didn't. When all the options were checked out, the prognosis was not hopeful. By July 25, the seismometer was more or less written off. "We are sending up commands . . . which will try to uncage it," said Jim Martin. "I guess I don't believe that we'll be successful; and we are, in fact, planning how to use the bit allocation, the data allocation bits that had been assigned to the seismometer. We'll use those for other purposes."

The failure of the seismometer was a blow to the geologists, who hoped to learn more about the Martian interior. Even if the seismometer aboard Lander 2 worked perfectly, the scientists would not now be able to pinpoint the location of Marsquakes, as they would have if both seismometers had been functional.

A second problem cropped up two days after landing. The Lander's transmitter was capable of working at 1, 10, and 30 watts, depending on the needs of the moment. During the active mission, it was supposed to operate at 30 watts, to achieve the maximum bit rate. But on July 22 and 23, it came on in the 1-watt mode, for no apparent reason. A team at RCA in New Jersey was put to work. According to Tom Young, "In the one-watt mode you can get slightly over seventeen minutes worth of data from the Lander to the Orbiter. We had built the mission on getting back a little over eighteen minutes of data, but if we're able to operate in thirty-watt mode, we probably can get something like thirty to thirty-two minutes of data. So that's the fundamental limitation."

On the morning of the twenty-fourth, the relay link came up in the 30-watt mode. "We don't know why it came on at thirty today ... or why it came on at one watt two days before," said a mystified but pleased Jim Martin. The link continued in the 30-watt mode for the rest of the mission, and the anomaly was ascribed to thermal problems.

Another communications problem resulted when the Lander's Receiver No. 1 failed to lock up on earth. Fortunately, Receiver No. 2 worked well, so there was no impact on the mission. An anomaly team fiddled with the problem for weeks, and occasionally managed to get the No. 1 receiver in lock, but for all practical purposes, it didn't really matter.

The most serious problem was in the Surface Sampler Arm. The collector head was protected during landing by a shroud, which was ejected after touchdown. As part of the ejection sequence, the sampler arm was supposed to extend a few inches and then return to its stowed position. It did extend, but when it tried to reel back in, it stuck.

Viking's ears (the seismometer) were already lost. If the sampler arm failed to function, then its sense of touch and "taste" (biology and GCMS) would also be lost, leaving the Lander with only its eyes. Yet another anomaly team was put to work on the sampler arm glitch.

The solution to the problem turned out to be simple. There was a latching pin in the arm assembly which was supposed to drop out when the arm was extended. The original computer commands had been for the sampler arm to extend about a foot, but somewhere along the line someone had rewritten the program, causing the arm to extend just six inches, which was not far enough to allow the pin to drop. When the arm retracted, the pin jammed it. The sampler arm motor clutched, then turned itself off. All that was required to set things right was a simple command to extend the arm 13 or 14 inches, far enough to allow the pin to fall out. On the twenty-fifth, the plan was executed, and photos showed that the pin had, indeed, fallen out.

The stuck arm was cured with apparent ease, but the true significance of the operation was that it showed that it was possible to diagnose and correct mechanical problems on the Lander from 212 million miles away. Later, more severe problems were to plague the sampler arm, but by using the same kinds of procedures that freed the jammed pin, the engineers were able to keep the sampler in operation.

Before separation from the Orbiter, the Lander was given an Initial Computer Load (ICL) which contained all the commands necessary for the Lander to carry out a 60-day mission even without further communications from earth. But since communications were not impaired, the mission planners were able to modify the ICL in order to get the most out of the mission. This ability to make changes and adaptations was one of the most important aspects of *Viking*.

Commands were sent to *Viking* via a procedure known as uplink. Working in three-day cycles, the uplink teams planned *Viking*'s daily agenda. Actually, "day" is somewhat inappropriate here; Martian days were called "Sols" to distinguish them from terrestrial days, which are 42 minutes shorter. July 20 was Sol 0, since there were only a few hours left in the Sol at the time of landing. Sol 1 began late on July 20. The first uplink occurred on Sol 3.

The uplink procedure was intricate and time-consuming, and the real heart of the mission. Lander Imaging is a good base from which to follow the uplink system, since virtually every command sent to Viking had an impact on Lander Imaging.

If Jim Martin or Tom Young decided that it would be a good idea to take a picture of the sampler arm immediately after a sample acquisition, the request would be made to Lander Imaging. There were three separate LI uplink squads, with three members and an intern each, plus a late-adaptive squad, responsible for making last-minute changes. Despite the fact that each squad planned two weeks ahead, the late changes were virtually inevitable.

The uplink squad, having received the picture request, then discussed it to make sure that the picture asked for was the picture that was really needed. Frequently, a request for several pictures could be boiled down to just one or two, saving both time and bits.

The picture requested was then put together with all the other pictures to be taken on that Sol, and after a series of meetings, a Science Requirement Strategy (SRS) was evolved, listing the specifics of each picture. The SRS passed on to the Lander Science Systems Staff (LSSS, or LS-cubed), where the requests were matched with possibilities.

LSSS got the uplink plans in the form of Science Instrument Parameters, known as SIPs. The SIPs were computer printouts produced by the uplink squads, and consisted of specific commands to the Lander. Lander Imaging had 56 commands available, and each one could be altered to fit specific needs. One of the major difficulties of uplinking was keeping track of the command changes made in previous uplink cycles. An uplinker might order command number 40, thinking it was an instruction to rotate a camera 90 degrees to the right, only to find out later that on the last cycle, command 40 had been changed to a 90-degree rotation to the left.

After the SIPs were produced, LSSS looked at them and made sure that no one had gone over his data allocation. From LSSS, the uplink requests went to Lander Computer Simulation, or LCOMSIM. The computer ran the commands, simulating what would happen on the actual Lander. Here conflicts were to be discovered, if they existed. With limited power available to the Lander, it was important that the uplink commands should not result in an overtaxing of the Lander's resources. Another important consideration was the effect of the commands on the Lander's temperature. Using power tended to raise the Lander's internal temperature, and in order to keep everything functioning optimally, there were limitations on the kinds of things that could be done at the same time. The Pyrolytic Release Experiment, for example, required heating of the experimental oven to about 900°F; the GCMS also involved temperatures in that range. They could not be run simultaneously without overheating the Lander. LCOMSIM identified such conflicts.

The result of the LCOMSIM procedure was a Lander Sequence (LSeq), which was checked over by all the various uplink squads. The LSeq was then sent to the mission planners, where final changes were requested. The uplink squads then rewrote their sequences, as necessary. Any last-minute revisions were handled by the late-adaptive squads, which could change commands up to about two days before the actual uplink. Finally, the commands were loaded into the computer, relayed to the DSN, and sent to Mars.

Uplinking was a tedious and nerve-wracking business. It was theoretically possible to wreck the Lander by sending up the wrong commands; more realistically, a badly designed sequence could result in wasted bits and lost science opportunities. The uplinkers worked long and difficult hours, and feuds were not uncommon. The Hatfield-McCoy battle of the mission was between Lander Imaging and GCMS, which continually made complex changes at the last possible moment, resulting in more work for the uplinkers.

Despite the preoccupation with mechanical glitches and the nuts and bolts of day-to-day operations, *Viking* sent back to earth a treasure trove of scientific data, beginning on the day of the landing. The Entry Science team was the first group to get its load of new knowledge, and they reported their preliminary findings on the evening of July 20.

Team Leader Alfred Nier described his instrument, the Upper Atmosphere Mass Spectrometer, reviewing the manner in which the UAMS knocks electrons off of gas molecules and separates them according to mass. As expected, there was a big peak in the data at mass 44, which is carbon dioxide. But there were two highly significant surprises. There was another notable peak at 14—and that could only have been nitrogen.

The search for nitrogen in the Martian atmosphere had been going on for a long time, but this was the first hard evidence that it had actually existed. As Dr. Tobey Owen, of SUNY, put it a few days later, "I am personally just delighted that we have finally found nitrogen in the Martian atmosphere. When I got interested in Mars back in the fifties, it was an established doctrine that the pressure on Mars was eighty-five millibars, plus or minus three millibars, and that the atmosphere was well over ninety-five percent nitrogen. Now, as time went along, the surface pressure went down and the concentration of CO_2 went up, and as the precision in the measurement was increased and increased, nitrogen just kept eluding us. And now we finally got it; it's really there." The tentative conclusion was that the Martian atmosphere was about 3 percent nitrogen—as opposed to 78 percent on earth.

The second surprise was the abundance of argon. Data returned from a Russian spacecraft suggested that the argon content of the Martian atmosphere might be as high as 35 or 40 percent, versus just 1 percent on earth. If the Russian data was correct, it would mean trouble for *Viking*, since the gas pump in the Gas Chromatograph Mass Spectrometer "choked" on argon. A high concentration of the inert gas would ruin the GCMS.

The UAMS found an argon peak, but it was much smaller than had been feared. It turned out that argon constituted no more than about 1 to 2 percent of the Martian atmosphere. Oxygen comprised another one-tenth to one-half of one percent, and the remaining 95 percent was CO_2.

The second Entry Science instrument, the Retarding Potential Analyzer, also provided some interesting data. *Mariner 9* observations indicated that a great deal of hydrogen was

228

escaping from Mars' upper atmosphere, and *Viking* confirmed it. There were also a lot of O_2+ ions escaping, so the loss of the two gases could be expressed in terms of water; Mars was losing about 60,000 gallons of water every day. Over the course of time, that was enough to have depleted the planet of about 3 meters of precipitable water. That provided one answer to the troubling question of what had happened to the water that carved the channels, but there was much more to the story.

Since water can't exist in any quantity on the present Martian surface, at some time in the past the Martian atmosphere must have been more massive. The Sagan-Ward cyclical climate theory postulated that most of the early atmosphere was locked in the polar caps and could be recycled in warmer times. But that theory was dependent upon the exact nature of the early atmosphere. The new *Viking* data now allowed scientists to "reconstruct" that early atmosphere, and perhaps find out what had happened to it.

There are two common isotopes of argon, argon-36 and argon-40. All the argon-36 in the solar system was produced in the interior of the sun; all of the argon-40 was created by the radioactive decay of potassium-40 in rocks. Both isotopes are released into the atmosphere from rocks. By comparing the relative amounts of the two isotopes present in the atmosphere, it is possible to gain some idea of how the atmosphere formed.

On Mars, the ratio of argon-36 to argon-40 is about 1:2750 ±500. This means that by comparison to earth, Mars has very little argon-36. Since both planets were presumably formed out of the same inventory of gases in the solar nebula, Mars ought to have a similar argon 36/40 ratio. It doesn't, and the implication is that much of the argon-36 is still locked in the rocks; Mars has outgassed about 100 times less efficiently than the earth. If true, then the early Martian atmosphere could not have been very massive.

There are other ways of reconstructing the early atmosphere, and different results are possible. Dr. Michael McElroy, of Harvard, looked at the problem from the perspective of nitrogen abundance. Mars presently has about 3 percent nitrogen, but in the past it must have had more. The reason is that, like hydrogen and oxygen, nitrogen escapes into space from the Martian atmosphere. In the upper atmosphere, nitrogen ions recombine with electrons to produce high-speed atoms traveling at 6.3 km per second. Escape velocity from Mars is 5.5 km per second; on earth, escape velocity is around 11 km per second. So the earth keeps nitrogen, Mars loses it.

Four billion years ago, Mars must have had considerably more nitrogen. It arrived early and gradually dissipated with time. But there is a problem with this theory. If Mars did have a greater abundance of nitrogen in the past, then at the present time it should have an enrichment of nitrogen-15 relative to nitrogen-14, since the ^{15}N is less likely to escape. The initial entry data didn't make clear whether or not there was a nitrogen-15 enrichment. Another difficulty was that the heavy inert gases xenon and krypton had not been discovered. If the earth-analogy theories were correct, and both planets did form from the same inventory, then xenon and krypton ought to be present in the Martian atmosphere.

Although the Entry Science instruments were not sensitive enough to detect krypton and xenon, the GCMS was able to continue the search on the surface of the planet. Using only the mass spectrometer part of the instrument, it was possible to do atmospheric analyses which confirmed and refined the UAMS measurements.

The GCMS had a better detection limit because of an ingenious enrichment process. Originally designed to detect the elusive nitrogen, the procedure also worked for the inert gases. After pumping the Martian air into the chamber, the CO_2 and CO was removed by a lithium hydroxide absorber, leaving only the other 5 percent of the atmospheric gases. By

230

repeating this process several times, the relative concentration of the other gases was increased, making them easier to detect. Unfortunately, the procedure could not be repeated indefinitely because the GCMS was needed for the analysis of Martian soil. But the work done on VL-1 pushed the detection limit for the noble gases down to the part-per-million (PPM) level. If they were present at all, the concentration of krypton and xenon had to be less than 20 and 50 parts per million, respectively. Plans were made to repeat the enrichment technique on VL-2 and push the detection limit even lower.

The atmospheric findings had important implications for the biology investigation. The discovery of nitrogen made it a lot easier for life to exist on Mars, since many terrestrial biological processes require the "fixing" of atmospheric nitrogen. In this respect, although the total amount of nitrogen was much lower, Mars actually may have more usable nitrogen than the earth. The high ultraviolet flux on Mars creates chemical reactions in the upper atmosphere which produce "a shower of fertilizer for the Martians," according to McElroy. On earth, "biology had to go to great steps to develop an elaborate mechanism to dissociate nitrogen and be able to absorb it. Mars, in some sense, is a more hospitable region in terms of supplying the reduced forms, the fixed forms of nitrogen, to the surface," McElroy explained. "I just do not feel that nitrogen in the Martian atmosphere is, in any sense anymore, a limiting factor in speculation about life."

The Martians, if there are any, would need more from their atmosphere than just "a shower of fertilizer." Water still seemed to be a necessity. Barney Farmer's MAWD experiment on the Orbiter had found considerable quantities of it in the atmosphere, with the highest concentrations at the warmer northern latitudes. But for water to flow in useful quantities, higher atmospheric pressure was needed. Hugh Kieffer's IRTM had taken measurements over the south pole which indicated that as much as a quarter of the entire atmosphere was freezing out there in the winter months. Presumably an equivalent amount of CO_2 was being released at the north pole, but good measurements of that region had not yet been obtained. The northern observations would be of critical importance, because they might answer the question of what had happened to some of that earlier, more massive atmosphere.

Mariner 9 had discovered curious laminated terraces near the north pole, indicative of many episodes of freezing and melting. This was supportive of the cyclical climate theory, but not conclusive. The joker in the deck was that Mars appeared to have two types of polar caps, one that formed and melted annually, and a permanent residual cap. The IRTM readings seemed to confirm that the annual cap was made of CO_2 frozen out of the atmosphere during the winter. But the residual cap was the key to the mystery. If it was CO_2, it was available for recycle into the atmosphere during warmer epochs. If it was H_2O, water ice, the missing CO_2 had to be elsewhere. The most likely place for it to be was chemically bound in the rocks, in which case recycle would be much more difficult.

It seemed necessary to come up with a recycle mechanism because the Orbiter Imaging Team kept coming up with strange geological discoveries that demanded running water, perhaps many episodes of it. Just four days after the landing, Hal Masursky proudly showed the latest photos of the Argyre region, a large basin in the Southern Hemisphere. Snaking across the basin were riverbeds, not simply broad channels. The rivers were complete with dendritic tributary networks, which could only have been formed by rainfall. Masursky said that the river-making process may have happened many times, since some of the tributaries looked quite young. Rainfall in recent times contradicted the early, more massive atmosphere that was being proposed by Owen and McElroy.

232

Owen maintained that "earlier is easier" in terms of getting a dense enough atmosphere to produce rainfall, but Masursky's channels seemed to be as young as a few hundred million years. Clearly, it was going to take awhile to come up with a new model of Mars that satisfied all the observations.

It was generally agreed that in order to have rainfall on Mars, the atmospheric pressure would have to have been around 100 millibars, or about a tenth of what it is on earth. Owen's reconstructed atmosphere model gave a maximum pressure of around 75 MB, while McElroy's model gave a slightly higher pressure. The only certainty was that by the time *Viking* reached Mars, the pressure was much, much lower.

The Entry Science readings gave a surface pressure at Chryse Planitia of just 7.3 MB, while the pressure at the mean surface level was 6.1 MB. That meant that the elevation of the landing site was about 2.9 km lower than the mean surface level. The temperature at Chryse was 241° Kelvin, or −30°F, which was somewhat warmer than had been expected. Since the Entry Science figures were simply extrapolations downward from 100 km above the surface, they were only preliminary data.

The first true weather report from another planet was delivered by Seymour Hess on the night of July 21. Although Hess admitted that this was probably "not the way Frank Field got started," he gave his report with gusto and considerably more clarity than one usually finds on the late news. The temperature at Chryse rose from an early morning low of −122°F to a high of −22°F in the early afternoon. Readings were not taken in the late afternoon, but indications were that the temperature probably rose somewhat above −22°F at around 3 or 4 P.M., local time. The atmospheric pressure held steady throughout the day at 7.7 MB. Winds, gusting up to 14.6 mph, were from the east early in the day, then shifted to southwesterly after midnight.

Hess continually claimed that he never made predictions, but meteorology data from the next two Sols tempted him to break his rule. The wind direction shifted almost exactly as it had on the first Sol, at the same time of day. Comparing the data, Hess said, "These are so much alike that if one of them were a Dow-Jones average and the other one my predictions, I would be a wealthy man ... if *Viking* has accomplished nothing else, it has converted meteorology to a reproducible science."

The repeating wind pattern shouldn't have surprised him, Hess admitted. "For twenty-six years I've been preaching the doctrine that the Mars atmosphere is a simpler and easier version of earth's atmosphere," Hess said. "If I'd had any sense, I should have predicted that there would have been this kind of repeatability."

Yet meteorology has its pitfalls, whether on Mars or the earth. On the twenty-fourth, Hess' colleague Conway Leovy reported that the diurnal wind pattern had, indeed, shifted. "If Seymour had invested any money," commented Leovy, "he would have lost his shirt."

If exact predictions are still impossible, long-term trends are nevertheless detectable. The diurnal wind variation seemed to be a function of downslope winds into the Chryse basin. As the night air chilled, it became more dense and simply slid downhill into Chryse every night. A more interesting long-term trend was that the atmospheric pressure was declining. Hess ascribed the decline to the freezing out of CO_2 at the south pole. The pressure fell by an average of .017 MB per day. "That's a rate," said Hess, "which in 500 Sols will cause the atmosphere to go away completely. I do not draw the conclusion from that that *Viking* landed just in time." The calculations based on the pressure drop agreed with the IRTM figures for the rate of CO_2 freezing at the south pole, so it seemed fairly certain that *Viking* was simply sensing the removal of mass from the atmosphere thousands of miles away. Commenting on the trend, Hess said, "I'm amazed. I seem to have intimidated the press. No one's asked me the usual question as to whether I'm willing to forecast. Today, I'm willing to forecast. The secular downward trend in pressure will not continue. It will level off and reverse and go up, but the time scale will be a matter of months."

"Happiness," Hess said a few days after landing, "is a well-behaved instrument in the thirty-watt mode." At that point, Hess was one of the few experimenters who could have considered himself happy. Between the seismometer failure and the sampler arm problems, Meteorology and Lander Imaging were about the only science teams with no complaints. Later on in the mission, a problem did develop in the wind quadrant sensor, but by that time the scientists had learned to tell the direction of the wind by looking at the cooling rates on the RTG covers—proving once again that you don't need a weatherman to know which way the wind blows.

For all the intriguing scientific data returned by the Lander, it was still the Lander Imaging pictures which caused the greatest excitement. The first two Martian pictures were printed on the front pages of newspapers all over the world. It was thrilling just to look at them, but the pictures also contained a wealth of scientific data.

One of the first things noticed by the Lander Imaging people was the brightness of the sky. It had been known that the Martian atmosphere contained a great many small particles, which made the sky somewhat hazy—"like a smoggy day in Pasadena," as one scientist described it. But the Lander pictures showed that the sky was perhaps as much as 100 times brighter than expected. Since the atmosphere itself was thin, the cause of the brightness had to be light scattering produced by a tremendous number of particles a few tenths of a micron in diameter.

The effect of all those particles was seen the next day when the first color picture was returned. "Incredible!" enthused Tim Mutch when he first saw it. "The more you look at it, the more interesting it becomes." The most obvious feature was the color. "The discovery that Mars is red," said Carl Sagan, "merely confirms a discovery made in about one million B.C. by someone named Og." But the surface was not merely red—it was *red*. Not lipstick red or fire engine red, but, as Jonathan Eberhart of *Science News* wrote, it was about the color of "an embarrassed brick." And above that red surface, there was a clear blue sky.

More or less.

The color picture was released in raw form, before it went through any image processing. The color balance was not exactly right. When the color was corrected a couple of days later, Sagan reported to the press that his colleague, Dr. James Pollack, had concluded that "the sky is not blue." The announcement was greeted with a chorus of boos and hisses from the press corps. "Typical earth chauvinist response," said Sagan. "The sky is, in fact, pink—an okay color."

On earth, the sky is blue owing to Rayleigh scattering; air molecules scatter blue light better than red. But on Mars the air is so thin that the blue scattering is very weak, and is overwhelmed by the red scattering of the tiny suspended particles.

Aside from making the sky look pink, Pollack reported that the particles may also help drive the Martian wind system by heating the air during the day. In the longer term, the gradual buildup of particles in the atmosphere may also be responsible for touching off the great Martian dust storms, such as the one seen by *Mariner 9*.

On the surface itself, there was no evidence of moving dust. Single-line rescan pictures showed no sign of any motion. In a way, this was fortunate, for it gave the scientists an effective zero point to work from. When the next dust storm began,

236

they would be able to observe the precise wind, temperature, and pressure conditions necessary to inaugurate a Martian sirocco.

The scene at Chryse did not show much evidence of long-term wind erosion. Contrary to expectations, there were very few rocks that had been ventifacted to any significant degree. There were wind tails of dust behind many of the rocks, but it did not look like an area where massive sandblasting was occurring.

Mostly, there were just rocks. Lander Imaging member Dr. Alan Binder, of Science Applications, Inc. in Tucson, began counting the different types of rocks that were visible, and came up with well over a dozen. If the number reached 25, he promised he would take the whole team out to dinner. The rock typing was based solely on visible traits, such as color, texture, granularity, shape, and size. The most common type of rock looked similar to earthly basalt.

To the left of the Lander, there was a feature that had been described as dunes on Sol 0. When the missing portion of the panorama was completed, it turned out that there was a substantial field of dunes. In the middle of the dunes rested a large black boulder, about three meters across, eight meters from the spacecraft. It would have thoroughly wrecked the Lander. The boulder was originally christened "Big Bertha," but due to what Tim Mutch called "sexist and militarist" implications, the name was later changed to "Big Joe."

On August 4, a high resolution photo of the dune field was taken at a low sun angle (about 7:30 A.M., Lander Local Time) in order to enhance the detail. The picture was spectacular, and produced the first oohs and aahs heard around JPL since the landing. "Some of you may recall," said Mutch, "that on Sol 0 I talked about how incredible the pictures were. I don't know what I would have done if I had seen this. I probably just would have levitated and gone up to the ceiling."

237

On closer inspection, it turned out that the dunes were not dunes at all, at least not in the strict geological sense. "There is a suggestion of a crust here on the surface," said Mutch. "I think you are seeing some sort of a stratification here in the depositing medium, rather than ripples." The dunes were reclassified as drifts, semipermanent features, rather than the transient desert dunes one might see in the Sahara.

The Physical Properties Team also made some interesting observations about the landing site. Footpad #2 had been seen in the first picture after landing, and it was sitting comfortably atop the surface material. But when a picture was obtained of Footpad #3, the scientists were shocked to see that it was buried five inches deep in loose material. The entire footpad was submerged, up to its "ankle."

Directly beneath the Lander, the fine material had been blown away, revealing what seemed to be either bedrock or hardpan. It was an exciting revelation for the geologists. By earth analogy, it was as if *Viking* had come down with one foot on the beach and the other in the ocean—rather incredible luck.

The surface material itself was extremely fine-grained and cohesive. "If you want to see how Martian material behaves," said Dr. Henry Moore of the USGS, "go down to the beach where the water washes up on the sand and then retreats, and right after it retreats you stick your heel in it and start pushing down, and you'll see a phenomenon like this." That observation was made after the digging of a trench by the sampler arm; the trench itself looked very much like the footprint that Moore spoke of, although, of course, the Martian surface was not at all wet. The trench picture was the most lifelike thing yet observed by *Viking*—evidence of a Martian Sasquatch.

Robert Hargraves' magnetic experiment was the poor relation of the sophisticated Lander investigations. Not only did it cost almost nothing, but Hargrave had to wait until late August to finally get a clear picture of his magnets on the sampler backhoe. The picture revealed that the Martian surface material was extremely magnetic. Both the strong and weak magnets were completely covered by small particles arranged in the magnets' characteristic bull's-eye pattern. Based on the color and size of the particles, Hargraves deduced that the material had to be one of four substances: magnetite, maghemite, iron, or sulfide-pyritite. Pyritite was eliminated by the X-Ray Fluorescence experiment results, and native iron seemed unlikely in an oxidizing environment. That left magnetite and maghemite. Since the two substances represent different stages of iron oxidation, the final results of the magnetic experiment could give important information about the chemical interaction between the Martian atmosphere and the surface.

The X-Ray Fluorescence experiment successfully determined the chemical composition of the soil. Since the experiment gave only the abundances of the various elements in the surface material, it was left to the scientists to figure out just how they all fit together, and in which compounds. The X-Ray analysis is essentially a statistical process, so the more data obtained, the better the accuracy. By early August, Dr. Priestly Toulmin and his colleagues had accumulated more than a billion bits of data.

The major constituents of the Martian soil were iron, calcium, silicon, titanium, and aluminum. Other elements were present, but at low levels; the X-Ray experiment put an upper limit on their possible abundances. One of the more interesting findings was that the iron oxide content was relatively low. It appeared that the iron oxides might be present simply as a stain—a very thin, or even discontinuous surface coating.

The experiment also found a surprisingly low amount of trace elements such as rubidium and zirconium. Relative to the earth and the moon, Mars was apparently very poor in the trace elements. The observation had possible significance in

239

the search for life, since trace elements are a necessity for earthly biology.

The Martian surface material was essentially unique, in that it was not exactly like any known terrestrial material. The closest match to the Mars soil was Molokai Basalt, from the Hawaiian Islands. The implication was that the Chryse surface had been formed by ancient lava flows.

All of the Lander investigations were valuable in increasing our understanding of Mars, but it was the biology experiment which held everyone's attention. For most people, the whole purpose of *Viking* was to find life on Mars. On the night of July 24, some people thought they had found it.

To give some idea of the flavor of the event, I'll quote directly from my notes of that evening: "Reports of writing on a rock—radio reports of 'numbers painted on a rock'—much nonsense. Pic looks interesting but hardly convincing. Streams of people coming up to the TV monitors and staring & pointing. I think I can see the hindside of an armadillo in the same pic. If any animal would be dumb enough to live on Mars, it would be the armadillo. Jim Martin seems amused by it all. Nevertheless, heavy guns are here for briefing."

The stir was caused when a Lander picture showed what appeared to be the letter "B" carved on a rock. Some people also thought they saw the letter "G" and the numbers 2, 3, and 4 on the same rock. Was this a message from the Martians? Or just some graffiti by fraternity brothers from the University of Barsoom? Or what?

The story immediately went out on the wires. All three networks ran bulletins reporting the finding. If the mission had its moments of high drama, then this was its counterpoint—low comedy.

Alan Binder calmly reported that the "B" was simply the result of a shadowing phenomenon caused by the rough texture of the rock. He showed pictures of terrestrial rocks

240

which had similar features, and demonstrated that when the sun angle changed, the letters went away. Binder also spoke of Percival Lowell, who thought *he* saw things on Mars which weren't really there.

Who was the first to see the "B"? "Well," said Binder, "I do not know what the rest of the world was doing, but I, unfortunately, was the first one to see it since my last name begins with B. As a Binder, I happened to notice that there was an interesting shape there and I think I was probably the first one to notice it—within the project—unfortunately." Hal Masursky gleefully dubbed the rock, "Binder's B Block." Later on in the same briefing, Mike Carr was showing orbital photos, and mentioned a particular crater: "I hesitate to point this out," he said, "because it looks remarkably like the letter 'O.' "

The press had jumped on the story. Millions of people heard the news and must have wondered just what was going on at JPL. There had already been stories circulating that life had been found on Mars but that the government had suppressed the news. An Italian writer even claimed that an Orbiter photo had revealed a buried Martian city. Around JPL, there were rumors that methane had been found in the Martian atmosphere—a biologically produced gas. "The CIA is not involved in this," said Tobey Owen. "We didn't see any methane." Yet there were people who were all too ready to believe that some conspiracy of silence was covering up the truth about life on Mars. The B-Block incident didn't help things any.

The *Viking* press corps varied in size from several hundred for the landings, to about a half-dozen during slack periods. Those who did the best and most accurate reporting were the ones who kept close to the project and had a real understanding of what was going on. The regulars included George Alexander of *The Los Angeles Times,* Tom O'Toole of *The Washington Post,* Dave Perlman, of the *San Francisco Chroni-*

241

cle, Dave Salisbury of *The Christian Science Monitor,* Jim Louden of National Public Radio, and Jonathan Eberhart from *Science News.*

Eberhart was practically a member of the project. *Viking* was his seventy-fifth space mission, and he knew more about it than a lot of the team members. With his long, graying hair, he looked more like an aging hippie than a science reporter, but when a new reporter arrived at JPL, he usually asked Eberhart to tell him what was going on. An accomplished folksinger, Eberhart provided *Viking* with its own musical accompaniment, including two songs he wrote for the occasion. One of them, a stately ballad about the old Mars, where the rivers ran and the winds blew, was a triumph of both music and science. In the interests of accuracy, Eberhart bugged the scientists for weeks, trying to get a look at a picture of the sunset. It was an intriguing question; if the sky is pink all day, what color is the sunset? It turned out to be sort of blue-green; Eberhart eventually got the picture and finished his song.

On the other side of the ledger, there were a lot of reporters who didn't know anything about Mars or *Viking,* and badly distorted events. Even the *New York Times* editorialized about the lack of carbon on Mars (there was plenty of carbon; the search was for carbon *compounds).* The worst offenders were the television reporters, who needed to boil down complex science to glib 30-second film spots. Gentry Lee, Science Analysis and Mission Planning Director, was interviewed by three separate TV reporters in the space of ten minutes one afternoon. Roy Neal of NBC wanted short, snappy answers to his questions about the stuck sampler arm. The reporter from a local station asked the same questions, but let Lee explain in some detail. The woman from the local NBC affiliate didn't even know his name.

Because *Viking* was such a complex mission and television is such a simplifying medium, television coverage of *Viking* tended to be shallow and misleading, although NBC did run two fine documentaries on the subject. But even the documentaries relied too much on neat generalities. The rundown sheet for the NBC show sums it up rather well: "Neal with Carl Sagan—(What All This Means) (5:15)."

The scientists and mission directors were generally extremely cooperative with the press, and sometimes more patient than saints. During a rather straightforward discussion of landing site options, a reporter from a local TV station (whose main problem seemed to be that she, literally, could not tell north from south) asked a question with this preface: "I'm very impressed with everybody in here, and I'm glad that you all know what you're talking about. However, I have to tell John Q. Public what it is that all of you are talking about ... and I'm wondering if you could phrase for me in a manner that you would tell your dumb cousin Clara...."

Dumb cousin Clara certainly exists, but "John Q. Public" is probably smarter than that—and the reporters who give him the news ought to be. The *Viking* scientists sometimes strayed into regions too technical for even the most dedicated and experienced science writers, but the tendency of the media (especially the electronic media) to oversimplify everything was equally galling. The single dumbest question of the mission was asked by an experienced television science reporter (whom I'll call, say, Jules Bergman). After Harold Klein, leader of the biology investigation, had spent twenty minutes explaining why it is so difficult to distinguish between an exotic chemical reaction and a purely biological reaction, Bergman asked, "Clearly and simply, if that is possible, and I'm beginning to doubt that it is, why wasn't there an instrument aboard that could tell us, without all this torture, whether we're seeing chemistry or biology?" Klein looked at the ceiling for a moment, then patiently responded, "The only instrument I know of capable of doing something like that would be a divining rod."

243

Part of the problem was that the press was being allowed a behind-the-scenes peek into the workings of real science. Probably never before in the history of science had scientists been in a position where they had to report to the press almost daily on the progress of complex experiments. Norman Horowitz, principal investigator on the Pyrolytic Release experiment, summed up the scientists' viewpoint: "I want to emphasize that if this were normal science, we wouldn't even be here—we'd be working in our laboratories for three more months. You wouldn't even know what was going on, and at the end of that time we would come out and tell you the answer. Having to work in a fishbowl like this is an experience that none of us is used to . . . You're looking over the shoulder of a group of people who are trying to work in a normal way in an abnormal environment."

On balance, the scientists did an excellent job of reporting their results—even their incomplete results—and the media did a generally good job on a difficult story. If *Viking* had been merely another spacecraft, things would have been much easier all around. But because *Viking* went to Mars to look for, among other things, evidence of life on another planet, the atmosphere around JPL was supercharged. No reporter wanted to miss the scoop of the century, and, as Horowitz put it, "Nobody wants to be wrong in public on a question as important as that of life on Mars."

13

Looking for Life—
"Nobody Wants To Be Wrong . . ."

> If we had observed these results in the laboratory, we would have concluded that we had a weak but positive biological signal. Weak, but definitely positive. But since the signal comes from Mars, which is an entirely different world and one that we don't understand yet, we have to be very careful in how to interpret these numbers.
>
> —Norman Horowitz,
> August 25, 1976

> At the risk of losing a friend, I'm going to tell you what Dr. Horowitz said to me when I first saw him after he saw these results. He said, "I'm overwhelmed!"
>
> —Gerald Soffen
> August 25, 1976

Jim Martin looked out into the lights and cameras and paused. He had just delivered his status report for July 31, Sol 11, and his consistently low-key style gave no hint that a dramatic announcement was coming. But that was typical of *Viking;* the routine and the mundane gave way to the spectacular without any warning.

"I wanted to state," said Martin, "that it's been project policy for seven years to make data available to the media when we have solid data. And today is no exception. We have received biology data that we believe to be good data. The engineering telemetry all indicates that the instrument is performing extremely well, and I think it is important that you and the public are aware of the data we have. I would like to caution all of you, I think Chuck Klein will continue to caution you, that the biology experiment is a complex one. We've seen that Mars is a complex planet. There are many things that we do not understand, so that in any research activity, one must proceed in a systematic, methodical manner, and this is what Dr. Klein and his team are in the process of doing."

With that cautionary preface, Dr. Harold Klein, leader of the biology investigation, stepped before the microphones and gave the first report on the results of the biology experiments aboard *Viking*. Klein, too, was low-key, and could probably have announced the Second Coming without apparent emotion. "In one of our experiments," said Klein, "the Gas Exchange experiment, we believe that we have at least preliminary evidence for a very active surface material. We believe that there's something in the surface, some chemical or physical entity, which is affording the surface material a great activity. And may, in fact, mimic, and let me emphasize that, may *mimic* in some respects biological activity."

It was a stunning moment. After centuries of speculation, there was now, at last, positive evidence that life of some sort might actually exist on Mars. Martin and Klein's cautions were all but forgotten, and the announcement received worldwide front-page coverage. Some went so far as to report that life had actually been discovered.

Not quite. Klein's announcement was merely the first tentative finding of an investigation that would probably take years to complete. In the days and weeks that followed, hopes were alternately raised and dashed as more data was returned from *Viking*. The search for life on Mars turned into a cosmic mystery story, complete with exotic clues, red herrings, suspenseful waits, and masterful deductions worthy of Holmes at his best.

246

The preliminary results from the Gas Exchange experiment indicated that the surface material in the sample was releasing an unexpectedly large amount of oxygen. "What we have found," said Klein, "is something like fifteen times as much oxygen ... as we can account for from known sources." One possible cause for the oxygen release was the presence in the sample of something that was alive. But there were still other possibilities which didn't depend on biology, and the biologists were inclined to regard them as more likely. It was possible that there were peroxides or superoxides present in the soil. When exposed to the "chicken soup" injection in the Gex, they reacted and gave off large quantities of oxygen gas.

The Labeled Release experiment had also sent back some surprises. Like the Gex, the LR experiment involved a small injection of nutrient into the test chamber. And like the Gex, the LR reported a massive evolution of gas following the injection. The LR response was in terms of the number of counts of radioactivity produced by the labeled carbon-14 in the nutrient. Immediately after the injection, the number of counts shot upward and plateaued at around 10,000 counts per minute.

The results of the two experiments were similar in that they showed that the soil contained a lot of volatiles. Their sudden release could be explained as a reaction to the nutrient after perhaps four billion years in a sterile environment. Yet, particularly in the LR, there may have been other factors at work. The LR curve was similar to curves produced by terrestrial samples, where biology was known to be present. "We are far too early in the game to say that we have a positive response," said LR experimenter Gilbert Levin. "There are many other factors that must be tested. All we can say, at this point, is that the response is very interesting and, be it biological or nonbiological, it's unanticipated."

The biologists were excited (if restrained) over the response, but were also happy just to have a sample. The troublesome surface sampler arm had misbehaved again, and yet another glitch had popped up in the GCMS experiment.

The Sol 8 sample acquisition had gone smoothly for the biology and X-ray experiments, but the GCMS did not send back a "level-full" signal, indicating that the surface sample had not been delivered to its hopper. There were two possible explanations: either the soil had somehow failed to get into the GCMS, or the level-full indicator was malfunctioning. The level-full indicator consisted of a very fine wire stretched across the cavity where the sample was delivered. When the cavity was full, the wire would be surrounded by the fine surface material, and a current running through the wire would have increased resistance. Since the wire was so fine, it was possible that a small rock in the sample could have broken it, preventing a level-full signal.

The mission controllers decided to acquire an additional sample for the GCMS, just in case. Photos were scheduled to catch the collector head poised above the GCMS hopper. But when the photos came back, they showed the GCMS hopper, but no collector head. The sampler boom was stuck again, and they didn't know where.

An anomaly team, headed by Joe Moorman, went to work on the problem. Meanwhile, a decision had to be made regarding the GCMS. It seemed likely that it had gotten its sample on Sol 8, and that the level-full indicator had malfunctioned—but there was no way to be sure. If they went ahead and performed an analysis, they might be wasting the second of the three ovens on an empty chamber. But if the sampler arm could not be fixed, a sample never would be acquired. Even if it could be fixed, the delay would ruin the mission timeline. In light of the positive biological signals, a GCMS analysis was imperative, since the discovery of organic compounds in the soil would be strong evidence that positive responses in the biology instruments were, in fact, due to a

248

Martian life form. It was decided to go ahead and run the analysis, even at the risk of losing the second oven.

Viking's good luck held; the GCMS did have its sample.

Meanwhile, Moorman's team figured out a solution to the sampler arm glitch. The anomaly team was an ad hoc group, whose members were chosen because of their problem-solving abilities, rather than for any special expertise on the sampler arm. Over 50 people worked on the problem for up to 18 hours a day—one of Moorman's biggest jobs was in getting people to go home and sleep before they fell over from exhaustion.

In the end, a series of maneuvers was worked out that freed the stuck boom. It had stopped at a 90-inch extension, probably due to the low temperature; the sample had been acquired early in the Martian day. The correction sequence was executed at a warmer time of day, and worked perfectly.

The sampler arm glitch, while important, had seemed like a minor distraction from the main event, which was the biology investigation. By August 1, the oxygen evolution in the Gex had slowed down considerably, supporting the theory that the release was due to superoxides in the soil. It's important to note that up to this point, the soil had not been in direct contact with the nutrient. During this "humid mode," the nutrient was suspended in the test cell; not until August 5 would the "wet mode" begin, when the chicken soup actually mixed with the soil.

On August 2, Dr. Levin gave an update on the LR experiment. The rise in counts was leveling off, and Levin and his colleagues examined the growth curve very carefully. "We have analyzed this curve," Levin reported, "and there is no exponential portion to it. That is, there is no evidence of any doubling of cells. No growth was occurring, and therefore, if there is any metabolism present, if this is a biological curve, we're monitoring metabolism only in the sense that we know it, no growth. On the other hand, if this is a chemical curve, we find that the chemical reaction took place at a very rapid rate initially, and then uncharacteristically slowed down and took a long time to plateau." Levin's conclusion: "We're surprised." The curve didn't correspond with known chemical *or* biological responses.

"We're in between," Levin admitted. "The most difficult imaginable explanation of any data that we get back from Mars is going to be that there is life there, because life is the most complex peak of evolution that we have seen. Therefore, we must try every other possibility to explain the responses by physical means, by chemical means, before absolutely being driven, you might say, to the conclusion that we can only explain it by living reaction." And Levin was still a long way from having been driven that far. Asked if he would put the chemistry versus biology odds at fifty-fifty, Levin replied, "I wouldn't even say fifty-fifty, because I think if I said fifty-fifty, that would be tending strongly towards the biological."

Levin's carefully noncommittal attitude was typical of all the biologists. It was all but maddening to those who wanted there to be life (which meant everybody) to have such intriguing results coupled with such bland statements by the biologists. They refused to be budged a single centimeter toward either biology or chemistry. But as Project Scientist Gerry Soffen explained, "No scientist worth his salt would make any commitments one way or the other at this point."

On August 7, data came back from *Viking* that tempted even the scientists to move at least a short distance in the direction of biology. While the Gex and LR had been returning data, the Pyrolytic Release experiment was still incubating its sample. The most Mars-like of the three experiments, the PR attempted to duplicate actual Martian conditions by incubating the soil at about 17°C for several days, under a xenon lamp which simulated sunlight. The at-

250

mosphere in the chamber was laced with labeled carbon-14, which was flushed out after incubation, providing the first peak. The second peak came after the soil was pyrolyzed at 600°C, and represented the number of counts produced by the ^{14}C which had been absorbed (in whatever manner) into the soil. A high second peak would be indicative of a biological response; a low second peak would mean that there was little or no reaction of any kind.

Dr. Norman Horowitz, with a good sense of drama, reported the second peak results only after a lengthy description of the workings of the instrument. The predicted number of counts for the second peak was 15 per minute. The actual second peak: 95.

"There's a possibility that this is biological," said Horowitz. "There are also many other possibilities that have to be excluded." But the high second peak was the strongest indication yet of biological activity on Mars. Even Klein cautiously admitted, "I am very tantalized." And Horowitz moved to that fifty-fifty point that Levin had shied away from a few days earlier. Asked where, if he were a betting man, he would put his money, Horowitz answered, "Half of it here and half of it here," indicating chemistry on one side of him and biology on the other.

One by one, nonbiological explanations were falling by the wayside. Instrument defects had been ruled out. The second peak in the PR eliminated the peroxides and superoxides that may have been responsible for the Gex reaction, since the PR had observed a reducing, rather than an oxidizing reaction. "If anything," said Klein, "the superoxides would tend to decrease the size of the second peak."

As the first cycle of biology experiments drew to a close, the scientists had a chance to catch their collective breath and do some hard thinking about what they had seen. Outside experts were called in to contribute their opinions. Chemists, in particular, were sought after for their expertise in exotic reactions which might not have been familiar to the *Viking* biologists; virtually all of the straightforward chemical explanations had already been eliminated. "We're seeing some fancy chemistry," said Leslie Orgel, "there's no doubt about that." The question was, how fancy? Biology, itself, is no more than a very specialized, very fancy form of chemistry. Orgel didn't think that the results were beyond what could be explained by chemistry alone. Nevertheless, Orgel, who had once volunteered to eat a sample of Martian soil (if one could be obtained), now withdrew his offer. He wasn't particularly afraid of Martian microbes, but the soil now appeared to be a lot more volatile than anyone had anticipated; he didn't want to get his mouth burned.

"We believe that Mars is really talking to us and is telling us something," said Harold Klein. "The question is whether Mars is talking with a forked tongue or giving us the straight dope." It was hoped that the next cycle of experiments might provide the answer.

"In biology, it's a cardinal rule that you don't believe it if it hasn't happened at least twice," said Dr. Norman Horowitz after the PR second peak data was returned. The results of the first cycle of experiments were intriguing, but far from conclusive. In the second cycle, both the LR and PR were run as control experiments, using sterilized samples. In the Gex, the experiment was put into a "recycle mode" in which the first batch of nutrient and gas was drained from the test chamber, and a second injection was added.

After the initial excitement over the release of oxygen in the Gex, that experiment proved to be the one which did the least to support a biological interpretation of the data. The oxygen levels dropped, and the evolution of other gases, such as argon and carbon monoxide, held steady. By August 20, Harold Klein admitted that, "there is no clear indication of any biological process going on in this experiment so far."

252

The LR experiment, however, was coming on strong. After the second injection of nutrient into the test chamber, the evolution of gas and the number of counts per minute unexpectedly went down, then leveled off. But at the very end of the first cycle, there was a very slight rise in the number of counts. Unfortunately, before there was a chance to fully analyze the data, the experiment shut itself off, as previously ordered. So there was another tantalizing bit of data to be considered, but it was too little to provide a positive indication of anything.

In the second cycle, the samples in the PR and LR were raised to a temperature of 160°C for three hours before beginning incubation. The heat was enough to kill any living organism in the sample, but probably not enough to destroy most types of chemical reactions. If the first cycle responses were due to biology, then the second cycle ought to have seen the extinction of those responses.

And it did.

"We were all looking forward to these first data from the control on the LR because the data could have ruled out the possible presence of biology in the soil," Klein said on August 20. "But," he added, "they did not. Indeed, the results are still consistent with a biological interpretation and, on the other hand, they are also still consistent with a somewhat narrower range of chemical interpretations."

In the first active LR cycle, immediately after the first nutrient injection, the number of counts per minute shot upward and eventually plateaued at around 10,000 cpm. In the sterile sample, after a brief initial rise to about 2,200 cpm, the curve dropped sharply and leveled off at about 1,200 cpm. "Had we seen these two curves on earth," said Gilbert Levin, "if we had run this experiment in the parking lot at JPL, we would have concluded that life is present in the sample."

Levin was quick to point out that the experiment was, in fact, run on Mars, and not in the JPL parking lot; and there are literally worlds of difference between the two sites. Because the data was being returned from an essentially unknown environment, it could not be taken as positive proof of biological activity. It was, nevertheless, an important result. "At least," said Levin, "we have significantly narrowed the range of possible chemical explanations." The results indicated that whatever chemical reaction might have been occurring, it had to be one which disappeared when the temperature was raised to the sterilization temperature. The biologists began to look carefully at a class of compounds known as heat labile oxidants. There were not a large number of them, so it would be possible to go into the laboratory and try to duplicate the LR results on the basis of heat labile oxidants.

Five days later, the second peak of the second PR cycle was announced. As with the LR, it was expected that if biology were present, the sterilization would have killed off the first cycle response, resulting in a low second peak, close to the predicted 15 cpm. The actual second peak turned out to be around 20 cpm, significantly lower than the 96 cpm observed in the active cycle.

The results, according to Klein, "leave us with either a biological interpretation for the data or some even fancier chemistry than we had talked about a week or two ago." There were now even tighter constraints on the kind of chemical reaction which could be at work in the Martian soil. The feeling around JPL was that the biologists were getting very close to announcing that life had been discovered on Mars. Levin and Horowitz now seemed to be leaning in that direction, although Klein remained very cautious. "I guess I'm a diehard," he said. "I think we're dealing here with a very puzzling phenomenon and if we're really going to be sincerely scientific, as long as there are credible alternative hypotheses, they have to be tested."

There was also one key element in the puzzle that was still missing: organics. The GCMS hadn't found any.

On August 7, Klaus Biemann reported the results of the first GCMS analysis. The sample was heated to 200°C, and about 300 mass spectra (about 15 million data bits) were returned. No carbon compounds were detected. The only surprise was the unexpectedly small amount of water that was evolved from the sample.

On August 13, the results of the 500°C analysis were obtained. The GCMS was run at different temperatures because there are many different types of organic compounds, and some of them can only be broken down at higher temperatures. At 500°C, the sample let loose a very large amount of water. That was both a surprise and a hindrance, since the water would tend to mask the presence of any large organic molecules. The sample was apparently composed of stable hydrates, which give up their water at 500° but not at 200°. But the sample did not contain any large organic molecules at the part-per-million level of detection.

The GCMS results were troubling, because if the PR and LR results were due to biology, one would expect to have organic molecules in the soil. However, at the part-per-million level of detection, it was still possible that organics were present, and that the GCMS was simply not sensitive enough to find them.

To illustrate the point, Dr. Klein showed that a reasonably rich sample of terrestrial garden soil, with ten million organisms per gram, would not necessarily provide enough organics for the GCMS. If all the organics in those organisms were put into the same compound, the detection limit would still be at the part-per-million level. If, as was more likely, the organics were spread around in ten or a hundred different types of compounds, the detection limit would be still lower. Even assuming ten dead bodies for every live one, it would still be difficult to find organics in that terrestrial sample.

Still, just as the biology experiments had imposed severe constraints on Martian chemistry, the GCMS was imposing similar constraints on the possible types of Martian biology.

The Martians had to be very efficient; they couldn't leave a lot of dead bodies lying around. In a harsh environment, that was a reasonable way for the Martians to behave; in other words, the Martians might be cannibals.

Another possible explanation was that the microbes (per-haps) observed in the biology experiment might not be indigenous to the Chryse site. If they had been carried in by wind from some other location, then there was no reason to expect that the sample would be rich in organics. Life might grow in some areas of Mars, and then be transported to other areas. The implication was that Mars, unlike the earth, was not teeming with life. Virtually anywhere you look on earth, you can find organics. On Mars, where conditions are tougher, life might be relatively scarce.

The remaining possibility was that there were no organics detected because there were no organics to be detected. And without organic compounds, there can be no life as we under-stand it.

Another GCMS sample was acquired on August 21, and the first analysis on that sample was performed at 350°C instead of 200°C. The strategy was to drive off the water at a lower temperature than 500°C, thus making the organics (if any) easier to see at the higher temperature. At 350°C, significant amounts of water were evolved, raising hopes that at 500°C the elusive organics would finally be discovered.

The results of the second 500°C analysis were reported on September 4, and they did not look very much different from the results of the first analysis—still no organics. There was less water this time around, and the detection limit was lowered to the range of 10 to 100 parts per billion. Even at that level, according to Biemann, there would have to be at least a million microorganisms in the sample—dead or alive—in order to detect them.

The complete absence of organic material was baffling. Organics have been detected in carbonaceous chondrite meteorites on earth; since Mars has been hard hit by meteorites, organics from the chondrites, if nowhere else, ought to be present in the Martian soil. According to some models, the meteorites would have mixed so thoroughly with the Martian regolith that the organics would be so dilute as to be beyond the detection level; other models suggest a thinner regolith in which the organic concentration would be higher.

What had happened to the organics? One strong possibility was that they were rapidly broken down by the ultraviolet light raining down on the Martian surface. The GCMS and biology samples were taken from just a few centimeters beneath the surface, not deep enough for them to have received significant long-term protection from the ultraviolet. In that case, however, the same ultraviolet light which destroyed the organic material should also have killed any microorganisms. The implication was that the results from the biology experiments were due to chemistry, not biology.

But the chemistry kept getting fancier. Norman Horowitz had stated three criteria necessary for the biologists to believe that the data they were getting was indicative of a living system. The first was that the original response had to be eliminated by heat sterilization; that was accomplished in the second cycle of the PR. The second criterion was that the original result had to be reproducible; the third PR cycle was aimed at that goal. And the third criterion was that organic molecules should be discovered in the soil—a continuing problem.

In the third PR cycle, an anomaly developed in the otherwise smooth-running biology package. During the first two days of the PR incubation, a cooler in the PR failed to turn itself on, resulting in a slightly warmer temperature of incubation. Instead of running at 17°C, as it had on the first cycle, the PR got as hot as 27°C.

The anomaly turned out to be a bit of good luck. The first cycle second peak was 96; on the slightly warmer third cycle, it was 28. The immediate implication was that the increased temperature had partially destroyed whatever it was that had caused the original high second peak. Very few chemical reactions can be eliminated by a 10°C rise in temperature; but a 10°C fever will kill a human being. It was possible that the microorganisms in the sample had been wiped out by the temperature rise, virtually eliminating the second peak. The result was one more tantalizing indication of the presence of biology. "I'm driven away from chemistry," said Klein.

However, Horowitz's third criterion was still unfulfilled. If organics were not found, it would be all but impossible for the scientists to be sure that they had found life on Mars. And in the meantime, there was still a lot of fancy chemistry to be checked out.

As the *Viking 1* mission wound down, in preparation for the landing of *Viking 2,* it began to look as if there would be no hard answers on the question of life for quite some time. "I think it's quite possible," said Klein on August 25, "that at the end of a year or so of *Viking* activities, we'll be in a position where the biological interpretation is still strong for one, two, or even perhaps all three of the experiments, and where we will need to go into the laboratory here on earth to do simulations and test some of the alternative theories that I'm certain will creep out of the woodwork as these results get announced. We are already hearing from our colleagues on the outside, getting letters suggesting this or that as a possible explanation. Some of these can easily be ruled out. Some cannot. But I think that it may very well be that we will find that after *Viking,* we will need a year or two of testing in the laboratory before we can come out and say, 'Well, we finally think we've got an answer.' "

There were additional experiments scheduled for *Viking 2,* at a site where most scientists thought that life would be more likely. Extended incubations were planned for the LR and PR experiments, on the theory that it takes time before milk

258

begins to smell bad. Perhaps, given more time, the Martian organisms might make their presence known in a less ambiguous manner. And perhaps not.

There is an old story, possibly apocryphal, about a newspaper editor who was preparing a story about Mars. He sent a telegram to a famous astronomer: NEED FIVE HUNDRED WORDS ABOUT LIFE ON MARS. WIRE COLLECT. The astronomer's reply: NOBODY KNOWS. NOBODY KNOWS. NOBODY KNOWS. NOBODY KNOWS. NOBODY KNOWS . . . two hundred fifty times.

Viking was sent to Mars for many reasons. One of them was to look for evidence of life on the Red Planet. Almost no one expected that *Viking* would give a definite answer to that age-old question. Whether or not life actually does exist there, *Viking's* results are important, for they immeasurably increased our knowledge and understanding of Mars. And yet, there has to be at least a small pang of regret that the answer to the Big Question is still: NOBODY KNOWS.

14

Utopia and Beyond

Space—the final frontier. These are the voyages of the starship *Enterprise;* its five-year mission—to explore strange new worlds, to seek out new life and new civilizations . . . to boldly go where no man has gone before.

—Captain James T. Kirk
U.S.S. *Enterprise*

Viking 2 swung smoothly into orbit around Mars on August 7. The Orbiter immediately began the search for a landing site at 44° north, but as had happened on *Viking 1,* the smooth-looking areas picked out by *Mariner 9* photography turned out to be considerably less than hospitable under the keener eye of *Viking.* The original B-1 site, in Cydonia, had already been surveyed by VO-1, and did not look promising. VO-2 reconnaissance went as high as 60° north, but found nothing that looked like a safe spot.

Site selection for *Viking 2* was made more difficult by the lack of radar studies of the surface. Since earth-based radar observations were impossible at that latitude, the Orbiter's Infrared Thermal Mapper was used as a substitute. By studying the heat-retention characteristics of a given area, it was possible to deduce the average size of the surface material. The IRTM was a useful tool, but it was still the orbital photography which weighed most heavily.

Cydonia was covered with large polygonal cracks on the surface, similar to "patterned ground" seen in arctic regions on earth. There were also a large number of pedestal craters, standing above the heavily eroded surrounding surface material. It didn't look like an inviting place to try to land a spacecraft.

The preselected backup site for *Viking 2* was farther west, near Alba Patera, to the north of Olympus Mons. The first pictures of the region looked very good, but as Hal Masursky explained, looks can be deceiving. "We were very excited when we first looked at this," said Masursky, "because comparing it with the photographs we got of the many sites we photographed, this is a smoother-looking, less cratered area than anything we've seen on the planet. But it reminded me of the pre-*Apollo* days when we were looking at Lunar Orbiter photographs.... We found as we counted craters across the planet, the crater counts varied enormously. And I soon clued in on the fact that those photographs with very high sun had very few craters. That is, the higher the sun, the fewer the craters. So we decided we would land the first *Apollo* at high noon when there wouldn't be any craters, and we'd be in great shape ... So I applied that principle to the pictures we just got of the B-2 site ... We have a very smooth area that has high sun and low exposure. So we decided we would immediately make a recommendation to the Project to land instantaneously, before we get any more data that ruins this beautiful image."

Unfortunately, Masursky's instantaneous landing was not possible, and the next set of pictures, taken at a low-sun angle, showed that there were craters galore. An instantaneous landing would have been desirable for other reasons, as well. If the search for a safe site continued much longer, the

261

landing of *Viking 2* might have to be delayed until after conjunction, sometime in December. The prospect didn't seem to trouble Jim Martin. "The Lander would probably be safer going through conjunction in orbit," he commented. However, the delay would have cost an extra twelve to fifteen million dollars in operational costs. Financially, scientifically, and probably emotionally, it was preferable to get *Viking 2* down in September.

With B-1 and B-2 virtually eliminated, the Orbiter was sent to take a closer look at another possible site, with the attractive name of Utopia. The Utopia area was about the size of the United States, so it offered many possibilities, but a great deal of searching.

The search eventually came to center on an area to the southwest of the crater Mie. From orbit, the terrain appeared to be heavily duned, but there seemed to be room for a landing ellipse. The decision was made, and a landing was scheduled for September 3 at 3:58 P.M. PDT, at 47.9° north, 225.9° west, about 4,500 miles from Chryse.

On the morning of the landing, Martin told the press, "I personally believe this is a safer landing site." He also conceded that, "There was not unanimity." Some were skeptical about the supposed dunes at the landing site; they might not be there, and if they were, would it be safe to land in them? Once again, the only way to find out was to go ahead and land.

The landing sequence for *Viking 2* was identical with that of *Viking 1*. Preseparation checkout went smoothly, although there was some slight worry about one of the Lander's landing radar systems. It was decided that the problem was not serious, and the go command was given.

Separation occurred as scheduled at 12:40 P.M. But within seconds of separation, things began to go wrong.

As later reconstructed, this was the sequence of events. Five seconds after separation, the primary gyros on the Orbiter began to lose power. Four minutes later, the Orbiter began to drift. Normally, it was always within a quarter degree of its lock on the sun, but now it was wobbling three times that far. The high-gain antenna link with earth deteriorated as the Orbiter's attitude changed.

At seven and a half minutes after separation the Orbiter's Attitude Control Electronics (ACE) system sensed too much attitude jet activity. The ACE signaled the computer that it was in trouble. Within a half second, the computer executed its failure program, switching from the high gain antenna to the low gain and replacing the primary ACE with its backup system. At separation plus ten minutes, the backup ACE sensed the same excessive jet activity that had bothered the primary system. The backup ACE then switched off the primary gyros and turned on the backup gyros. Within a minute, the Orbiter's oscillations dampened as the new gyros took control.

But the damage was done. The Orbiter was still receiving relay data from the Lander, but was unable to transmit it to earth. Except for the 8⅓ bit-per-second engineering data, the mission controllers were completely out of touch with VL-2. New commands were quickly sent up to the Orbiter so that it would turn on its tape recorder to preserve entry data from the Lander. Nothing would be lost, but the data could not be sent back to earth until the Orbiter was back on the high gain.

Meanwhile, the Lander was on its way down. Nothing happening aboard the Orbiter could affect it, but back in Pasadena, the mission controllers were flying blind. The only way they would know that the Lander was safely down would be the signal that the Lander had switched from 4 to 16 kilobits.

The wait for *Viking 2*'s landing was, in a different way, even more tense than the wait for *Viking 1* had been. It was suggested that the Project should get some new scriptwriters.

Touchdown was due at 3:58. The moment came, then

passed. An interminable 21 seconds later, the shout went up from the mission controllers: "There it is!" The Lander had switched over to 16 kilobits—it was down, safe, and sound. Pictures from *Viking 2* would have to wait, however, until the relay link with the Orbiter could be repaired.

Another post-touchdown press briefing was held. On his way into Von Karman Auditorium, Gentry Lee was heard to mutter, "Jesus, I'm telling you that was the longest minute and twenty seconds of my life!" This from a man whose first child was born just a few weeks earlier. Martin echoed Lee's sentiments: "It seemed to me that the last two minutes took about an hour."

The nerve-wracking descent was the main topic of discussion. One NASA administrator called it "two, the hard way." Martin observed that, "There were some chances that I might be here by myself." But the real achievement of the *Viking* team was not overshadowed by the narrow escape. Mission Director Tom Young spoke eloquently of his feelings at the moment: "I find that maybe the only other time that you go through something similar is when children are born. You also don't know what you're going to feel and what you're going to think until it happens. I see Gentry Lee saying that's true. The first cycle you go through is you say, God, if only it can be born. Then you say, gee, I kinda hope it looks pretty good. Then you say I'd like for it to be intelligent, and then you say, I'd like for it to grow into a mature, contributing adult, and then you say, I'd like for it to be respected by its peers. I believe *Viking 1* has gone through all those maturing states. We've watched it be a full contributing member by providing us more knowledge about Mars than we've ever really had before. *Viking 2* is in its infancy. I can't tell you how proud I am that it's born."

Young can be forgiven for anthropomorphizing a billion-dollar spacecraft. The *Viking* team was in many respects like a very close-knit family, complete with feuds, jealousies, growing pains, a stern father figure, and a problem child. *Viking's* success was not simply a triumph of science and engineering; it was the fulfillment of the hopes and dreams of a great many people—people who are just as emotional and just as human as anyone else.

A recovery sequence was designed for the Orbiter, and was executed that evening. The Orbiter was put through a slow 360° roll maneuver which allowed the Canopus sensor to build up a star map. Once the mission controllers knew exactly where the Orbiter was, they were able to send commands that would put it back in the correct attitude, in lock with the star Vega. High gain transmission was restored, and in the early morning hours of September 4, the first pictures from Utopia were seen.

In contrast to the mob scene at the first landing, the press center was all but deserted when the *Viking 2* pictures arrived. Carl Sagan and Robert Hargraves were there, along with a handful of correspondents, as Tim Mutch provided commentary for the closed-circuit television coverage.

The picture sequence was the same: a footpad picture, followed by a panorama. The first picture started to unfold, revealing a larger number of rocks than had been seen on the first photo from Chryse. One of them, Mutch remarked, looked "alarmingly large." One of them, in fact, was right next to the footpad, and may actually have been moved by the spacecraft.

The panorama revealed a surprise: no dunes. The scene looked amazingly like the view at Chryse, rock-littered and desolate. Another surprise was that the horizon appeared to be swaybacked. The explanation was that the curve was due to the way the camera functioned at a slant. *Viking 2* had landed at an 8.2° tilt.

Standing in front of the overhead monitors, Sagan periodically hopped up and down to get a better view of the pictures.

He and Hargraves pointed out features to each other and smiled frequently. After years of studying Mars, their enthusiasm was undiminished.

Viking 2, like its sister ship, provided a scientific bounty. The best news was that the seismometer had uncaged properly. Wind vibration of the Lander was minimal, so it was possible to turn the seismometer up to its full sensitivity, magnifying surface motions 200,000 times. At that level, the seismometer could sense a medium-sized quake anywhere on the planet. But in the first few weeks of operation, there were no quakes to sense. Mars was more active than the moon, but much less active than the earth.

The entry science data, delayed by the Orbiter anomaly, also provided a few surprises. There was evidence that Mars had a magnetic field after all. *Mariner 4* had found none, and subsequent missions had not included magnetometers. A Russian spacecraft did return data suggestive of a magnetic field, but American scientists tended to be a little suspicious of the quality of the Russian data, particularly after the argon incident.

Viking 1 had landed more or less on the night side of Mars, in the shadow of the solar wind. But *Viking 2* landed in the morning and came down right through the "bow shock" of the solar wind. Electron flux measurements by the Retarding Potential Analyzer indicated that there may be some sort of boundary layer at 2,000 km, where the solar wind interacts with the Martian magnetic field.

Meteorology data from Utopia was slightly different from that obtained at Chryse. The minimum temperature was −128°F (vs. −121° at Chryse) and the maximum was −35°F (vs. −29° at the VL-1 site). Unlike Chryse, the atmospheric pressure remained absolutely constant, at 7.78 MB. That reading implied that Utopia was even lower than Chryse, about 3 km below the mean surface level of the planet.

The geologists were intrigued by what looked like a sort of

266

dry wash running across the near field of the panorama. It might have been a very small ancient channel. Another theory was that it represented the extreme edge of an ejecta blanket from a nearby crater. Either way, it was another example of *Viking*'s good luck in finding landing sites where more than one type of geological terrain is in evidence.

One of the more interesting findings was that there was a general lack of intermediate-sized particles. There were large rocks and pebbles, and a lot of very fine-grained material, but the medium-sized stuff was missing. Dr. Roy Arvidson of Lander Imaging suggested that the intermediate particles had all been broken down into the fine material. "They may be kamikaze particles," said Arvidson. The implication was that the erosional process had been going on for a very long time, long enough to reduce all of the intermediate particles to dust.

There was also a spot in front of the spacecraft which looked to the geologists like a caliche deposit. Caliche is an evaporite product, the result of salts such as gypsum being percolated toward the surface by underground water. The water evaporates, leaving the salts. The caliche area was nicknamed Bonneville, after the salt flats in Utah, and a GCMS sample was dug from that location.

Before the GCMS did any organic analyses, it was used for the atmospheric enrichments that had been attempted on *Viking 1*. Another glitch in the surface sampler arm on *Viking 2* delayed the acquisition of the GCMS soil sample, so additional atmospheric enrichments were run. The atmosphere was enriched by a factor of 15, and the process resulted in the discovery of the inert gases krypton and xenon in the Martian atmosphere. The discovery helped to confirm the models of an early, somewhat more massive atmosphere for Mars.

Meanwhile, sophisticated analyses of the *Viking 1* entry data revealed that Mars did, indeed, have an enrichment of nitrogen-15 relative to nitrogen-14. That gave strong support to McElroy's theory of the nitrogen-rich early atmosphere.

267

The *Viking* Orbiters also added information about the atmosphere. Readings from the IRTM and MAWD showed that the residual northern polar cap had a surface temperature of about 200° Kelvin. That was too warm for it to be composed of frozen CO_2. The polar cap had to be made of water ice, H_2O. Orbiter pictures showed that some large craters were completely filled with ice, implying a thickness for the cap of between 100 meters and a kilometer.

The combined atmospheric data from several experiments added up to a consistent model of the early Martian atmosphere. It was mostly nitrogen, water-rich, and may have had a pressure as high as 800 MB, although it seemed more likely that it was closer to 100 MB. In either case, that was enough to account for the rainfall and the channels. It also meant that the channels had to be, for the most part, billions of years old. There may have been some intermittent periods of a thicker atmosphere and warmer temperatures due to volcanic activity, but the theory of a cyclical climate seemed doomed. There was no reservoir of frozen CO_2 in the poles. According to Hugh Kieffer, that suggested that, "the CO_2 we see on Mars now represents a good fraction of all that has ever evolved." Some of it may have been bound in the regolith, but that was not easily available for recycle into the atmosphere.

Thus, it seems that Mars once had an atmosphere rather similar to earth's. But the weaker Martian gravity could not hold on to the nitrogen, and most of it escaped into space or was reduced to nitrates in the soil. Earth's oxygen was mainly produced by biological action, but Mars has very little oxygen, implying the absence of large-scale biology. As the nitrogen disappeared over the course of three or four billion years, CO_2 became the major constituent of the atmosphere, with nitrogen and oxygen just barely present. Pressures declined, the temperature dropped, and Mars came to look as it does today.

It did not add up to a promising picture as far as life was

concerned. But the question was still very much open. The *Viking 2* biology experiments added more data and excluded more chemical possibilities, but were unable, by themselves, to provide a definitive answer one way or the other.

The Gex experiment showed an evolution of gases similar to that observed by *Viking 1*, but at a lower level. The LR also achieved familiar results. In the PR, it was decided to run the experiment "in the dark," with the xenon lamp turned off. A low second peak in the dark could mean that *Viking 1* had observed microorganisms which live by photosynthesis; it could also mean that the results were due to a form of photochemistry. The second peak turned out to be 21.5, ± 1.3—a result so marginally positive that Horowitz decided to abandon that line of attack and go back to a lights-on incubation. But the result was supportive of both photosynthesis and photochemistry, so biology was still in the ballgame, and the range of chemical options was further limited.

The GCMS organic analysis results were also similar to the *Viking 1* data. On the first series of analyses, no organic molecules were found. The mysteries of Chryse were still there in Utopia . . . and still unexplained.

As Mars and the earth raced toward conjunction with the sun, the *Viking* team began preparations for the extended mission. *Viking* Orbiter 2, recovered from its separation anomaly (which was probably caused by damage from an explosive bolt), was put through a plane-change maneuver. Its orbital inclination was changed to 75° by a long 343 mps burn, and the spacecraft began a long "polar walk," during which it would take pictures of the intriguing north polar region and a number of other areas which were of interest. VO-1 was moved to a position from which it could maintain the VL-2 relay link, in place of the walking second Orbiter. *Viking* Lander 1 was put into a reduced mission mode and maintained contact with the earth through its daily direct link.

Spectacular Orbiter pictures of Phobos were obtained, showing details as small as 40 meters. There were curious parallel striations on the small moon, possibly the result of fracturing during separation from another body—perhaps Deimos. The pictures were obtained by slewing, or turning, the cameras to compensate for the smear that would be produced by the spacecraft's relative motion at close range. The procedure worked so well that plans were made to reduce the orbit of one of the Orbiters to a periapsis of just 300 km.

On November 8, 1976, Mars went into conjunction with the sun. Interference from the solar corona prevented active communication with the Landers and Orbiters, although one radio link was maintained as part of a relativity experiment to study the sun's gravitational effect on radio waves. Conjunction lasted until December 13, providing the *Viking* personnel with a much-needed respite.

After months of long hours and high tension, the *Viking* people were exhausted. One of the top *Viking* officials had remarked following the landing of *Viking* 2 that the only thing that kept him going was the knowledge that he would be able to rest during conjunction. The *Viking* hardware was still performing excellently, but the human component was wearing out.

When Mars emerged from behind the sun in December, the *Viking* mission was under new leadership. Project Manager Jim Martin, who had completed his task of building, flying, and landing *Viking*, left NASA and took a job with Martin Marietta, the prime *Viking* contractor. Mission Director Tom Young took an administrative post with NASA back in Washington. G. Calvin Broome, from NASA at Langley, put on both hats and became the new Project Manager and Mission Director.

From December 13 through December 17, the *Viking* spacecraft were brought back to operational status. Actually,

270

they had never been turned off, even though they were out of touch with the earth. Data had been acquired during conjunction and was stored aboard the tape recorders for post-conjunction playback.

The scientists learned that *Viking 2* had observed two "seismic events" during November. The first was a major marsquake, registering more than 6 on the Richter scale, centered some 7,200 km from Utopia. The second event was no more than a mild tremor, 2 on the Richter scale, about 100 to 200 km from *Viking 2*. There was now positive proof that Mars had a geologically active interior, although it seemed to be considerably less active than some scientists had anticipated.

On December 20 *Viking Orbiter 2* was maneuvered to a new periapsis of 795 km in an effort to get high-resolution pictures of the north polar region before the annual polar "hood" formed. The maneuver was too late; the hood had already formed.

VO-1 was dropped even lower on March 11, 1977, all the way down to a periapsis of 298 km. Again, the maneuver came too late to reap all the possible benefits. It was now autumn in the northern hemisphere, and the atmosphere had become so cloudy that it was impossible to obtain the kind of sparkling-clear orbital photos that had caused so much excitement the previous June. In the southern hemisphere, spring brought the onset of the Martian dust storms, similar to the one which had greeted *Mariner 9*. Spectacular pictures were obtained of the huge dust clouds, but the surface itself was obscured. The atmospheric conditions even affected the two Landers; new photos from Chryse and Utopia were noticeably less sharp and clear than the pre-conjunction pictures.

Only at the South Pole did the atmosphere remain clear. Rising temperatures caused the frozen CO_2 to sublime into the atmosphere, creating a huge high-pressure system that kept the winds flowing outward from the Pole.

271

While the planet itself was getting hazy, Viking scientists got their best-ever look at Phobos. VO-1 passed within 125 km of the inner moon and returned some impressive pictures. On close examination, the puzzling parallel striations on the surface of Phobos turned out to be chains of very small craters, probably the result of orbital collisions between Phobos and swarms of rocks and debris.

The close pass enabled scientists to calculate the density of Phobos and arrive at a determination of its composition. Phobos has a density of about 2 grams per cc (one scientist called it "more marshmallow than rock"), which is consistent with the density of the carbonaceous chondrite meteorites. Phobos, and probably Diemos as well, is therefore not simply a leftover chunk of Mars material, but probably a captured body.

Down on the ground, the Landers continued to function, but they were beginning to show signs of wear and tear. In March, a short-circuit in the GCMS ion pump on VL-1 endangered the entire Lander. Mission controllers decided to pull the plug on the GCMS, since it had already done all its soil analyses and was now doing only atmospheric analyses.

At Utopia, VL-2 was put into a "Survival Automatic Mission" (SAM) in anticipation of the harsh Martian winter. By March the temperature at Utopia had dropped to −190°F, too cold for the Lander to continue its science investigations. All power was diverted to the heaters, in the hope that the Lander would be able to survive the winter and resume operations in October or November. During its extended hibernation, VL-2 would continue to collect meteorology and seismology data, and perhaps take an occasional picture, if all went well.

The biology investigations continued at both sites, but yielded no clear answers to the many questions that had been raised by the initial results. The focus had shifted from Mars back to the earth, and if any answers were to be found, they would come not from *Viking* but from terrestrial laboratories. The weight of scientific opinion shifted slowly—but not conclusively—toward chemistry and away from biology. Vance Oyama, the Gex experimenter, claimed to have come up with a purely chemical explanation for all the results. Other scientists weren't so sure; one claimed he had come up with a purely chemical explanation for Oyama.

The extended *Viking* mission has been funded at least through May of 1978. The Orbiters have fuel enough to function much longer than that, and the nuclear-powered Landers, if they survive the winter, may be able to carry on meteorological and seismological observations for up to five years.

So the story of *Viking* is far from finished. Much more data will be returned, and scientists will spend years analyzing it. The biologists will return to their laboratories, away from the spotlight, and attempt to duplicate the reactions they observed on Mars. Chemistry still seems the more likely alternative, but biology is still very much alive. The final answers may be years in coming, or they may not come at all from the data obtained so far; we may have to go back.

Mars, after all, is a planet with a surface area equal to the total land area of the earth. Only two small spots have been seen from the surface. There is much more to be learned.

On September 17, 1976, attention was briefly diverted from *Viking* by the rollout ceremonies of the first prototype of the Space Shuttle. The Shuttle is the beginning of a new generation of spacecraft which will be reusable, relatively inexpensive, and adaptable to a wide variety of tasks. It is expected to be operational by 1981.

The rollout was held at the Rockwell International assembly facility at Palmdale, California. In response to a nationwide letter-writing campaign, President Ford announced that the first Shuttle would bear the name of *Enterprise,* after the

273

starship in the *Star Trek* television series. Although there was a faint tinge of exploitation about it, the name was a good choice. The *Enterprise* was to become the world's first true spaceship, and naming it after the fictional starship was a symbolic recognition of the fact that the exploration of space is really just beginning. The fantasy of the Trekkies may someday become a reality.

The ceremony was attended by a number of politicians and dignitaries, including the crew of *Star Trek*'s *Enterprise*—with the exception of Captain Kirk (William Shatner), who was presumably busy elsewhere with Star Fleet business. As an Air Force band played the *Star Trek* theme, the Space Shuttle was towed slowly out from behind a hangar.

The Shuttle is about the size of a DC-9; the scorched *Apollo 14* capsule on display nearby looked like a toy in comparison. It will be launched by a rocket booster, like a conventional spacecraft, but once in orbit, it will be able to maneuver freely and return to earth like a glider. The Shuttle will have an operational lifetime of over 100 missions, which should take it into the 1990s.

The days when only highly trained astronauts could venture into space are now ending. The Shuttle will carry scientists, engineers, construction workers, and perhaps even a writer or two, into orbit. Its huge cargo bay will be used to carry as many as five separate satellites or larger items such as astronomical observatories and sections of space stations. Future planetary probes will get a free ride into space aboard the shuttle. Previously launched satellites can be retrieved by the Shuttle for repairs; and unfriendly satellites could be hijacked in the same manner.

There are enormous benefits to be realized from the continued exploration of space. Some of them are practical, such as weather prediction, pollution control, resource management, communications, and perhaps even zero-G manufacturing. Other benefits are less tangible but no less real; if there is such a thing as "the human spirit," then space exploration is probably one of the purest expressions of it. One of the first reactions to the *Viking 1* pictures of the Martian scene was, "I wonder what's over that horizon." Mankind had just leaped over the longest horizon in history, yet there was still another horizon ahead, and the urge to explore it was undeniable. If man ever does stop wondering what's over the horizon, he will have lost the very thing that separates him from, in Wells' phrase, "the beasts that perish." But in space, the horizons are literally endless.

Yes, it costs money. The Shuttle price tag will be around 10 billion dollars. Undoubtedly there are better ways to spend that kind of money—but there are worse ways, too. The world's biggest industry is the manufacture of weapons, and compared to that, the money spent on space exploration is a pittance.

Eventually, the space program may help save us from all those weapons. Already, it has helped us preserve the fragile environment of our own world. Studies of the atmosphere of Venus led to the discovery that fluorocarbons in our own atmosphere may destroy the ozone layer, which protects us from ultraviolet radiation; and Mars is a prime example of what happens to an unprotected world. Shortly after the landing of *Viking 2*, the National Academy of Science came forth with a recommendation that something should be done about the release of fluorocarbons from spray cans. As Dr. Michael McElroy pointed out, "A fourteen-billion-dollar-a-year industry was affected by a branch of atmospheric science on the earth whose total funding is less than about fifteen million dollars a year." It may be too much to hope that the exploration of space will someday put the arms industry out of business, but it's clear that what we learn in space can be of incalculable value here on earth.

And so, we will be returning to Mars. The timing will be determined by what Congress and the American people are willing to spend, but sooner or later, Mars will again be the host to an interplanetary traveler.

Viking 3 will probably be a Rover, equipped with wheels or treads to enable it to traverse thousands of kilometers of Martian terrain in the course of its extended mission. According to Jim Martin, an advanced *Viking* could be launched in the early 1980s for around 350 to 400 million dollars. The launch vehicle would probably be the Space Shuttle, since the Titan III-C booster is now out of production.

A 1984 *Viking* mission might well be powered by a solar sail. The concept is exciting: a huge, half-mile-across sheet of thin material such as mylar could be erected in orbit and used as a sail to catch the solar wind. The solar sailer would be fast, cheap, and reusable, since after delivering its payload to Mars, it would be capable of tacking into the wind and back to earth.

Another possibility is a sample return mission, using the solar sailer. Much more could be learned about Mars if it were possible to take a sample of its surface material into a terrestrial laboratory. Unfortunately, the problem of possible contamination by Martian microbes may prevent a sample return. As Dr. Fred Brown, a TRW biologist put it, "There is little possibility of back-contaminating the earth with an *Andromeda Strain* kind of thing, but if we do, the consequences are so terrible that when you multiply the chances by the consequences, you come up with something you have to worry about—it's an issue you can't ignore." Jim Martin also pointed out the *Catch-22* nature of a sample return mission. If there is life on Mars, we couldn't take the chance of back-contamination; if there isn't life on Mars, there wouldn't be much interest in obtaining a sample.

Any manned mission to Mars would also have to contend with the contamination problem. Moreover, the cost of such a mission would be enormous, on the order of 100 billion dollars. "As a taxpayer," said Martin, "I'd be against it. We

276

could fly 100 *Viking* missions or more for the cost of one manned mission." The consensus seems to be that man will someday travel to Mars, but almost certainly not in this century. On the other hand, genius is where you find it, and tomorrow or next week there could be a breakthrough that would permit easy travel to Mars or even the stars. It's not likely, but the possibility exists.

For the foreseeable future, the exploration of Mars and the other planets will continue to be by unmanned probes similar to *Viking*. But for all its sophistication, *Viking* is merely a beginning. "*Viking* is about as intelligent as a grasshopper," says Carl Sagan. Instead of spending billions on projects such as the Space Shuttle, Sagan would prefer to see the money devoted to the development of artificial intelligence. The day may come—and rather soon—when the solar system is teeming with robot explorers with the intelligence and judgment to conduct missions that will make *Viking* seem as quaint as the Wright Brothers' first flight at Kitty Hawk. Already, the robotics laboratory at JPL is developing the technology that will permit the *Viking* Rover to find its own way among the rocks and ravines of the Red Planet.

The Mars seen by *Viking,* and the Mars yet to be discovered, is vastly different from the world imagined by the Chaldeans and Copernicus, Herschel and Lowell, Burroughs and Bradbury. Gone are the Tharks and crystal cities, the ancient gods and the ancient canals. It is a dry, cold, hostile world, and very possibly a dead world. But, at the very least, Mars has given us a better understanding and a deeper appreciation of "the cool green hills of earth."

The red fire of Mars burns as bright as ever in the night sky and in the hearts of men. Mars has always been much more than just the next planet out from the sun. Mars is the place where dreams and reality meet—and form new dreams for the curious and questing people of the earth to follow.

Selected Bibliography

Bradbury, Ray, et al. *Mars and the Mind of Man*. New York: Harper and Row, 1973.

Caidin, Martin. *Destination Mars*. New York: Doubleday, 1972.

Jackson, Francis, and Patrick Moore. *Life on Mars*. New York: Norton, 1965.

Ley, Willy. *Watchers of the Skies*. New York: Viking, 1963.

———, and Wernher Von Braun. *The Exploration of Mars*. New York: Viking, 1956.

Moore, Patrick. *Guide to Mars*. London: Frederick Muller Ltd., 1956.

Richardson, Robert S. and Chesley Bonestell. *Mars*. New York: Harcourt, Brace, & World, 1964.

Rousseau, Pierre. *Man's Conquest of the Stars*. New York: Norton, 1961.

Sagan, Carl. *The Cosmic Connection*. New York: Doubleday, 1973.

Shklovskii, I.S. and Carl Sagan. *Intelligent Life in the Universe*. San Francisco: Holden-Day, 1966.

Thiel, Rudolf. *And There Was Light*. New York: Knopf, 1967.

Velikovsky, Immanuel. *Worlds in Collision*. New York: Macmillan, 1950.

For a detailed account of the *Viking* mission, see issues of *Science News* through the summer and fall 1976. Also valuable is the September 1975 issue of *Scientific American,* which was devoted entirely to articles about the solar system.

278

Appendix A
Mars As a Planet

	Mars	Earth
Mean distance from sun	227.9 million km	149.6 million km
Maximum distance from sun	249.1 million km	152.1 million km
Minimum distance from sun	206.7 million km	147.1 million km
Period of revolution	687 days	365.26 days
Period of rotation	24 hrs, 37 min, 23 sec	23 hrs, 56 min, 4 sec
Inclination of axis	23° 59′	23° 27′
Orbital eccentricity	.093	.017
Orbital velocity	24.1 km/sec	29.8 km/sec
Mean equatorial diameter	6,795 km	12,756.28 km
Surface gravity (Earth = 1)	.38	1
Mean temperature at surface	−23°C	+22°C
Mean surface pressure	5.5 millibars	1,016 millibars
Known satellites	2	1

Appendix B
The Martian Atmosphere

Carbon Dioxide	95%
Nitrogen	2–3%
Argon-40	1–2%
Oxygen	0.3%
Argon-36	4–7 Parts Per Million

Krypton and Xenon present at Parts Per Billion level

Appendix C
Surface Composition

(Percent by weight)

Al		2–7%	Cu	<	0.5%
Si		15–30%	Zn	<	0.1%
P	<	10%	Ga	<	0.03%
S		0–6%	As	<	0.02%
Cl		0–3%	Se	<	0.015%
K		0–2%	Br	<	0.015%
Ca		3–8%	Rb	<	0.01%
Ti		0.5–2%	Sr	<	0.02%
V	<	3%	Y	<	0.02%
Cr	<	5%	Zr	<	0.02%
Mn	<	7%	Nb	<	0.025%
Fe		14 ± 2%	Mo	<	0.05%
Co	<	7%	Tc to U	<	2%
Ni	<	5%			

Appendix D
Glossary of Abbreviations

ACE	Attitude Control Electronics
DAPU	Data Acquisition and Playback Unit
DSN	Deep Space Network
ERT	Earth Received Time
FPAG	Flight Path Analysis Group
GCMS	Gas Chromatograph Mass Spectrometer
GCSC	Guidance Control and Sequencing Computer
Gex	Gas Exchange Experiment
ICL	Initial Computer Load
IPL	Image Processing Laboratory
IRTM	Infrared Thermal Mapper
JPL	Jet Propulsion Laboratory
LI	Lander Imaging
LR	Labeled Release Experiment
LSS	Landing Site Selection
LSSS	Lander Science Systems Staff
MAWD	Mars Atmospheric Water Detector
MOI	Mars Orbit Insertion
MOT	Mars Orbit Trim
PR	Pyrolytic Release Experiment
RPA	Retarding Potential Analyzer
RTG	Radioisotope Thermal Generator
SIP	Science Instrument Parameter
SFOF	Space Flight Operations Facility
SRS	Science Requirement Strategy
UAMS	Upper Atmosphere Mass Spectrometer
VL	*Viking* Lander
VO	*Viking* Orbiter
XRFS	X-Ray Fluorescence Spectrometer

Appendix E
Costs of *Viking* Project

Lander:	$549 million (mostly Martin Marietta Aerospace)
Orbiter:	243 million (mostly Jet Propulsion Laboratory)
Support:	<u>138</u> million
Total:	$930 million
Launch Vehicles (2):	<u>70</u> million
GRAND TOTAL:	$ 1 billion

Viking Science Costs
(millions of dollars)

Science Teams: Orbiter	$ 3.3	
Lander & Radio	11.2	
		$ 14.5
Orbiter Investigations:		
Imaging System	$ 13.2	
Water Vapor Mapping	5.1	
Thermal Mapping	<u>4.8</u>	
	$ 23.1	
Lander Investigations:		
Biology	$ 59.2	
Molecular Analysis (GCMS)	41.3	
Imaging System	27.4	
Entry	10.1	
Meteorology	6.1	
Seismometry	4.0	
X-Ray Fluorescence	3.7	
Radio (X-Band)	0.9	
Physical Properties	0.2	
Magnetic Properties	<u>0.</u>	
Subtotal	$152.9	
Total for Investigations:		$176.00
Support for Investigations:		
Orbiter	$ 5.7	
Lander	30.5	
		$ 36.2
GRAND TOTAL:		$226.7

extended mission   Oct. 76-Oct 77 $20 million

Index

Abbreviations used in this
  index:
  VL 1–*Viking* Lander 1
  VL 2–*Viking* Lander 2
  VO 1–*Viking* Orbiter 1
  VO 2–*Viking* Orbiter 2
Aeroshell, 172
Agathodaemon, 148
Air Force Project Blue
  Book, 100
Alba Patera, 203, 261
Aldiss, Brian, 87
Alexander, George, 241
All-Story Magazine, The,
  75
Almagest, 29
Aluminum, in Martian soil,
  239
Amazing magazine, 79
American Association for
  the Advancement of
  Science (AAAS), and
  Velikovsky, 96–97
Anaximander, 28
Anaximenes, 28
Anderson, Dr. Don L., 191
Anomaly team, 248–49
Antoniadi, E. M., 64, 149
Apollo, 20
Arab astronomers, 29, 30
Argon, in Martian
  atmosphere, 177, 228,
  229
Argon-40, 229
Argon-36, 229
Argosy, The, 75
Argyre region, 232
Aristarchus of Samos, 28
Aristotle, 28–29, 31, 32, 36,
  38–39
Arrhenius, Svante, 56, 63,
  112

Arsia Mons (South Spot),
  137. *See also* South
  Spot
Arvidson, Dr. Roy, 267
Ascraeus Mons (North
  Spot), 137
Asimov, Isaac, 82, 87, 91
Astonishing magazine, 79
Astounding magazine, 79
Astrology, 23–26
Astronauts, ancient, 97–99
Astronomy, 23
  Chaldean, 26–28
  Greek, 28–30
  Roman, 30
Atlas-Agena booster, 127
Atmosphere, Martian
  and development of life,
    119–20
  early, 229–30, 267–68
  identification of elements
    in, 109–10
  preliminary *Viking* data,
    228–34
  temperature
    measurement, 170
  Viking experiments, 176–
    79
  water vapor in, 167–69,
    229, 231–32
Atmospheric pressure on
  Mars, 233, 234, 266
  early, 268
Attitude control electronics
  subsystem (ACE), 163,
  263

Back contamination, 276
Basalt, 153, 237
B-Black incident, 240–41
Beer, Wilhelm, 45
Bergen, Edgar, 73–74

Between Planets (Heinlein),
  82
Biemann, Dr. Klaus, 189,
  255, 256
Big Medicine Wheel, 31
Binder, Dr. Alan, 237, 240–
  41
Biological experiments, on
  Viking Lander, 181–
  89, 246–58
  Gas Exchange (Gex),
    183, 184–85, 186–87,
    246–47, 249, 250, 251,
    252, 269, 273
  Labeled Release (LR),
    183, 185–86, 247–50,
    253, 254, 258, 269
  Pyrolytic Release (PR),
    183, 184, 186, 187,
    250–54, 258–59, 269
Biological laboratory, on
  Viking Lander, 181–89
  cost, 186
  problems building, 186–
    87
Bioshield, 172
Blue Book Magazine, The,
  76
Blue clearing phenomenon,
  106–7
Bradbury, Ray, 14, 15, 19,
  77–78, 86–90, 212, 215,
  277
Brahe, Tycho, 34–36, 37–38
Brand, Max, 76
Brashear, John, 55
British Interplanetary
  Society, 131
Broome, G. Calvin, 270
Brown, Dr. Frederick S.,
  160–61, 185, 188, 276
Bruno, Giordano, 39, 45,
  97

Bunsen, Robert, 107
Burgess, Eric, 131–32
Burroughs, Edgar Rice, 13, 14, 18, 75–78, 79, 84, 89, 159, 277

Calcium, in Martian soil, 239
Caliche deposits, 267
Cameras, Lander. *See* Lander Imaging System; Pictures
Camera systems
  on *Mariner* 4, 126, 129–30
  on *Mariner* 9, 135–36
Canals, Martian, 49–66, 130–32, 134, 148–49
  as rift valleys, 132
Canopus sensor, 128, 163, 265
Carbonaceous chondrites, 153, 256–57, 272
Carbon Assimilation experiments. *See* Pyrolytic Release
Carbon-based chemistry, and life on Mars, 182–83. *See also* Organic compounds
Carbon dioxide
  frozen, in polar cap, 232, 234, 271
  in Martian atmosphere, 228, 232, 234, 271
Carbon-14, 247
Carr, Michael, 166–67, 204, 206, 209, 241
Carter, Jimmy, 212
Cassegrainian telescope, 166
Cassini, Jean-Dominique, 43
Cavalier, The, 76
Chaldean astronomers, 26–28
Chaotic terrain, of Mars, 134
Chemistry vs. biology, in search for life on Mars, 250 ff., 269, 273
Chinese astronomers, 30
Christian Science Monitor, The, 242
Chryse, Basin, 218, 234, 271

Chryse Planitia (Plain of Gold), 202–3, 207, 233
Chung K'ang, 26
Civilizations, Martian, 56–57, 60, 62, 148, 149–50
Clarke, Arthur C., 82, 84–86, 89
Color of Mars, 17, 22, 25, 236
Columbus, Christopher, 28
Comenici, Nadia, 212
Cemmentary (Copernicus), 32
Communications system, *Viking,* 174–75
  problems with, 223–24
  sending commands to VL1, 225–27
Comparative planetology, 115
Computer, *Viking* Lander. *See* Guidance, control, and sequencing computer
Computer programs, for *Viking* navigation, 196–97
Condon Report, The, 101
Conjuction, of Mars and sun, 208, 262, 269, 270, 271, 272
Copernican theory, 32–33, 35, 37, 38
Copernicus, Nicolaus, 27, 31–35, 36, 39, 41, 277
Coprates Rift Valley (Valles Marineris), 139–40, 148, 209
Cosmic cataclysms, pseudoscientific theories of, 92–93
Cosmic Connection, The (Sagan), 121
Crabbe, Buster, 121
Crab Nebula, 30
Craters, Martian, 142–43, 154
Crosby, David, 84
Cummings, e. e., 260
Cyclical climate theory, 229, 232, 268
Cydonia, 203, 209, 260–61

Data acquisition and processing unit (DAPU), 175

Data storage memory unit, on *Viking* Lander, 175
Day, Martian, 16, 43. *See also* Sol(s)
Deep Space Network (DSN), 126, 213–14
Deferents, 29
Deimos, 16, 47–48, 149–54, 270
  formation of, 151–53, 272
  pictures of, 270, 272
De-orbit engines, on *Viking* Lander, 172
De Revolutionibus (Copernicus), 32, 33–34
Descartes, René, 116
Descent engines, on *Viking* Lander, 173
Dialogue Concerning the Two Chief World Systems (Galileo), 41
Diurnal wind variation, 234
Dollfus, Audouin, 109, 111
Doppler, Christian, 108
Doppler effect, 108–9
Doubleday Books, 94
Double Star (Heinlein), 82
Douglass, A. E., 57
Doyle, Arthur Conan, 76
Drifts, Martian, 238
Dunes, Martian, 237–38
Dust storms, Martian, 236–37, 271

Earth
  and birth of solar system, 117–18
  origin of life on, 114
  "Earth chauvinism," 147–48, 182
Earth Received Time (ERT), 199
Eberhart, Jonathan, 141, 236, 242
Einstein, Albert, 80, 94
Elysium Planitia, 203
Entry Science, 176–79, 266
Entry Science team, preliminary findings, 227 ff.
Eolian deposition, 145, 147
Epicycles, 29, 37

Erosion, on Mars
water, 174
wind, 133, 143, 237
Escape velocity, 230
Evolution, theory of, 94–95
Exobiology, 114
Explorer satellite, 20, 122

Famous Story Magazine, 76
Farmer, Dr. Crofton B.
(Barney), 141, 168–69,
231
Farrell, Win, 209
Firesign Theater, The, 91
Fletcher, James, 187, 221
Flight Path Analysis Group
(FPAG), 196
Flinn, Ted, 209
Fluorocarbons, 275
Fontana, Francesco, 42–43
Footpads and legs, on
Viking Lander, 173–74
Footpad #2, 238
Ford, Gerald, 273
Fox, Paul, 49, 148, 149
Fraunhofer lines, 107, 109
Frederick II, 34, 35

Gagarin, Yuri, 122
Galileo, 38–42, 46, 97
Gas Chromatograph Mass
Spectrometer
(GCMS), 188–89, 227,
228, 230–31, 267
malfunction, 197, 248–
49, 272
and search for organic
compounds, 254–58
Gas Exchange experiment
(Gex), 183, 184–85,
186–87
on VL1, 246–47, 249,
250, 251, 252, 273
on VL2, 269
Gemini project, 20
Geocentrism, 27–28, 35
Geological investigation,
189, 191, 220–21, 237,
267
Goddard, Robert H., 121
Gordon, Flash, 121
Greek astronomers, 28–30
Guidance, control, and
sequencing computer
(GCSC), 175–76

Haggard, H. Rider, 76
Haldane, J. B. S., 91
Hall, Angelina Stickney,
47, 48
Hall, Asaph, 47–48, 50, 51,
150
Hargraves, Dr. Robert B.,
192, 208, 238–39, 265–
66
Heat labile oxidants, 254
Heat source, on *Viking*
Lander, 176
Heberspacher, Chris, 209
Hebrew calendar, 26
Heinlein, Robert A., 14, 18,
78, 81–84, 86, 89
Heliocentrism, 32–33, 35,
36, 38, 41
Hellas, 133
Heraclitus, 29
Herschel, Friedrich
Wilhelm, 43–45, 150,
277
Hespiria, 51
Hess, Dr. Seymour L., 191,
233–35
Hi, 26
Hibbs, Dr. Albert, 13–14,
20, 215–17, 219
Hinners, Dr. Noel, 221
Ho, 26
Hohmann, Walter, 127
Horoscopes, 26
Horowitz, Dr. Norman,
183, 244, 245, 251–52,
257–58
Houseman, John, 73
Hoyle, Fred, 91
Huber, Peter J., 96
Huggins, Sir William, 46
Huygens, Christian, 40, 43
Hydrated iron oxide, 113
Hydrogen, in Martian
atmosphere, 228–29
Hygroscopic salts, 112

Iliad (Homer), 93
Image Processing
Laboratory (IPL), 166
Imaging System. *See*
Lander Imaging
System; Orbiter
Imaging System
Infrared Thermal Mapper
(IRTM), 169–70, 231–
32, 234, 260–61, 268

Initial Computer Load
(ICL), 175, 225
Iron, in Martian soil, 239
Itek Corporation, 181

Jansen, Zacharias, 40
Janssen, Pierre, 46
Jet Propulsion Laboratory,
127, 159, 195, 201–2,
212
birth of, 122
Jupiter, 25, 27, 29, 30, 41,
46, 48, 93
atmosphere, 108
and origin of solar
system, 117
Jupiter-C rocket, 122

Kant, Immanuel, 116
Kennedy, John F., 123
Kepler, Johannes, 27, 35,
36–38, 39, 42, 46, 48
Keyhoe, Donald E., 101–2
Kieffer, Dr. Hugh H., 170,
231, 268
Kirchoff, G. R., 107
Klein, Dr. Harold P., 183,
184, 243, 246, 247, 251,
252, 255, 258
Koch, Howard, 69, 73
Krypton, on Mars, 230–31,
267
Kuiper, G. P., 109

Labeled Release
experiment (LR), 183,
185–86
on VL1, 247–50, 253,
254, 258
on VL2, 269
"Lament for a Red Planet"
(Eberhart), 141
Lander, *Viking. See Viking*
Lander; *Viking*
Lander 1; *Viking*
Lander 2
Lander Computer
Simulation
(LCOMSIM), 226–27
Lander Imaging System,
179–81, 226, 227. *See
also* Pictures
Lander Imaging Team,
218–19, 222, 235. *See
also* Pictures
Lander Local Time, 218

285

Lander Receiver No. 1, 224
Lander Receiver No. 2, 224
Lander Science Systems
  Staff (LSSS), 226
Lander Sequence (LSeq),
  227
Landing date
  choosing, for VL1, 198,
  202–12
Landing site
  choosing, for VL1, 202–
  12
  choosing, for VL2, 261–
  63
  observations of, 238
Landing Site Selection
  Team, 206–7
Langley Research Office,
  158, 159
Laplace, Pierre-Simon de,
  116
Lasswitz, Kurd, 72
Launch vehicles, 194
Lava mantle, on Mars, 143
Law of gravity, 37, 39
Lederberg, Joshua, 114
Lee, B. Gentry, 204, 242,
  264
Leovy, Conway, 234
Levin, Dr. Gilbert V., 183,
  247, 249–50, 253, 254
Life, origin of
  on earth, 114
  nebular hypothesis, 116
Life on Mars, 15, 114, 149–
  50, 240 ff.
  atmosphere and, 119–20
  biology vs. chemistry,
  250 ff., 269, 273
  vegetation theory, 110–
  12
  Viking experiments, 161,
  181–89, 254–59
  water availability, 147–
  48
Lift-off, 194–95
Lippershey, Hans, 40
Liquid-fueled rockets, 121
London, Jack, 76
Los Angeles Times, The,
  241
Loudon, Jim, 242
Lovecraft, H. P., 76
Lowell, Abbott Lawrence,
  53

Lowell, Amy, 53
Lowell, James Russell, 53
Lowell, Percival, 49, 52–66,
  69, 76–77, 80, 82, 95,
  105, 110, 134, 137, 144,
  148, 150, 241, 277
Lunar calendar
  Chaldean, 26–27
  Mayan, 31
Lunik, 20
Luther, Martin, 32, 33
Lyman, Pete, 213

McCarthy, Charlie, 73
McDonald, James E., 100
McElroy, Dr. Michael, 21,
  230, 231, 232–33, 267,
  275
McLaughlin, Dean B., 113
Macmillan Publishers, 94
Mädler, J. H. von, 45
Maghemite, 239
Magnetic field, on Mars,
  130–31, 266
Magnetism, in Martian
  surface material, 238–
  39
Magnetite, 239
Manned space flights, 123
  to moon, 135
  vs. unmanned, 170, 221,
  276–77
Mantle, lava, on Mars, 143
Maraldi, Giacomo, Filippo,
  43
Mariner 1, 20, 123
Mariner 2, 123
Mariner 3, 124
Mariner 4, 66, 102, 124–32,
  133, 135, 266
Mariner 6, 132–34
Mariner 7, 132–33, 134
Mariner 8, 135
Mariner 9, 102, 135–40,
  163, 165, 191, 196, 202,
  203, 205, 228, 232, 236,
  260, 271
  new data provided by,
  141–54
Mariner 10, 142
Mars, 37–38, 41
  and astrology, 25–26
  atmosphere, 106, 109–10,
  119–20, 130–31, 132–
  33, 144–45, 168, 170,

176–79, 190–91, 216,
  228–34, 267–68, 271
  atmospheric pressure,
  233–34, 266, 268
  blue clearing
  phenomenon, 106–7,
  133
  canals, 49–66, 130–32,
  134, 148–49
  channels, 138–39, 144–
  47, 205, 232–33
  civilization on, 56–57, 60,
  62, 148, 149–50
  color, 17, 22, 25, 236
  craters, 142–43, 154
  day, 16, 43, 225
  distance from earth, 17
  drifts, 238
  dunes, 237–38
  dust storms, 236–37, 271
  early astronomers and,
  37–38, 41, 42–48
  eolian deposition, 145,
  147
  erosion, 133, 143, 147,
  237
  life on, 110–12, 114, 119–
  20, 140, 147–50, 161,
  181–89, 240 ff., 245–
  59, 268–69, 273
  magnetic field, 130–31,
  266
  mantle, 143
  marsquakes, 271
  mascons, 138, 151, 163
  mass, 16
  moons, 16, 46–47, 50,
  149–54, 270
  mountains, 134, 137
  orbit, 16, 38
  and origin of solar
  system, 118–19
  polar caps, 16, 58–59, 62,
  112, 133, 145, 232, 268
  pseudoscientific theories
  of, 93
  rainfall, 233
  retrograde motion, 27,
  37–38
  riverbeds, 232–33
  rocks, 220–21, 237
  science fiction and, 69–
  78
  seasons, 58–59, 63, 107,
  110 ff.

size, 15–16, 132
sky, 236
surface appearance, 200–
21, 236–38, 267
surface material, 238–40
surface temperature, 133,
169–70, 266
symbol of war, 22, 25,
30, 47
temperature, 133, 144,
190
topography, 133–34, 144,
190, 220–21, 236–38,
267
and UFO phenomena,
101–2
volcanoes, 137–38, 143,
145, 147, 151
water erosion, 147
water on, 147–48, 167–
69, 205, 229, 231–33,
268
weather, 190–91, 233–35
wind erosion, 133, 143,
237
wind pattern, 233–34
year, 16
Mars 1, 123–24, 125, 160
Mars 2, 135, 140, 160
Mars 3, 135, 140
Mars 6, 177
Mars (Lowell), 56
Mars As an Abode of Life
(Lowell), 56
Mars Atmospheric Water
Detector (MAWD),
167–69, 268
Mars and Its Canals
(Lowell), 56
Mars and the Mind of Man
(Murray), 105
Mars Orbit Insertion
(MOI), 163, 199–201
Mars Orbit Trim (MOT)
#5, 163, 211
Marsquakes, 271
Martian Chronicles, The
(Bradbury), 15, 86–89
"Martian Odyssey, A"
(Weinbaum), 81
Martin, James, 157, 158–
59, 160, 213, 216, 221,
223, 224, 225, 240, 245,
262, 264, 270, 276
choosing VL1 landing

site, 198, 200, 207, 209,
210–11
Martin-Marietta, 159, 186,
187, 223, 270
Mascons, on Mars, 138,
151, 163
Mass, of Mars, 16
Mästlin, Michael, 36
Masursky, Harold, 137,
139, 206, 207, 209, 210,
212, 232–33, 241, 261
Maunder, E. Walter, 64,
149
Mayans, 31
Mercury, 25, 29, 142
Mercury project, 20
Mercury Theatre, The, 72–
73
Meteorological
investigation, 189,
190–91, 233–35
Meteorology team, 235
Michael, Dr. William H.,
192
Middle Spot (Pavonis
Mons), 137
Mie, 262
Miller, Stanley, 114, 119
Mineralogical investigation,
189–90
Molecular analysis, on
VL1, 188–89
Moon, 40, 117, 191
craters, 142, 143
Moons of Mars, 16, 46–47,
50, 149–54, 270. *See
also* Deimos; Phobos
Moore, Dr. Henry, 238
Moore, Patrick, 64
Moorman, Joe, 248–49
Morrison, Philip, 100
Mountains, on Mars, 134,
137
Murray, Dr. Bruce, 105,
144
Mutch, Dr. Thomas (Tim),
180, 218–21, 236, 237,
265

Narratio Prima (Rheticus),
33
National Academy of
Science, 275
National Aeronautics and
Space Administration,

(NASA), 157, 159, 186,
187
National Investigations
Committee on Aerial
Phenomena (NICAP),
101
National Public Radio, 242
Navigation systems, 196–97
NBC television coverage,
of *Viking* landing,
242–43
Neal, Roy, 214, 242–43
Nebular hypothesis of
origin of life, 116
Neptune, 65
and origin of solar
system, 117
Newton, Isaac, 42, 48, 107
New Yorker magazine, 282,
285, 292, 296, 302
New York Times, 131, 242
Nier, Dr. Alfred O. C.,
178–79, 227
Nitrogen, in Martian
atmosphere, 228, 230–
31, 268
Nitrogen-14, 230, 267
Nitrogen-15, 230, 267
Nix Olympica (Olympus
Mons), 136–37
North Spot (Ascraeus
Mons), 137
Northwest Territory, 209
Novara, Domenico Maria,
31

Olympus Mons, 144. *See
also* Nix Olympica
O'Neill, Dr. William, 196,
197, 199, 201
On Two Planets (Lasswitz),
72
Opik, E. J., 110–11
Orbit, Martian, 16, 38
Orbiter. *See Viking
Orbiter; Viking
Orbiter 1; Viking
Orbiter 2*
Orbiter Imaging System,
165, 167, 179
and landing site
selection, 204, 209
Orbiter Imaging Team,
166–67, 206, 232

Orbiter-Lander relay link, 163, 164, 174–75, 221
Organic compounds, search for, 112, 182–83, 188–89, 254–58, 269
Orgel, Leslie, 114, 119, 252
Origin of Species, The (Darwin), 94
Osiander, Andreas, 33
O'Toole, Tom, 241
Owen, Dr. Tobey, 228, 232–33, 241
Oxygen, in Gex experiment, 247, 249, 252
Oyama, Dr. Vance I., 183, 185, 273

Page, Thornton, 101
Paul V, 41–42
Pavonis Mons (Middle Spot), 137
Pearre, James, 215
Perlman, Dave, 241
Phobos, 16, 47–48, 149–54
    composition, 272
    density, 272
    formation, 151–53
    pictures of, 270, 272
    secular acceleration, 149, 151
Photographs. *See* Lander Imaging System; Orbiter Imaging System; Pictures
Physical properties investigation, 192
Physical Properties Team, 238
Pickering, William H., 55, 57, 63
Pictures, 204–5
    of dust clouds, 271
    first, post-landing, by VL1, 218–21, 232, 237
    first color, 236
    of Phobos and Deimos, 270, 272
    use of, in landing site selection, 204, 209, 260–61
    of Utopia, 265–66, 271
    by VO1, 204–5, 270, 272
    by VO2, 270
Pieri, David, 146, 209

Pioneer, 20
Planetary astronomy, 105 ff.
Planetary scientists, 138
Planetology, comparative, 115
Planets, birth of, 116
Pluto, discovery of, 65
Podkayne of Mars (Heinlein), 82
Polar caps, Martian, 16, 58–59, 62, 112, 133, 145
    frozen carbon dioxide in, 232, 234, 271
    frozen water in, 268
    northern, temperatures, 268
    two types of, 232
Pollack, James, 113, 236
Power source, on *Viking* Lander, 176
Press coverage, of *Viking* mission, 240–42, 244
Princess of Mars, A (Burroughs), 13, 75
Project Stratoscope, 124–25
Pseudoscience, 91–102
Ptolemy, 29–30, 36, 37
Pyrolytic Release (PR) or Carbon Assimilation experiment, 183, 184, 186, 187, 227, 244, 269
    incubation problem, 257–58
    and search for life on Mars, 250–54
Pythagoras, 28

Radiation belts, lack of, on Mars, 130–31
Radio experiments, *Viking* Lander and, 192–93
Radio-isotope thermoelectric generators (RTGs), 176, 235
Radio tracking system, 197
Rainfall on Mars, 233
Ranger project, 20, 161
"Rayed" craters, 143
Rayleigh scattering, 236
Red Planet (Heinlein), 82
Red shift, 108
Redstone rocket, 122

Retarding potential analyzer, 177–78, 228, 266
Retrograde motion, of Mars, 27, 37–38
Rheticus, 33
Richardson, Dr. Robert S., 52, 91, 112
Riverbeds, Martian, 232–33
Rockets, development of, 121
Rocks, Martian, 220–21, 237
Rockwell International, 273
Roddenberry, Gene, 78, 213, 215–16, 219
Rolling Stones, The (Heinlein), 82
Roman astronomers, 30
Roosevelt, Teddy, 61
Rubidium, in Martian soil, 239
Rudolf II, 35

Sagan, Carl, 20, 49, 78, 113, 114, 116, 121, 141, 147, 148–49, 182, 202, 211, 222, 236, 243, 265–66, 277
    and canal theory, 148–49
    and channels, 145–46
    and Martian seasonal changes, 113–14
    and Phobos and Deimos, 150–51
    and UFOs, 101
    and Velikovsky, 96–97
Sagan-Ward cyclical climate theory, 229, 232
Salisbury, Dave, 242
Sands of Mars, The (Clarke), 85
S and X band subsystem, 164
San Francisco Chronicle, 241–42
Saturn, 25, 27, 29, 40–41
    and origin of solar system, 117
S band link, 174–75
Schiaparelli, Giovanni, 50–52, 54, 56, 57, 59, 65, 66, 110, 134

288

Science fiction, 69–78, 79–90
scientific realism in, 80 ff.
space opera, 80, 82
Science Instrument Parameters (SIPs), 226
Science News, 236, 242
Science Requirement Strategy (SRS), 226
Science Test Lander, 220
Scientific establishment vs. pseudoscience, 91, 92, 95, 99–102
UFO forum, 101
and Velikovsky, 96–97
Scott, Al, 213
Seasons, Martian, 58–59, 63, 107, 110 ff. See also Cyclical climate theory
Secondary craters, 143
Secular acceleration, 149, 151
Seismometer, 191
failure of, on VL1, 222–23
on VL2, 266
Seismometry Team, 222
Sharpless, B. P., 149–50
Shatner, William, 274
Shklovskii, I. S., 149–50
Shorthill, Dr. Richard W., 192
Silicon, in Martian soil, 239
Silicon-based life, 81
Simulations, 198
Sinton, William M., 112
Size, of Mars, 15–16, 132
Sky, Martian, 236
Skylab, 20
Slipher, E. C., 106
Snyder, Dr. Conway, 204
Soderblom, Larry, 146
Soffen, Gerald, 194, 210, 245, 250
Soil, Martian, 239–40
major constituents of, 239
search for life in, 250–54
superoxides in, 249
Solar plasma detector, 128
Solar sailing, 276
Solar system, birth of, 115–20

Solar wind, 266
Sol(s), 225
Sourcebook on Space Sciences (NASA), 66
South Pole, Martian, 271. See also Polar caps
South Spot (Arsia Mons), 137–38, 144
Soyuz, 20
Space Cadet (Heinlein), 82
Space exploration, 274–75
manned vs. unmanned, 170, 220, 276–77
Space Flight Operations Facility (SFOF), 201
Space opera science fiction, 80, 82
Space Shuttle, 273–75, 276, 277
Sputnik, 20, 122
Sterilization, of Martian spacecraft, 160–61
Stout, Rex, 76
Stranger in a Strange Land (Heinlein), 82, 83
Sturgeon, Theodore, 92
Sulfide pyritite, 239
Sullivan, Walter, 213
Sun
conjunction of Mars and, 208, 262, 269, 270, 271, 272
and origin of planets, 117
T-Tauri winds, 117
Supernova of 1054, 30
Supernova of 1572, 34
Superoxides, 249
Surface material, Martian, 238–39, 240. See also Topography
Surface Sampler Arm, 174
on VL1, 224–25, 248–49
on VL2, 267
Surveyor, 20
"Survival Automatic Mission" (SAM), 272
Swift, Jonathan, 46, 48
Syrtis Major, 43

Telescope, invention of, 39–40
Temperature of Mars, 133, 144, 169–70, 190, 266

Tharsis volcanoes, 137–38, 143, 151
Thermal radiation, Martian, measurement of, 169–70
Time Machine, The (Wells), 71
Titan-Mars '73, 159
Titan III-C missiles, 194
Titanium, in Martian soil, 239
Tombaugh, Clyde, 65–66
Topography, Martian, 133, 144, 190, 220–21, 236–38, 267
Toulmin III, Dr. Priestley, 190, 239
Trace elements, 239–40
Trajectory, calculating, of Viking 1, 196–97
Transmitter problems, 223–24
"Triad" (Crosby), 84
TRW, Inc. 184, 185, 186, 187
Tsiolkovsky, K. E., 121
T-Tauri winds, 117
TV coverage of Viking landing, 242–44

UFOs, 99–102
UFOs, A Scientific Debate (eds. Sagan/Page), 101
Union of the Soviet Socialist Republics (U.S.S.R.), and U.S. space competition, 122–23
United States Air Force, and UFOs, 100–1
Universe
geocentric concept of, 27–28, 35
heliocentric concept of, 32–33, 35, 38, 41
Unmanned space exploration vs. manned, 170, 221, 276–77
Uplink communication procedure, 225–27
Upper Atmosphere Mass Spectrometer (UAMS), 178, 189, 227–28

preliminary data, 227
Uranus, 44
  discovery of, 44
  and origin of solar
    system, 117
Utopia, 262, 265, 272
  geology, 266–67
  meteorological data
    from, 266
  pictures of, 265–66, 271
  VL2 landing at, 262, 265

V-2 rockets, 122
Valles Marineris (Coprates
  Rift Valley), 139–40,
  148, 209
Vanguard rockets, 20, 122
Vega sensor, 163
Vegetation theory, of life
  on Mars, 110–12
Velikovsky, Immanuel, 91–
  97, 99
Venera 3, 160
Venera 4, 160
Venera 5, 160
Venera 6, 160
Venus, 25, 29, 40, 275
  attempted landings on,
    160
  pseudoscientific origins
    of, 91–92, 96
  Russian probe, 123
  U.S. probe, 123
Veverka, Dr. Joseph, 150–
  51
Vidicon tube television
  camera
  on Mariner IV, 126, 129–
    30
  in Viking Orbiter
    Imaging System, 165–
    67
Viking 1, 121, 164, 195–
  217, 267
  entry data analysis, 267–
    68
  landing, 13–15, 20–21,
    77–78, 84, 89, 212–17
  landing date and site
    selection, 198, 202–12
  lift-off, 194–95
  Mars Orbit Insertion,
    199–201
  trajectory, 196–97

See also Viking Lander;
  Viking Lander 1;
  Viking Orbiter; Viking
  Orbiter 1
Viking 2, 164, 196, 207,
  258–73
  biology experiments, 269
  entry science data, 266
  landing, 263–64
  landing site selection,
    203, 260–61
  Mars Orbit Insertion,
    207
  Marsquakes,
    measurement of, 271
  pictures, 265–66
  See also Viking Lander;
    Viking Lander 2;
    Viking Orbiter; Viking
    Orbiter 2
Viking Flight Team, 195
Viking Lander, 157, 164,
  170–76, 194–95, 197
  biological laboratory and
    experiments, 181–89,
    246–58, 269, 273
  body, 171–72
  building of, 159–61
  communication system,
    174–75
  data acquisition and
    processing unit
    (DAPU), 175
  data storage memory
    unit, 175
  de-orbit engines, 172
  descent engines, 173
  external components,
    172
  footpads and legs, 173–
    74
  guidance control and
    sequencing computer
    (GCSC), 176
  imaging system, 179–81
  internal components, 172
  mission requirements,
    171
  Orbiter relay link, 174–
    75
  original plans, 158
  parachute, 172–73
  power and heat source,
    176
  selection of, 159

sterilization of, 160–61,
  172, 175
surface sampler, 174,
  224–25, 248–49, 267
Viking Lander 1 (VL1),
  207–8, 212 ff.
  extended mission, 269,
    272
  pictures taken by, 218–21
  post-landing problems,
    222–25, 248–49
  preliminary scientific
    testing and data, 227–
    44
  sending commands to,
    225–27
Viking Lander 2 (VL2),
  207, 208, 262–63
  extended mission, 272
  Orbiter relay link
    problem, 263–64
  surface sampler arm
    problem, 267
  "Survival Automatic
    Mission" (SAM), 272
Viking mission, 81, 154,
  157–93, 218–44
  anomaly team, 248–49
  biological laboratory,
    161, 183–87
  biology experiments,
    240, 245–59, 269
  birth of, 157
  conjunction, and loss of
    communication, 208,
    262, 269, 270, 271, 272
  cost, 193
  entry science, 176–79,
    266
  extended mission, 269–
    70, 273
  future mission, 276
  geological investigation,
    189, 191, 267
  landing date and site,
    198, 202–12
  launch vehicles, 194
  lift-off, 194–95
  magnetic investigation,
    189, 191
  meteorological
    investigation, 189,
    190–91
  mineralogical
    investigation, 189–90

molecular analysis, 188–
89
navigation systems, 196–
97
organic compound
search, 182–83, 188–
89, 254–58, 269
physical properties
investigation, 193
pictures, 204, 209, 218–
21, 232, 236, 237, 260–
61, 265–66, 270, 272
press coverage, 240–42,
244
radio tracking system,
197
science teams, 197–98
scientific data return,
227–44
scientists vs. engineers,
210–11
search for life, 181–88
simulations, 198
sterilization problem,
160–61
team, 195, 264–65, 270
TV coverage, 202, 242–
44
Viking Orbiter, 159, 162–
65, 194–95
communications relay
link, 163, 164, 174–75,
221
communications system,
163–64
data storage system, 164
design, 162
guidance system, 163
imaging system, 165–67
power source, 162
propulsion system, 162–
63
redundant computer
system, 164–65
weight, 162

Viking Orbiter 1 (VO1),
269, 271, 272
pictures taken by, 204–5
Viking Orbiter 2 (VO2),
260, 271
atmospheric data, 268
extended mission, 269
recovery sequence, 265
separation problems,
262–63, 269
Viking Rover, 276, 277
Viking spacecraft,
propulsion system
leak, 199
Violet shift, 108
Vishniac, Dr. Wolf, 186
Visual navigation system,
197
Volcanoes on Mars, 137–
38, 143, 145, 147, 151
Volcano theory, 113
Von Däniken, Erich, 91,
92, 97–99, 102
Von Karman, Dr.
Theodore, 122
Vostok, 20
Voyager mission, 158

Wac-Corporal rocket, 122
Wac rocket, 122
Wallace, Alfred Russel, 63
War, Mars as symbol of,
22, 25, 30, 47
War of the Worlds, The
(radio play), 69, 73–75
War of the Worlds, The
(Wells), 70–72, 86
Ward, William, 145
Washington Post, 241
Water on Mars, 147–48,
167–69, 205, 229, 231–
33, 268
in Gas Chromatograph
Mass Spectrometer
(GCMS) tests, 255

loss through Martian
atmosphere, 229, 231–
33
and Mars Atmospheric
Water Detector
(MAWD), 167–69, 268
Water erosion on Mars,
147
Weather, Martian, 190–91,
233–35
Weinbaum, Stanley G., 81
Welles, Orson, 72–75, 99
Wells, H. G., 14, 70–72, 79,
88, 275
Wilford, John Noble, 213
Wind on Mars
erosion, 133, 143, 237
pattern, 233–34
Wireless World magazine,
85
"Wolf's trap," 186
Worlds in Collision
(Velikovsky), 92, 94
Wright, Orville, 20
Wright, Wilbur, 20

Xenon, 230–31
discovery of, on Mars,
267
X-Ray Fluorescence
Spectrometer (XRFS),
189–90
experiments, 239

Year, Martian, 16
Young, A. Thomas, 192,
213, 214, 218, 220, 223,
225, 264, 270
Young, Richard S., 19

Zirconium in Martian soil,
239
Zodiac, signs of the, 26–27